NAZARENES
EXPLORING
EVOLUTION

NAZARENES EXPLORING EVOLUTION

Sherri B. Walker **&** Thomas Jay Oord

EDITORS

SacraSage

Many of these essays were originally published online at exploringevolution.com

Published in Boise, Idaho by Russell Media
ISBN: 978-1-937498-41-2

Cover design: Jay Akkerman
Cover image: Thomas Jay Oord
Interior design: Sherri B. Walker

Library of Congress Cataloging-in-Publication Data
    Walker, Sherri B. and Oord, Thomas Jay
    Nazarenes Exploring Evolution
ISBN: 978-1-937498-41-2

This book is dedicated to H. Orton Wiley who wisely said...

> *"God sufficiently reveals Himself through His works, as to lay in nature a sure foundation for theology... [Humans] may be led to seek after God by nature, to feel for Him in conscience, but only through the added revelation of His Word can [we] find Him in the knowledge of salvation." (CT I, 54)*

CONTENTS

Introduction   13
  Thomas Jay Oord

SECTION 1: A FOUNDATIONAL PERSPECTIVE

1. Nazarenes and "Origins"   33
   Al Truesdale

2. Evolution(ism), Creation(ism), Canon, and Creed   41
   Brent A. Strawn

3. A Pedagogy of Hospitality   49
   Kerry Fulcher

4. Evolution, Irony, and the Future of God's Favorite Mechanism   55
   Brint Montgomery

5. Conversations on Evolution and Christian Faith   61
   Dan L. Boone

6. Robust Conversation and Collective Discernment   67
   Eric Vail

7. Taking Scripture Seriously   71
   Shea Zellweger

8. Creative Love   75
   Deanna Hayden

9. Evolution: A Stumbling Block for Evangelicals 79
John W. Dally

10. All Creation Sings 87
Mark Winslow

11. Regarding the Virtue of a Full Diet 93
Henry Spaulding

12. Evolution, the Bible, and Human Intellect 97
Jim Edlin

13. Preface to the Dialogue 101
Dee Kelley

14. Looking Forward: How Millennial Voices Will Shape 105
the "Science-Religion" Debate
Grant Miller

15. I've Evolved Too 111
Stan Ingersol

SECTION 2: A SCIENTIFIC PERSPECTIVE

16. On This We All Agree... In the Beginning God 117
Nancy Halliday

17. Exploring Evolution Through the Reproductive Process 123
Jennifer Chase

18. Darwin and the Farmboy 127
Dennis Williams

19. Breaking Away from a False Dilemma 133
Steven Smith

20. Nothing Makes Sense in Herpetology Except   139
    In Light of Evolution
     John Cossel

21. Permission to Explore Evolution   145
     Dianne Anderson

22. Anxiety, Cognitive Biases, and the Need for Embodied   149
    Charity and Hospitality: The difficult process of
    exploration and dialogue on origins
     Ronald W. Wright

23. Echoes from My Journey of Faith   155
     Lowell H. Hall

24. Providence and Evolution   163
     Burton Webb

25. Evolutionary Battle Fatigue   167
     Donald A. Yerxa

26. God is the Creator of All That Is   173
     Max W. Reams

27. The Perspective from Geoscience   177
     Charles W. Carrigan

SECTION 3: A THEOLOGICAL PERSPECTIVE

28. Creative Evolving Conversations: Reflections on   185
    Scripture, Evolution, and the Christian Faith
     Stephen Riley

29. Making the Pieces Fit   191
     Timothy Crutcher

30. Faith Seeking Understanding   197
    Robert Branson

31. Considering Evolution   201
    Carl M. Leth

32. The Bible Celebrates the Creator   205
    Marty Michelson

33. Some Reflections on the Genesis Story of Creation   213
    Alex Varughese

34. Genesis and Reading the Scriptures   219
    Hans Deventer

35. Common Observations on the Character of   223
    the Creation Account in Genesis 1-2
    Thomas J. King

36. Two Reasons Why I Believe the Theory   229
    of Evolution is Scientifically True
    Samuel M. Powell

37. Origins and Outcomes   235
    Randie L. Timpe

38. Evolutionary Theory and Moral Development   241
    Mark A. Maddix

39. My Struggle with Evolution   247
    Kevin Twain Lowery

40. Theological Implications of the Evolution Debate   255
    Joseph Bankard

41. Humanity in the Image of God   259
    Michael Lodahl

42. Much Needed Conversation 263
 Mark R. Quanstrom

43. Evolution and Faith: My Journey Thus Far 271
 Daniel Hamlin

44. Christology and Evolution 275
 Rusty Brian

45. Creation, Incarnation, and Evolution 279
 Mark H. Mann

46. Godless Evolution? 285
 Rob L. Staples

SECTION 4: A PASTORAL PERSPECTIVE

47. Evolution: A Missional Consideration 291
 Roland Hearn

48. A Reflection on the Church and Evolution 297
 Stephen L. Borger

49. Ernesto and Evolution 303
 Steve Rodeheaver

50. Don't Get Sidetracked 309
 Kyle Borger

51. Beginning to Listen: Creative Loving Congregations 313
 Bethany Hull Somers

52. Out of the Dragon's Grave: Lesson in Faith and Forgiveness 319
 Jeremy Scott

53. My Evolutionary War 325
 Wilson Deaton

54. Mending Wall: Good Fences Make Good Churches   329
    Jeremy Hugus

55. Evolution and Creation   335
    Mike Schutz

56. Growing Pains and Brave Humility: Learning to Learn   339
    Seth Waltemyer

57. Exploring Evolution: Does it Matter to the Church?   343
    Trent Friberg

58. Putting Childish Ways Behind Us   347
    Joe Foltz

59. Setting God Free   351
    Ryan Scott

60. My View from the Window   359
    Eric Frey

61. Evolution and Orthodoxy   363
    Steve Estep

62. Bread, Cup, and a Barrel of Monkeys, Wolves, and Lambs   367
    Jon Middendorf

INTRODUCTION

Thomas Jay Oord

Few issues are more important than how God created the universe. And few are more contentious!

Virtually all Christians agree that God is Creator. And virtually all believe the biblical witness to God's creative activity. But how God acts as Creator is disputed. And Christians disagree with one another on how to best interpret the Bible's statements about creation.

In 2013 and 2014, a group of leaders in the Church of the Nazarene undertook a project to explore the possibility that God creates through evolution. The project shares the title of this book: Nazarenes Exploring Evolution. In a loving, constructive, and humble endeavor, the project tried to help the Church of the Nazarene consider how evolution can complement rather than contradict Wesleyan-holiness theology.

The project was conceived and led by Thomas Jay Oord, professor of theology at Northwest Nazarene University. Sherri Walker served as his assistant in the project. Project leadership also included Robert Branson, Jennifer Chase, T. Scott Daniels, Kerry Fulcher, Philip Hamner, Mark Mann, and Mark Winslow. A conference with the project name was hosted by Point Loma Nazarene University in January of 2014, with Mann and Oord serving as conference directors.

The Nazarenes Exploring Evolution project worked to foster greater understanding among members of the Church of the Nazarene about the potential fruitful relation between Wesleyan-holiness theology and evolution. Its goal was not to ridicule those who hold non-evolutionary views of creation, such as Young Earth Creationism, Progressive Creationism, or some versions of Intelligent Design. Instead, it offered Theistic Evolution or Evolutionary Creation to the denomination as a viable alternative among accounts of how God creates the universe.

NAZARENE SCIENTISTS ON GOD CREATING THROUGH EVOLUTION

In a 2009 Pew research study, 97% of scientists said humans and other living things have evolved over time by natural processes, guided by God, or evolved in some other way.[1] Prior to the Nazarenes Exploring Evolution project, no polls had been taken to find out how scientists in Church of the Nazarene colleges and universities think about evolution. But some scientists in the denomination had previously published their views on the subject.

Karl Giberson, long-time professor at Eastern Nazarene College, had affirmed evolution in a variety of books and publications. In one book, he writes, "I think evolution is true. The process, as I reflect on it, is an expression of God's creativity, although in a way that is not captured by the scientific view of the world… God's creative activity must not be confined to a six-day period - 'in the beginning' - or the occasional intervention along the evolutionary path. God's role in creation must be more universal – so universal it cannot be circumscribed by the contours of individual phenomena or events."[2]

Darrel Falk, professor at Point Loma Nazarene University, had written in one of his books on the subject that "for the past century and a half, thousands of scientists from disciplines as diverse as physics, geology, astronomy, and biology have amassed a tremendous mass of data, and the answer is absolutely clear and equally certain. The earth is not young, and the life forms did not appear in six twenty-four-hour days. God created gradually."[3]

Rick Colling, a long time scientist at Olivet Nazarene University, had said that "some people, on religious grounds, choose to aggressively ignore or deny many scientific concepts and principles, especially in the domain of evolution… The problem, as I see it, is that we tend to squeeze God into small rigid boxes… Unfortunately, this approach to religious faith is fraught with liability because it prevents God from truly being God – a creator capable of using any means He chooses for His creation."[4]

Fred Cawthorne, professor at Trevecca Nazarene University, argued that "evolution by no means contradicts the fact that God is the Maker of heaven and earth and that he has been actively guiding and sustaining the universe for all time. If we say God cannot create through a gradual, progressive process such as evolution, then we limit God's transcendence and immanence."[5]

Before the Nazarenes Exploring Evolution project polling, it was difficult to know if these views represent the majority of Nazarene scientists. But the polling results to be offered shortly confirm most Nazarene scientists believe the evidence for evolution is strong and evolution does not necessarily conflict with the belief God is Creator.

NAZARENE BIBLICAL AND THEOLOGICAL SCHOLARS ON GOD CREATING THROUGH EVOLUTION

There is little doubt some people reject evolution based on their interpretation of the Bible. The Bible says little to nothing about evolution. And the first chapters of Genesis, when read literally, do not easily fit the theory of evolution.

Many biblical scholars, theologians, and philosophers in the Church of the Nazarene, however, believe the Bible should not be interpreted as a straightforward science or history book. For instance, many believe Genesis 1 reads like a hymn of praise. Others believe it draws from Jewish Temple literature, which is religious and not scientific. Most Nazarene theology, Bible, and philosophy scholars believe the main point of Genesis and other creation texts is theological: God is Creator. Genesis and other books of the Bible need not mention the specific ways God creates for this main point to be true.

Like several Nazarene scientists, some religion scholars in the Church of the Nazarene had published their views on science, evolution, theology and the Bible. For instance, Robert Branson, a long-time professor at Olivet Nazarene University, said that "it is one thing to say we believe that God is the Creator. It is quite another to say that in Scripture God described with scientific accuracy 'when' and 'how' he created."[6]

Alex Varughese, professor of Mount Vernon Nazarene University, and his Nazarene co-writers of *Discovering the Bible* say that a "careful reading of Genesis 1:1-2:4a shows that the focus of the text is on the Creator and what He made. Our usual questions of why, how, and when are not answered in this account."[7]

Dennis Bratcher, a long time Bible scholar in the Church of the Nazarene and manager of an important ministry website, said that "sometimes it is hard for us to realize that the Bible, particularly the Old Testament, is an Oriental book... The thought world of Oriental culture is radically different from the thought world of Western culture, particularly when we recall that there is a period of three thousand years between us and that culture... That's why they are not writing about evolution in Genesis 1; that's 3,000 years in their future."[8]

Michael Lodahl, profess or theology at Point Loma Nazarene University, has published several items on issues of creation. In his book, *God of Nature and of Grace*, Lodahl said that "a Wesleyan reading of Genesis – and of the world – need not and should not shy away from the dominant ideas of the contemporary natural sciences. It is obvious that if the evolutionary story of the universe (including our own planet and all of its living inhabitants) is generally accurate, then the opening chapters of Genesis cannot be assumed to be giving a straightforwardly literal account of the creation of the world."[9]

Thomas Jay Oord, of Northwest Nazarene University, has also published significant writing on the subjects of evolution and creation. He says that "the Bible tells us how to live abundant life. It does not tell us scientific details about how life became abundant. The Bible also tells us how to go to heaven. It does not provide the science to tell us how the heavens go."[10]

The Nazarenes Exploring Evolution poll of religion scholars reveals that the ideas expressed in the quotations above represent well the majority of biblical scholars, theologians, and philosophers in the denomination. Most scholars in Bible, theology, and philosophy seem at least open to the possibility that Wesleyan-holiness theology is compatible with evolution. And many are convinced the two are compatible.

THE DIVIDE BETWEEN SCHOLARS
AND THE PUBLIC

The 2009 Pew Research poll revealed that the majority of scientists in the United States believe in evolution. In fact, more than 9 of 10 professional scientists believe the evidence for evolution is compelling.[11] While the theory of evolution comes in a variety of forms, virtually all forms say that gradual changes occurred to produce new species over long periods of time.

Not only do the majority of scientists affirm evolution, the general features of evolutionary theory – including an old earth and natural selection – are widely accepted in American culture today and in societies around the world. Most public television and scientifically-oriented programs simply assume the general truth of evolutionary theory.

That same Pew research also shows, however, that more than half of white American Evangelicals believe humans and other living things have existed in their present form since the beginning of time.[12] Those who hold this view typically believe the world is relatively young. And they interpret Genesis (and other books of the Bible) in a particular way to support their young earth view.

This difference between 1) many Evangelicals and 2) the vast majority of American scientists represents the difference between most laity and most scholars in the Church of the Nazarene. Many denominational scholars in various disciplines – scientific, biblical, and theological – believe the general theory of evolution is compatible with Wesleyan-holiness theology. Yet, many non-specialists in the Church of the Nazarene reject evolution. Dan Boone, president of Trevecca Nazarene University, sums it up: "The bulk of our Christian scholars/scientists are in a camp different from the bulk of our laity [on issues of evolution]."[13]

TWO POLLS ON NAZARENE VIEWS

One particularly interesting aspect of the Nazarenes Exploring Evolution project was the polls it conducted. One poll with a set of questions was placed on the project website. Anyone who visited the site was welcome to answer the questions in the poll. While both members of the denomination and nonmembers participated, the results below show the response of the 285 who reported being members of the Church of the Nazarene. Here are the results of that public poll:

Question 1:
The Bible can properly be interpreted as compatible with the theory of biological evolution.

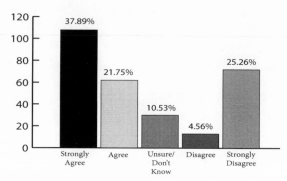

Question 2:
Genesis and other biblical texts require Christians to believe the earth was created less than 15 thousand years ago.

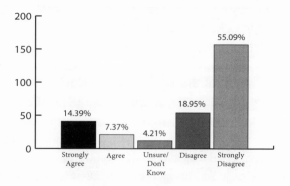

Question 3:
Geology, astronomy, and physics have established that the world is billions of years old.

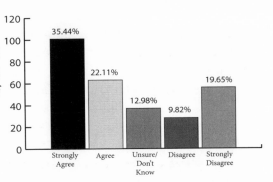

Question 4:
Humans likely became a species as God worked with the biological evolutionary process.

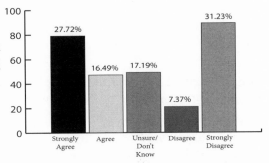

Question 5:
The Church of the Nazarene should allow the theory that God creates through evolution as one acceptable view of creation among others.

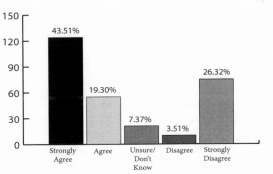

Much could be said about these polling results from the public survey. The only known poll of Church of the Nazarene member views on evolution prior to this was in 2007 and conducted by the Pew Research institute. In that poll, only 21% of Nazarenes questioned "mostly agreed" or "completely agreed" that evolution is the best explanation for the origins of human life on earth." [14] Among other things, the public Nazarenes Exploring Evolution poll suggests more Nazarenes today feel comfortable with the idea human themselves are a part of the evolutionary process.

POLLS OF NAZARENE SCHOLARS

The second poll conducted by the Nazarenes Exploring Evolution project was not open to the public. Instead, private invitations were sent to scholars in science and in religion who teach in Church of the Nazarene educational institutions in the United States. All of the major American universities and colleges of the Church of the Nazarene were contacted, including Nazarene Theological Seminary and Nazarene Bible College.

Here are the results of this invitation-only poll of scholars working in the U.S. Church of the Nazarene educational institutions. A total of 81 professors participated in this poll: 39 were from the sciences, 42 were from Christian ministry departments.

Question 1:
Genesis and other biblical texts require Christians to believe the earth was created less than 15 thousand years ago.

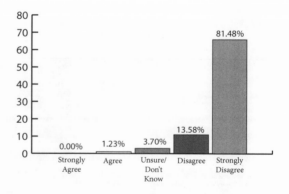

Question 2:
The Bible can properly be interpreted as compatible with the theory of biological evolution.

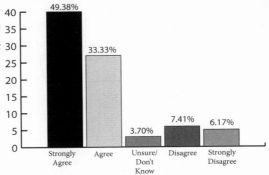

Question 3:
Wesleyan-holiness theology can be reconciled with the theory of biological evolution.

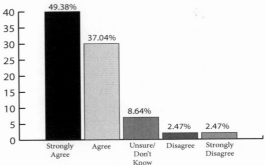

Question 4:
References to Adam in the New Testament are compatible with the idea the earth is old.

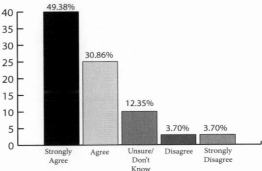

Question 5:
God is creator.

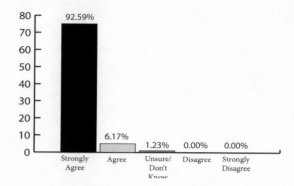

Question 6:
Scientific evidence sup-
ports the general theory
of biological evolution.

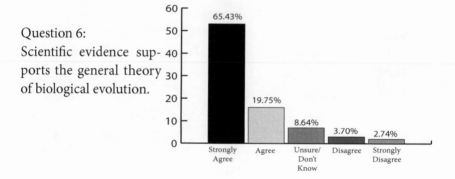

Question 7:
Humans likely became a
species as God worked
with the evolutionary
process.

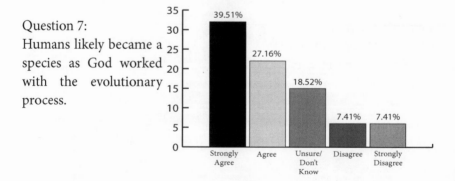

Question 8:
The universe is billions of years old.

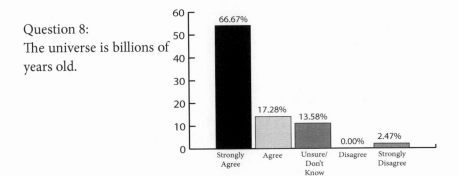

Question 9:
Some species and organisms show evidence of design.

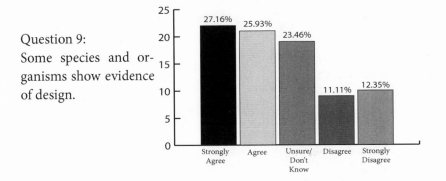

Question 10:
Geology, astronomy, and physics have established that the world is billions of years old.

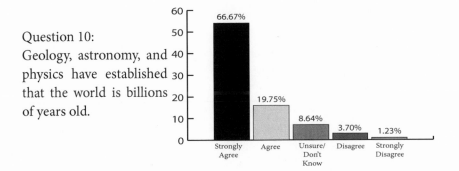

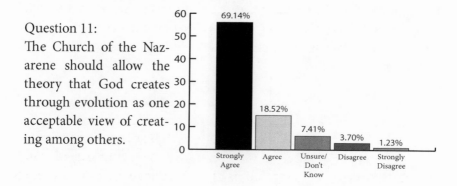

Question 11:
The Church of the Nazarene should allow the theory that God creates through evolution as one acceptable view of creating among others.

This set of results from scholarly views and the online results from the public polls confirms Dan Boone's statement that we find in the Church of the Nazarene a marked difference between how laity and scholars think about evolution. One goal of the Nazarenes Exploring Evolution project was to address this divide and to argue that how we think about evolution makes a difference.

DOES IT MATTER?

Even those mildly interested in questions of theology and evolution know the science-and-religion discussion has a history of conflict. Any progress toward insight or reconciliation comes slowly, if at all. Veterans of the discussion are prone to weariness, and denominational leaders might wonder if the "fight" is worth the trouble. Does addressing the issues of evolution really matter?

Christians have long believed that truth matters. Although Christians may not ever know all truth because we "see through a dark glass" (1 Cor. 13), we are called to search for truth in our attempts to love God with our minds. Because the natural and social sciences are primary avenues for discovering truth about existence, these sciences can play a central role in helping Christians discern how to love God and others as oneself.

Al Truesdale, long-time professor at Nazarene Theological Seminary, summarizes the importance of seeking truth in the Church of the Nazarene: "Denominations that stand in the Wesleyan tradition [such as the Church of the Nazarene] are at their best when they advocate a vital faith that seeks understanding through a bold examination of the results of all human exploration, whether in technology, in the sciences, or through historical research."[15]

One reason this discussion matters, therefore, is that the search for more adequate understandings of God and the world God creates relies upon a variety of sources, not the least of which are the sciences. If evolution is widely accepted among those who have studied the natural world most intently – scientists – it matters how Christians engage the science of evolution in light of Christian Faith.

This brings us to a second reason why the discussion of evolution and theology matters. It matters because many (but not all) scientists in the Church of the Nazarene affirm the general theory of evolution. These scientists often feel ostracized, get labeled as ungodly, are marginalized, or considered deceived.

The testimony of Nazarene biologist, Darrel Falk, is similar to the testimonies of many Nazarene scientists: "One of the biggest deterrents (to entering a Nazarene community) was my impression that I could never become part of an evangelical fellowship because of my belief in gradual creation.... Unless the church begins to downplay the significance of believing in some variety of sudden creation, there will continue to be thousands of individuals ... who will be denied true fellowship in God's kingdom."[16]

CHRISTIAN WITNESS TODAY

A third important reason why the evolution and Christian theology discussion matters is the nature of Christian witness. And the Christian witness pertaining to evolution is especially true for how young people think of God and Christian faith.

In a recent Pew study, more 18- to 29-year olds reported having a positive view of science than those in any other age category. More specifically, sixty-one percent of young people believe life evolved over time due to either natural process or divine guidance. Seventy percent of all college graduates – no matter their age – affirm some form of evolution. In sum, young people and those with degrees in higher education are more likely to trust scientists who argue for the validity of evolution.

Statistics also show, unfortunately, that young people leave the church and/or become atheists because they perceive the church to be opposed to science in general and evolution in specific. In his book, *You Lost Me: Why Young Christians are Leaving the Church and Rethinking Faith*, David Kinnaman uses the data from Barna Group research to show why 18- to 29-year olds are leaving the Church. Nearly 3 in 10 say the church is out of step with science, and one quarter say Christianity is anti-science. About one quarter of young people are turned off by the creation vs. evolution debate, and about one-fifth say Christianity is anti-intellectual.[17]

Kinnaman quotes one young person and why he left faith over the church's failure to accept science: "To be honest, I think that learning about science was the straw that broke the camel's back," says the young person. "I knew from church that I couldn't believe in both science and God, so that was it. I didn't believe in God anymore."[18]

Stories from Nazarene parents, youth pastors, and university professors indicate that some young people are leaving the Church of the Nazarene for the reasons Kinnaman reports. These young people think they cannot affirm the idea that God creates through evolution and still feel welcome in the denomination.

Dan Boone, president of Trevecca Nazarene University, asks an important question of himself that also applies to the Church of the Nazarene, "Will I engage a young generation in an open-minded biblical conversation that welcomes scientific discovery, reasoned philosophy, and careful logic? Or will I ignore all of these in favor of an interpretation of creation that is barely one hundred years old and rooted in the fear of science?"[19]

THIS BOOK

At the heart of the Nazarenes Exploring Evolution project were more than 50 essays from Nazarenes on issues of evolution. These 1,000-

word essays were published weekly in 2013 on the project website: exploringevolution.com. Essayists were invited to explore whatever dimension or issue in evolution they wanted. They were also encouraged to speak from their hearts and to tell their stories, whenever appropriate.

This book offers in print most of the essays offered online in 2013. Some of the essays are identical to their online versions; others have been expanded significantly by their authors for this book. The editors have organized the essays to foster continuity among the diverse ideas.
This book provides a powerful testimony in itself to the compatibility most essayists believe exists between the general theory of evolution and Christian faith.

The editors are grateful to many people for their support and encouragement. We especially appreciate the BioLogos Foundation for graciously supporting the project with a grant. In addition to thanking all who wrote essays for this book and/or for the website, we thank the following: Jay Akkerman, Kathryn Applegate, Dan Boone, Clayton Borah and 6foot4, Robert Branson, Jennifer Chase, Ken Crow, T. Scott Daniels, Darrel Falk, Kerry Fulcher, Karl Giberson, Deborah Haarsma, Ryan Hanson, Lydia Heberling, Rich Houseal, Mark Maddix, Mark Mann, Jesse Middendorf, Northwest Nazarene University, Point Loma Nazarene University, Mark Russell, Al Truesdale, Burton Webb, and Donald Yerxa.

ENDNOTES AND SUGGESTED READING

1 Research Center for the People & the Press. http://www.pewforum.org/science-and-bio-ethics/public-opinion-on-religion-and-science-in-the-united-states.aspx   Accessed 1/18/13. See also, http://www.people-press.org/2009/07/09/section-5-evolution-climate-change-and-other-issues/ Accessed 1/22/13

2 Karl W. Giberson, *Saving Darwin: How to be a Christian and Believe in Evolution* (New York: HarperOne, 2008), 216.

3 Darrel R. Falk, *Coming to Peace with Science: Bridging the Worlds Between Faith and Biology* (Downers Grove, Ill.: Intervarsity, 2004), 214.

4 Richard G. Colling, *Random Designer: Created from Chaos to Connect with the Creator* (Bourbonnais, Ill.: Browning, 2004), 107.

5 Fred Cawthorne, "The Harmony of Science and the Christian Faith," in *Square Peg: Why Wesleyans Aren't Fundamentalists*, Al Truesdale, ed. (Kansas City, Mo.: Beacon Hill Press, 2012), 105.

6 Robert Branson, "The Bible, Creation, and Science," in *Square Peg: Why Wesleyans Aren't Fundamentalists*, Al Truesdale, ed. (Kansas City, Mo.: Beacon Hill Press, 2012), 105.

7 Alex Varughese, ed. *Discovering the Bible: Story and Faith of the Biblical Communities* (Kansas City, Mo.: Beacon Hill, 2006), 65.

8 Dennis Bratcher, http://www.crivoice.org/biblestudy/bbgen1.html Accessed 1/18/13

9 Michael Lodahl, *God of Nature and of Grace: Reading the World in a Wesleyan Way* (Nashville, Tenn.: Kingswood, 2003), 63.

10 Thomas Jay Oord and Robert Luhn, *The Best News You Will Ever Hear* (Boise, Id.: Russell Media, 2011), 25. See also Oord, *Divine Grace and Emerging Creation: Wesleyan Forays in Science and Theology of Creation* (Eugene, Or.: Pickwick, 2009) and Oord, *Defining Love: A Philosophical, Scientific, and Theological Engagement* (Grand Rapids, Mich.: Brazos, 2010), ch. 4.

11 Research Center for the People & the Press. http://www.pewforum.org/2009/11/05/public-opinion-on-religion-and-science-in-the-united-states/#evolution-and-related-issues Accessed 1/18/13. See also, http://www.people-press.org/2009/07/09/section-5-evolution-climate-change-and-other-issues/ Accessed 1/22/13

12 Ibid.

13 Dan Boone, *A Charitable Discourse: Talking about the Things that Divide Us* (Kansas City, Mo.: Beacon Hill Press, 2010), 106.

14 2007 U.S. Religious Landscape Survey, collected by Pew Forum on Religion & Public Life. http://www.thearda.com/denoms/families/profilecompare.asp?d=1001&d=801&d=&d=&d= Accessed 9/19/2013

15 Al Truesdale, "Introduction," in *Square Peg: Why Wesleyans Aren't Fundamentalists*, Al Truesdale, ed. (Kansas City, Mo.: Beacon Hill Press, 2012), 10.

16 Darrel R. Falk, *Coming to Peace with Science*, 230. For similar testimonies, see Richard G. Colling, *Random Designer*, and Karl W. Giberson, *Saving Darwin*.

17 David Kinnaman, *You Lost Me: Why Young Christians are Leaving the Church and Rethinking Faith* (Grand Rapids, Mich.: Baker, 2011), 136.

18 Ibid., 131.

19 Dan Boone, *A Charitable Discourse*, 102.

SECTION 1

A

FOUNDATIONAL

PERSPECTIVE

1

NAZARENES AND "ORIGINS"

Al Truesdale

Al Truesdale is Emeritus Professor of Philosophy of Religion and Christian Ethics at Nazarene Theological Seminary.

It might appear that the place to begin when discussing how members of the Church of the Nazarene should assess and respond to Neo-Darwinism ("the modern synthesis," a fusion of genetics and evolutionary biology) is an examination of Wesleyan theology *vis-à-vis* the natural sciences. In fact, a prior "origins" topic that deals with the history of the denomination needs to be considered.

I

Some among us, including this writer, have spilled a lot of ink explaining how we are "Wesleyan" and that being "Wesleyan" generates a disposition toward "the modern synthesis," which makes it possible to affirm what the Bible teaches while also accepting the findings of the empirical sciences. We have told Nazarenes to "line up" or live with the consequences of betraying the theological convictions that define the denomination. However, will historical accuracy and fairness support such a judgment?

Presently, the Church of the Nazarene is home to an intense and sometimes bitter controversy over how Nazarenes should respond to Neo-Darwinism. Many believe themselves to be "Wesleyan" as opposed to "fundamentalist" and that such a posture permits compatibility between the Christian faith and modern evolutionary science. Others are equally confident that "Nazarene" and "Darwin" are mutually exclusive. Between these sharp edges are many who adopt what they believe to be properly mediating positions. Still others judge the topic unworthy of debate.

Some essays in the current series will tell of how their authors migrated from fundamentalism to a more Wesleyan appraisal of the natural and social sciences. Does the denomination's "origins" permit one camp or the other to present itself as the correct representative of how the denomination should assess Neo-Darwinism? Or does its history require some other formula for learning to live together?

To answer, we must refer to the denomination's beginnings. As students of our history know, the denomination was at first largely the result of a series of mergers. The 1922 merger between the Church of the Nazarene and many members of the Laymen's Holiness Association probably contributed more than any other to the current disagreement between classical Wesleyans and what Timothy L. Smith called "Wesleyan fundamentalists."[1]

After vigorously defending the "nondenominational idea" and opposing denominational affiliation, or "organized holiness," Joseph Grant Morrison, head of the Laymen's Holiness Association, joined the Church of the Nazarene in Minneapolis in the spring of 1922. The Association was a large network of disaffected Methodist clergy and laypersons staunchly committed to the doctrine of entire sanctification and pre-millennialism. They were equally opposed to modernism in the churches, science as influenced by Darwin, 'godless' education in the public schools and universities, and all hopes that the kingdom of God could advance on earth through Christian social action. They were marked by what Timothy Smith labels "rural fundamentalism" because they combined rural (e.g. antipathy towards labor unions and a feeling of alienation from urban culture) with theological interests.[2]

Morrison labored to bring as many members of the Laymen's Holiness Association as possible into the young denomination. He and others successfully wooed "Laymen" ranging from Michigan to the mountains of Montana, from Missouri, Kansas, Indiana, and even as far west as California and Oregon. Paul M. Bassett says Morrison "was given a wide and warm welcome into the Church of the Nazarene."[3]

Morrison's future and influence in the Church of the Nazarene blossomed. He became President of Northwest Nazarene College in 1926. In 1936, Nazarenes elected him general superintendent, a post he held until his death in 1939. That he and many clergy and lay members of the Laymen's Holiness Association were welcomed into the Church of the Nazarene without being required to shed their "Wesleyan fundamentalism" is without question. They abhorred what they saw as ecclesiastical compromise with "modernism," explained as a failure to stress the doctrine and experience of entire sanctification, acceptance of modern critical studies of the Scriptures, and reconciliation between the Christian faith and modern science as it relates to Darwinism.

According to Smith and Bassett, by the time J.G. Morrison joined the Nazarenes, the theological tide in the denomination was already shifting toward fundamentalism.[4] Bassett notes the fundamentalist influence of J. B. Chapman, editor of the *Herald of Holiness* from 1923 to 1928, but also points out that, thanks largely to H. Orton Wiley, fundamentalism was not unambiguously triumphant.[5] Nevertheless, there would have been little reason for Morrison to feel uncomfortable in his new home. His growing influence expanded his platform for strengthening fundamentalism. The brand of fundamentalism that came to characterize much of the denomination was "clearly Wesleyan," as distinguished from its Calvinist counterparts. This "drew a circle of isolation around the young church."[6]

Nothing has happened since "the Laymen" became Nazarenes that officially rejects the terms of their entrance. They and their progeny remain franchised Nazarenes.

A subsequent chapter in the denomination's history was the emergence of a vibrant exploration and teaching of classical Wesleyanism by a growing number of Nazarene theologians. They believed they had recovered the intended soul of the denomination. Increasingly, they composed the theological faculties of the denomination's universities and seminary. They began to dominate the church's publications and to feed a steady stream of clergy and professors into parishes and classrooms. They also undergirded a growing number of science professors in Nazarene universities who showed students how to achieve reconciliation between vital Christian faith and modern science. The brand of Wesleyanism the Wesleyan theologians taught was diametrically opposed to much of what characterized "Wesleyan fundamentalism." Representatives of the latter saw no reason to abandon their convictions and often believed they had well-established cause to oppose the likes of H. Ray Dunning, Rob L. Staples and Mildred Bangs Wynkoop.

II

One can see how ground work was laid for the current cleavage between the two positions, particularly as it relates to "the modern synthesis." Historical fairness seems to rule out telling "Wesleyan fundamentalists" they can't continue to hold their position if they want to be good Nazarenes. That question was settled when members of the Laymen's Holiness Association were warmly welcomed into the denomination on grounds other than fidelity to classical Wesleyan theology. Predictably, the two positions will probably continue to compete to define the denomination theologically and sociologically. Classical Wesleyans can legitimately tell Wesleyan fundamentalists they can't hold to their position if they want to be true to Wesley's theology, especially to his doctrine of Scriptures. But can they legitimately exclude them as *bona fide* Nazarenes? Our biblical scholars can painstakingly show why Genesis 1-3 doesn't support fundamentalism. But they should have little hope of generally changing a fundamentalist worldview whose sources transcend theology. Can each position grant living space to the other and together embrace a shared mission that marginalizes disagreements regarding Neo-Darwinism? Recent controversies suggest that on this topic "the jury is still out."

Given the energy and tenacity that fuel opposition to "the modern synthesis" and to fairly-well established theory regarding cosmogenesis (viz., the "Big Bang" and subsequent universe development) by many in the Church of the Nazarene in North America, one is left to wonder if Merton's "law" of unintended consequences has been at work in the denomination's history. Has opposition to the modern synthesis in many instances functionally replaced the doctrine of entire sanctification as the denomination's *raison d'être*?

III

A topic that cannot be marginalized is the philosophy of education that should guide the denomination's colleges and universities. It seems appropriate to ask, how serious is the Church of the Nazarene about higher education? It could not legitimately claim to educate persons as informed leaders in today's world based upon a fundamentalist response to established biological, paleontological, and geological science. Fundamentalism cannot equip students to love God with all their minds. However, fundamentalists will have a difficult time supporting a philosophy of education they believe to be inimical to some of their defining convictions and as the vanguard of apostasy.

A danger faced by theologically conservative denominations is that they will advertise themselves as providing a bold integration of faith and science in their universities while being strongly influenced by a significant number of fundamentalist stakeholders who require that "integration" be decided by a fundamentalist world view.

The faculties and administrators of Nazarene universities are well-equipped to help students develop a well-informed integration of faith and science. But the universities fulfill their potential only if they have the denomination's strong theological and intellectual support. To balance this, the universities have a responsibility to be faithful to the denomination by adhering to its Articles of Faith, its conduct of the Great Commission, and its fidelity to the Wesleyan tradition as it is faithful to the Scriptures and the Apostolic Faith. Holistic Christian education of lay and clergy leaders must be central to a Nazarene university's mission.

In *The Bible, Rocks and Time*, authors Davis A. Young and Ralph F. Stanley plead with evangelicals to avoid the human "shipwrecks of the faith" that occur when products of their churches and educational institutions eventually come to believe they must choose between modern science and a Christian Faith that rigorously casts its lot with pseudo-science.[7] Wesleyans have all the resources needed to avoid such crises.

The universities of the Church of the Nazarene are well positioned to offer society an important counterweight to what Harvey Mansfield, professor of government at Harvard University, describes as a "brazen politicization of the classroom" and "disregard of greatness in general" that characterizes much of contemporary American higher education.[8] As did the monasteries in the Middle Ages, Nazarene universities can offer a haven for cultivating the spirit and mind. But they must not be burdened by fundamentalist constraints that would obstruct their efforts.

IV

Finally, it has been argued that what really matters in Christian discipleship in the Church of the Nazarene is knowing and loving Jesus Christ, and bearing witness to him through works of love. What one believes about the age of the earth and human origins plays no significant role in vital piety. While no doubt we should champion the importance of vital piety, it must also be noted that the Christian faith is not an esoteric cult that fulfills its meaning when a personal relationship with Jesus Christ has been achieved. When it claims Jesus Christ is Lord of all, the Christian faith makes comprehensive and affirmative claims regarding truth, thought, the world, the mind, and the whole human enterprise. Christians simply cannot retreat to pietistic interiority, exclude the realm of modern science, abandon the canons of public discourse, and still claim to be faithful to historic Christianity and the Christ it confesses. Fleeing into a pietistic ghetto has always been deadly when practiced in the Christian church. It is now as costly as ever.

For the Church of the Nazarene to have a viable future that extends beyond private religiosity, at all levels it must hold itself accountable for the quality of its fidelity to, and representation of, historic Apostolic Christianity, and to the whole human enterprise as being included in Christian redemption. A fundamentalist worldview cannot equip a denomination for such a challenge. But Wesleyan theology, governed by the Scriptures and the historic faith, can.

ENDNOTES AND SUGGESTED READING

1 Timothy L Smith, *Called Unto Holiness* (Kansas City: Nazarene Publishing House, 1962) 308.

2 Ibid., 318.

3 Paul M. Basset, "The Fundamentalist Leavening of the Holiness Movement: 1914-1940," *Wesleyan Theological Journal*, Volume 13 (Spring 1978): 75.

4 Smith, 316.

5 Basset, 76-77.

6 Smith, 316.

7 Davis A. Young and Ralph F. Stanley, *The Bible, Rocks and Time* (Downers Grove, IL: IVP Academic, 2008) 476-7. See the poignant and tragic illustration given by Kerry Fulcher, "A Pedagogy of Hospitality," Chapter 3.

8 Harvey Mansfield, "The Higher Education Scandal," *Claremont Review of Books*, Volume 13 (Spring 2013) 10-11.

2

EVOLUTION(ISM), CREATION(ISM), CANON, AND CREED

Brent A. Strawn

Brent A. Strawn is Associate Professor of Old Testament at the Candler School of Theology and Graduate Division of Religion at Emory University.

Growing up in the Church of the Nazarene, when I did (born 1970) and where I did (Southern California), meant that I was somehow given a lot of what could be called run-of-the-mill, nondescript conservative evangelicalism—of the Wesleyan-Arminian variety, to be sure, but also of the general North American variety. Included in that nondescript, run-of-the-mill evangelicalism was a decent bit of anti-evolution thinking. Somewhere in my childhood, though I can't recall exactly when, I learned of evolution and got the distinct impression that it was something bad. I remember, if nothing else, the standard jokes about—or rather *against!*—humans being descended from monkeys.

Like many young people at that time, my devotion and piety were often manifested by listening to Christian music, listening to Christian radio (which included, invariably, its fair share of radio preachers), and regular study of the Bible. The first two of these—the music and the radio preachers—often took prominent stands against evolution, reinforcing their point with a sufficient supply of the standard monkey jokes. The cumulative effect of all this devotional "input"—including that from the Bible, too, at least to some degree (but see further below on Genesis 1)—left the impression that good, devout Christians just didn't side with evolution. If nothing else, there were the monkey jokes to consider.

EVOLUTION(ISM)

But then there was school. Science classes in my public schools didn't shy away from evolution, and since my parents (devout Christians) didn't either, neither did I. For some reason, my adolescent brain realized that despite the Christian music and the radio preachers, even the mesmerizing power of Genesis 1, there was something true about scientific inquiry, scientific results, and the scientific method.

But how was I to put these different truths together? Somewhere along the way, probably in my church youth group, I was given a crucial tool by which to draw a distinction between evolution—the scientific theory—and "evolution*ism*," which could be considered a much broader ideology if not religion. I think that it is this latter entity, evolution*ism*, that many well-meaning Christians think of when they speak against "evolution," but the two are not the same. Evolution-the-scientific-theory is a well-established fact in scientific literature for how biological life grows and develops; evolution*ism*-the-religion is a *non*-scientific but heavily philosophical and (a)theological deduction from science to argue that, given evolutionary processes, natural selection, random mutations, and so on and so forth, there is no God, no Creator, no purpose in life, etc. But I am getting ahead of myself.

CREATION(ISM)

The evolution vs. evolution*ism* distinction helped me through my secular school years but also, surprisingly enough, in my Christian college where I encountered a good number of people who were convinced that evolution and evolutionism *were* identical. Precisely because of this conflation, they were forced to do some serious mental gymnastics in their college science classes, buying into some but not too much of what they were learning there. All the while, they were second guessing the faith of any of their professors who happened to subscribe to evolution-the-theory, and they were reinforcing their mental gymnastics with a rather rigid and mechanistic understanding of the Bible, what it was about, and how it worked. I felt the latter issue acutely, though I couldn't yet articulate its problems, during my freshman year when I participated in a Bible study that had its fair share of anti-evolution (or, rather, anti-evolution*ism*) folks. So, imagine some college students, a faculty member or two, the biblical stories about David, Jesus, Moses, Paul...and throw in a few monkey jokes.

Experiencing this group and seeing firsthand the strangeness of the positions—not on the scientific side, mind you, but on the *biblical* side—revealed that just as evolution (not a problem, in my view) could become evolution*ism* (a definite problem, in my view), so, too, could the idea of creation (a core theological doctrine and therefore definitely not a problem) become "creation*ism*." I would define "creation*ism*" as a religion not unlike evolution*ism*. It frequently makes recourse to creation-science, and the two are often closely linked. But in terms of the Scriptural side of things, "creation*ism*" is limited, as far as I can tell, to an inexplicable valorization of Genesis 1 above all other texts in the Bible that concern creation.

Great help in better understanding the issues at work in evolution(ism) and creation(ism) came in a biology class taught my senior year by Dr. Darrel Falk. The help came in two forms: First, in an assigned textbook by Richard T. Wright, a Harvard trained Ph.D. who taught biology at Gordon College, entitled *Biology through the Eyes of Faith* (San Francisco: Harper & Row, 1989). The book took up not just evolution in general, but human evolution specifically—along with many other important issues—and treated them all reasonably and, or so it seemed to me, with complete competence in terms of both science and Christianity.

The second and more important help came in Dr. Falk himself. He was a fantastic teacher, an expert in his field, a top-notch scientist fully at home in and at peace with evolutionary theory, and a deeply committed Christian to boot (and at root). Here, in the flesh, was an instantiation—incarnation even!—of the paradigm that I had heard of with the ear but hadn't yet seen with the eye (to allude to Job 42:5), the paradigm that I knew inchoately, that is, but which lacked key pieces and much evidence. I will never forget the time Dr. Falk told his own moving story about how he looked at his children playing one day and felt sad because they would lack the church upbringing he had enjoyed. Why would they lack that?

Because he was a scientist, convinced of the truthfulness of evolutionary theory, and he was, as a result, sadly convinced that no church would have him for that reason and for that reason alone.

But a church would have him! In this case it was the Church of the Nazarene, a Wesleyan-Arminian denomination that understood Scripture less rigidly (but no less seriously) than some other branches of North American evangelicalism. And so, happily, Dr. Falk found his way to my college and to my home church. The daughters he felt sorry for ended up as key members of my church's youth group.

I will also never forget the hours Dr. Falk invested in me, meeting with me outside of class as I began to put together the implications of evolution within a larger theological framework—a point I was most anxious about since I was a religion/Bible major.

CANON

As I have already indicated, Scripture was present from the very beginning in my thinking about creation and evolution. Growing up Wesleyan helped a great deal. Indeed, I suspect that it is precisely the Wesleyan aspects of my evangelical heritage and upbringing that enabled me, despite my deep, primal love of Scripture and the well-meaning monkey jokes, to be able to see and agree with that distinction between scientific theory (evolution) and scientific religion (evolution*ism*)—though I realize the term "scientific religion" is something of an oxymoron. I don't mean to suggest that religion and science have no overlapping relationship whatsoever.[1] But I do mean to say that science is not, as such, religion.[2]

In any event, after college I went to seminary and then did a Ph.D. in Biblical Studies with a focus on Old Testament. Since then I've been teaching seminarians, some of whom have had serious questions about creation(ism) and evolution(ism). It was in the course of teaching students about the Bible, especially about Genesis 1, that I came to see that the Bible itself is not of one mind about how God created the world. It *is* of one mind—if the Bible can be said to have a "mind"—on *the fact that* God created the world and all that is in. But *how* God created the world is a matter of opinion in the Bible. There is no getting around Genesis 1, front and center as it is, but while that is an important text, a breakthrough came when I realized that its seven-day schema of creation was never repeated elsewhere in the Bible.[3] Rather than simplistic and extensive repetition of Genesis 1 elsewhere in the Bible, what we find instead are a lot of other texts about creation, texts like Genesis 2 (immediately adjacent to Genesis 1!), which suggest that God created things in different ways and in different sequences than what is set forth in Genesis 1. Consider Psalm 74:12-17, which uses creation language in conjunction with God's combat against the sea dragon (a long-standing creation motif in the ancient world), or Proverbs 8:22-31, which says that the first thing God created wasn't light, as Genesis 1 would have it, but Wisdom personified. And this doesn't mention still other texts from the Old Testament let alone the New Testament. For the latter, one need only think of John 1:1-4 or Colossians 1:15-20, which contribute to the discussion but also complicate it by placing Jesus, the Word of God, present at the creation. In brief, there is a lot to be said about creation in the Bible. A lot more than just Genesis 1.

What do all these different texts with their different "takes" on creation mean? Well, there can be no doubt that they mean a number of things, but here's one obvious conclusion: *any overly obsessed focus on Genesis 1 to the expense of all other texts about creation in the Bible is seriously mistaken.* On what grounds should one favor Genesis 1 over Genesis 2, over Proverbs 8, or over John 1? *All* of these texts are canonical; all of them, that is, are *Holy* Scripture, not just one of them and certainly not just the first in the series. And here's the crucial point: these different, holy, canonical writings disagree on the *how* of creation. But here's the next, equally important point: they are in full agreement on the *fact* of creation—or, better, on the *Who* of creation, which is to say, they agree on the fact that it is *God* who created heaven and earth, even if God had Jesus or Wisdom (or both!) near at hand in the process.

CREED

And that is why we find the Apostles' Creed affirming our belief in "God...Creator of Heaven and Earth" but without any further discussion or qualification. The Creed moves on immediately after that to "and in Jesus Christ, his only son, our Lord." The Creed does not tack on a rider to the creation part indicating *how* God created (e.g., "in seven twenty-four hour days"). And that is not because the Creed is afraid of (or somehow infatuated with) Darwin, but because the Creed is *thoroughly biblical*. The Creed knows—if a Creed can be said to "know" something—that the Bible affirms the fact that God created, but it also knows that how God created is not clearly portrayed in Scripture, at least not unequivocally.

If the Creed had mandated belief in seven twenty-four hour days, it would have reflected only one Scriptural perspective on creation (and only one particular interpretation of that perspective) to the neglect of all the others. That would do injustice to the full witness of Scripture. And so the Creed doesn't do it. Why? *Because the Bible itself doesn't do it.* Why, then, do some Christians insist on doing it? No doubt they mean well, but their well-meaning runs seriously afoul. In their zeal for Genesis 1, and in their defense of Genesis 1, they end up doing serious damage to the rest of Scripture and what it has to say on this crucial subject. And note that the difficulties I am mentioning here are only on the biblical side of "creationism"; I haven't even begun to mention the scientific problems inherent in the same.

It was in the classroom, then, that my journey came full circle, much like it had begun in the classrooms of my youth at school and at church. It was a journey from Genesis 1 and creation*ism*, to evolution and evolution*ism*, and back to creation and Genesis 1. In light of all that, I see no reason to affirm "evolution*ism*." In fact, Canon and Creed combine to indicate that I *cannot* affirm it. Instead, I confess belief in the Triune God who created heaven and earth. But I also see no need to affirm "creation*ism*." Scripture includes far more than Genesis 1, the Creed agrees, and my theological tradition affirms God's truth everywhere it can be found, even outside Canon and Creed—places like the amazing natural world that God created along with its many scientific laws and processes. I see no reason not to believe that all of these things—the world with its scientific processes—also include evolution, just as I affirm that all of them, of whatever sort, are created, redeemed, and sustained by the Lord.

ENDNOTES AND SUGGESTED READING

1 The celebrated atheistic evolutionary biologist Stephen Jay Gould argued just that: religion and science do not overlap. See his *Rocks of Ages: Science and Religion in the Fullness of Life* (New York: Ballentine, 1999), a book that, in its own way celebrates religion. I myself believe science and religion do overlap and interrelate in many ways—some of which are quite close, none of which, however, are exactly coterminous. See the helpful book by William P. Brown, *Seven Pillars of Creation: The Bible, Science, and the Ecology of Wonder* (New York: Oxford University Press, 2010).

2 Perhaps it would be better, in light of what I've said above about evolutionism, to say that science can be a religion of sorts—which is to say that it can be an ideology and philosophy that moves outside of the laboratory, the scientific method, hypotheses and verification/falsification, etc. But at that point, it is no longer a privileged repository of "hard data": it is yet another religion or ideology in a large marketplace populated by many others and must take its turn competing for attention and adherents, justifying its claims and so on and so forth. Unfortunately, there are no test tubes that prove science-as-religion correct. The scientific endeavor can't, in the end, prove or disprove religion as such. There's no mixing Jesus up in a test tube, let alone God; nor are the notions of revelation or inspiration capable of replication in a lab.

3 There is, to be sure, a reference to God resting on the Sabbath day in Exod. 20:11, but that is not found in the parallel text in Deut. 5:15. Even in Deuteronomy 5 there is no repetition of the seven twenty-four hour day schema—if, in fact, the days in question are twenty-four hour days, which is a point of debate in some circles, though I see no compelling reason to think that the Hebrew text suggests otherwise.

3

A PEDAGOGY OF HOSPITALITY

Kerry Fulcher

Kerry Fulcher is the Provost and Chief Academic Officer at Point Loma Nazarene University.

For many years, I have started my introductory lectures to both my major and non-major freshmen-level biology courses with a lecture titled, "Where do you draw the line?". The image being drawn upon here is one of friends or siblings growing up together and drawing a line in the sand or taping a line down the middle of the room that indicates to the other, "If you cross this line, we are going to have a fight on our hands." It is not just kids who do this, but it is also happening in our churches over a variety of issues, especially issues dealing with creation and evolution.

As bad as it is to see this happening within congregations, unfortunately it spills out into all sorts of relationships both within the Christian community and as our "witness" to a secular society. We see the battle played out on the freeways with bumper stickers of the symbol of the "Christian fish" growing legs to become the "Darwin fish." Not to be outdone, we have the "Jesus fish," with its ferocious teeth, swimming in to eat the "Darwin fish." We are tempted to smile at this clever example of "one-upmanship," but before we do, perhaps it would be worth the time and effort to count the cost that has accumulated thanks to the culture generated by the creation/evolution debates. While my essay could focus on a wide variety of issues at the interface of Christian faith and science, I choose not to focus on the issues themselves but on the WAY we address the issues within the church and beyond.

Anecdotally, I have seen many friends and students who have been raised in the Church and have ended up jettisoning their faith because the views they were taught regarding creation, portrayed to them by well-meaning people of influence as "the Christian view," can no longer be reconciled with what they are learning about creation from well-supported mainstream science. Given the choice of believing what they were taught as true versus accepting what they can clearly see as contradictory data, they are forced into either abandoning their faith or ignoring what to their minds seems to be compellingly clear information from their scientific studies.

I remember my first exposure to this when I went to graduate school. I had a fellow graduate student who had been raised in a Christian home and went to a Wesleyan undergraduate university. I approached her thinking that she would be someone I could talk to and discuss the faith/science questions I was having. I was not prepared for the story that she told me. She shared that she had gone through the questioning phase as an undergraduate and had turned to her church for help reconciling what she was learning with what she had been taught. Over the period of a couple of years, after being counseled to quit her scientific studies in order to preserve her faith, she came to a decision point after a church-sponsored seminar where the speaker indicated that one could not be a Christian without accepting that the earth was young. After the seminar, she asked one of the "dear old saints" of the church, as she put it, how she could account for the fossils of the dinosaurs. The lady told her that she believed that Satan had put them there to confuse and trick humans (a view you can find in books at the local Christian book stores lest you think this silly).

At that point, my friend decided that if being a Christian meant that she had to believe as her church seemed to be telling her, she could no longer do this. She turned her back on her faith and became fully devoted to her search for truth as determined by her scientific studies alone. I was dumbfounded...I was angry...I was totally unprepared to contribute anything of value to the conversation (unfortunately my undergraduate training had ignored the issue to avoid controversy). All I knew was that something was not right with people rejecting their Christian faith over disagreements on the mechanism of how God created...not over the Gospel message or teachings of Christ...but over the age of the earth. This was the defining event that started me on a long journey of study and engagement with this issue as a scientist and a follower of Christ.

My initial strategy, unfortunately, was motivated out of anger for what "those people" did that caused my graduate school friend to abandon her faith. So I studied and learned how to demolish and destroy the arguments of "those people," and when I first started teaching that was "the gift" I brought to my classroom. When the surveys given in my classes identified that 60-75% of my students identified themselves with "those people," you might guess that my attempts to "set them straight" did not go so well using my "demolish and destroy" pedagogy. This is when the second, and more important defining moment happened in my journey.

My best friend that I had grown up with and knew for my whole life came down with his wife to visit us. It turned out that my best friend also identified his beliefs with "those people," so naturally I launched into my impassioned attempt to "set him straight." To my dismay, none of my arguments or evidences seemed to have any effect on my friend. He was well educated with a Master's degree in School Counseling, but he did not understand my arguments that were steeped in genetics, molecular biology or developmental biology–but then again, I am not sure why I expected he should. Finally, long after our wives had wisely gone to bed, my friend concluded the matter with an affirmation of his belief in me and the way God was using my life and ministry...and the suggestion that we would agree to disagree on these issues. He indicated that he had a simple faith that sustained him and that he just could not go where I was asking him to go.

This was a turning point in my journey because here was someone who I knew was a "magnet" for Christ and had a profound ministry and influence on high school students. How could I justify holding this over his head in judgment and think of him the way I had come to think of "those people"? That is where I learned to separate the "ism" from the "ist"...the idea (creationism) from the people who held the idea (creationist). I had conflated the two and in doing so had been taking out my anger over what happened to my graduate school friend on anyone associated with the ideas that contributed to her leaving the faith. I realized my approach would have to change, and I would need to offer my students the same grace that I was willing to offer my best friend. Up to that point, I had been content to enter into science/faith dialogues in ways that were defined either by the culture wars of the creation/evolution debates or the theoretical world of the academy through its scholarly pursuits. In my view neither of these satisfactorily modeled Christ in the classroom. So through trial and error, many interactions with my colleagues, and a lot of prayer, I developed a different pedagogy…a pedagogy of hospitality.

While I don't have time to go into the details of each step and how that played out in the classroom, the following 6 steps became the framework that, in my experience, modeled how to approach controversial issues like these in a Christ-honoring way.

1. Begin by disarming/diffusing, which creates an openness to listen and discuss vs. feeding the flame that threatens others and causes them to be closed to real dialogue.

2. Create a reason for the audience to be engaged or care about the topic by helping them understand why open discussion or dialogue about the issue might be helpful to them.

3. Recognize the complexity of the issue and how an individual's faith can rightly or wrongly interact with it in foundational ways.

4. Set the tone of discussion as one of mutual respect for individuals that honors right relationships above right answers.

5. Set goals of education that promote greater understanding vs. advocacy that promotes winning the argument. This puts us in the uncomfortable position of being OK with others understanding our position without necessarily accepting or believing it.

6. Honor the individual and their journey by remembering our own – It has taken years and a lot of study and thought to get where I am on this issue, so don't expect others to make huge leaps in their own positions… be gradual.

The principles upon which this pedagogy of hospitality are based are rooted in our core Christian beliefs about who Christ calls us to be in community with fellow believers and who Christ calls us to be as a witness to an unbelieving world (John 13:34-35, 1 John 3:14 and 4:20). It recognizes that the ultimate answers we arrive at in the discussion are not as important as how we interact with each other in the discussion. God calls us to righteousness, which is right relationship to Him. What makes us righteous is salvation through our Lord and Savior Jesus Christ. When we understand the Gospel message, everything changes (or should change) in how we interact with others. We recognize that we can no longer feel superior to others because our good works get us no closer to salvation than the misdeeds of the wicked, as all of humanity falls short of God's glory (Rom 1-3). Because our salvation is not based on our good works or even our right thinking, there is no room for arrogance or superiority in our dealings with others.

As we approach brothers and sisters in Christ who hold different views than what we hold on issues not essential to our salvation, our first priority is to be in right relationship with them versus trying to prove who is right or wrong on these issues (1 Cor 8, Rom 14). Reversing these priorities runs the risk of "destroying the work of God over food..." or whatever the current non-essential topic of the day might be. This idea runs counter to the culture both inside and outside of the Church, which values right answers over right relationships...and it is a hard message to hear for both scholars and lay people alike because it runs counter to the default postures of our heads and hearts, which are inclined towards self. Nonetheless, the Gospel of Christ is a transforming Gospel that aims to renew both head and heart, fixing their inclination to self and aligning their posture towards Christ.

I close my first class by telling my students where I draw the line. I draw the line at "God created." Of this, I have no doubt. While I may have ideas about how He did it, and it is interesting to talk about these ideas, they are not important enough to set as a stumbling block for non-believers or as something to split the body of Christ over. So in general, before we delve into the issues of faith and science regarding the mechanisms of God's creation, it is important that we recognize that according to our understanding of Scripture, these are not issues that are essential to our salvation. Because of this, our approach should heed the scriptural warnings described above and the sage advice, whose origin is in question but was often quoted by Bresee, *"In essentials unity, in non-essentials liberty, in all things charity."*

4

EVOLUTION, IRONY, AND THE FUTURE OF GOD'S FAVORITE MECHANISM

Brint Montgomery

Brint Montgomery is Professor of Philosophy at Southern Nazarene University and serves as Director for the philosophy program.

"I'm sorry to hear that you've been so misinformed about evolution." These words, from Major Dean, a genetic warfare officer at Eglin Air Force Base in 1984, where I had been assigned temporary duty, brought me up short. I had just told the Major that science had shown evolution and religion are not compatible, so one cannot both believe in Christianity and still hold to evolution. At that time in my life, I was not a Christian. Yet here before me sat as clear a counter-example as any that God in heaven could have provided. Indeed, perhaps He did.

Major Dean was a fully committed Christian man leading a Navigators Bible study group almost every evening, while every morning working a job that specialized in the most existentially excruciating technology of our time -- biological weaponry. The new generation of young technocrats with their Glasnost ideas had not yet arisen in the Soviet Union, and men like Major Dean were considered a necessary evil for (what now sounds insane) the Strategy of Mutually Assured Destruction. Clearly he outranked me, a mere Senior Airman. He was "cocked, locked, and ready to rock," as the saying went, when it came to his full arsenal of educational achievements: first college and then onto graduate school in Biology, not to mention the top-secret clearance and nefarious training he had to master in order to even become a genetic warfare officer. So here he was: educated, friendly -- even loving; tall, a picture of good health and with a well-adjusted, mature character; moral, socially connected, and worst of all -- *Christian.*

I was 21 and really thought I had a basic idea of how the categories of the world stood: there were friends, acquaintances, and enemies; time and money, politics or personal relationships; and cool-headed scientists or crazy religious people. It was this last pair that began to crack first, though all the others would eventually collapse as well when, within a couple of days, Major Dean would pray-through with me at my conversion to Christianity.

In light of this origin regarding my own faith, it is easy to see why I do not *prima facie* consider evolution a threat to the Christian life; from the start, I saw a man who successfully and victoriously lived-out the compatibility. God calls us to defend the widow and the orphan, or calls us to an act exactly like it by loving one's neighbor as oneself. The Bible, also, notes how the life of Christ was lived-out with love and care, though he nevertheless was crucified on a cross. How is evolution supposed to threaten these commitments? Archeology would seemingly offer more immediate, defeasible counter-evidence to classical doctrines of Christianity were, say, scientists to dig up a box or excavate a cave filled with bones and sundry items, all (somehow overwhelmingly) pointing to the non-resurrected body of Jesus. Under those circumstances, my theological intuitions would go with the Apostle Paul when he writes, "and if Christ has not been raised, your faith is worthless; you are still in your sins" (1 Corinthians 15:17 NASB). Yet there is hardly a wafting scent of suspicion over *that* particular application of science to matters concerning Christianity. So there must be something deeper than the argument that evolution, as science, is a threat to religion, for it seems to demand the too powerful assumption that *all* science is a threat to religion.

Science is committed to a simplicity of explanation. Thus, when fully fleshed out, this results in what is called "methodological naturalism." On this view, one does not want to bring in any entities that are other than what the observable world offers, or what could otherwise be used to deduce something about an observable state of affairs in the world. A Christian holds that there are indeed some truths about reality that can only be reconciled by positing God, but scientists and other thinkers have rightly pointed-out that God has often been invoked far too early in explanations throughout the history of science. However, if one holds that God is not (and would never be) required for any explanation for reality, this then moves beyond mere methodological commitments into a philosophical position, one called "ontological naturalism." This would indeed be a rival philosophical claim to Christianity and, being a purely metaphysical one, would not be justifiable by science.

Many Christians think that evolution is only at issue for properly reconciling the past, generally manifesting as a fight over how one should interpret the Bible. What can be said about this matter? The Bible is at the origin of a collection of values that has survived well through various systems of ideas and cultures. Based on that text, Christianity's descent and occasional modification has continually made it a strong survivor, and even today it successfully contends in the ecosystem of ideas and cultural values. Some have erroneously presumed that the problem is essentially (and all too conveniently) located in the book of Genesis, such as worrying about how the word translated "days" is not literal or how the exact order of creation is not scientifically sensible.

Since I think these issues have been comprehensively addressed elsewhere, I would only pause to mention one line of worry as it concerns the status of human beings in God's creation. More specifically, since God breathed his spirit into Adam, this makes humans qualitatively distinct from all else in creation. Unless one is committed to a non-spatial, non-temporal being blowing 78% Nitrogen, 21% Oxygen, 1% Argon and a few other trace elements into a naked primate, then it's a helpful understanding of "breath," as used in Genesis (and elsewhere in the Bible), to represent the abstract order that makes a thing what it is, such as standing for the structure of what are sometimes called "natural laws" or for the unique organization of something's attributes -- its "form" to use classical philosophical language. Furthermore, since both breath and spirit are related terms in the Bible, this can even account for an understanding of the form of what makes humans at least discernibly different from other animals – moral consciousness. Thus, with this interpretation of God's breathing life into Adam, the origin of humans need not be accounted as a radically distinct act in God's creation. Yes, humans are functionally distinct; but, no, they are not radically different.

Again, evolution is not only at issue for properly reconciling the past but is also a pivotal issue for the future. Contemporary applications in modern artificial intelligence use evolution to come up with solutions that are not easily or perhaps even possibly addressed by classical mathematical techniques. Here the concept of evolution moves beyond what merely applies to biology. Of course, it is not surprising that evolution is typically thought of in terms of biology, since that is where it arose as a scientific matter, even if conceptually the idea is much older and can be generalized: "variations occur in reproduction and will be preserved in successive generations approximately in proportion to their effect on reproductive fitness."[1]

Biological creatures happen to have DNA which, as is well known, is shaped in a double helix formed by base pairs attached to a sugar-phosphate backbone. Yet as long as there are traits that can be inherited and modified, probabilistic laws -- first identified by Gregor Mendel, blessed be he for his methodological, monastic gardening hobby -- will describe how those traits can be modeled and even passed-along in *non-living* things. Indeed this has been done in many ways within a field called evolutionary computation.

For some decades now, engineers have been developing algorithms which take their inspiration from natural evolution to generate solutions for problems that are too difficult to tackle with other methods of mathematics. Today evolutionary computation is a major area of machine learning. Its techniques are used in hardware design and reconfigurable electronic circuits, computer assisted manufacturing, internet search engines, materials production, and most recently in robotics. As an overall distinction, one might say that biological entities evolve toward what's true when those entities find survival stasis within their ecological niche; while artificial intelligence structures evolve toward what's true when their variables, equations, or programs find an optimal fit to their modeling goals.

How ironic that a process which we see in virtually all arenas of God's creation is denigrated within some quarters of Christianity as somehow being *incompatible* with a life of faith. On the contrary, evolution is God's favorite mechanism of developing his creation, and, by his grace, God has made this mechanism practically accessible even to us, the self-sentient products of that very mechanism used throughout its unfolding. So here's my view on evolution: eyes have not seen nor ears heard what God has provided for an open and wondrously novel future.

ENDNOTES AND SUGGESTED READING

1 Stuart Russel and Peter Norvig, *Artificial Intelligence: A Modern Approach*, 3rd ed. (Upper Saddle River, New Jersey: Prentice Hall, 2009) 130.

5

CONVERSATIONS ON EVOLUTION AND CHRISTIAN FAITH[1]

Dan L. Boone

Dan L. Boone serves as University President for Trevecca Nazarene University after serving in pastoral ministry for more than thirty years.

May I share an honest confession? I was initially hesitant to participate in this project because of my role as president of a Christian university. At Trevecca Nazarene University, we are willing to ask hard questions and converse with a maturing generation. However, I know that many people have already discovered all the answers they are willing to consider on issues of creation and science. They prefer not to be confused with other facts. Sadly, a conversation will not be possible, and their decision about a college for their sons and daughters may be the way they protest my involvement. I find that administrators have to think about safety for the institution as well as courage for the kingdom of God. I don't like the choices these realities give me.

But with the release of my book, *A Charitable Discourse: Talking About the Things That Divide Us*, I have discovered a hunger for intelligent, informed, respectful, Wesleyan dialogue on divisive issues. It is time for the church to discuss the elephant in the middle of the creation dialogue – evolution. The bulk of our Christian scholars/scientists are in a different camp than the bulk of our laity, and the battleground will most likely be the minds of our youth. If there is a widening gap between Christian universities and local church pews, how will the church deal with the potential divide?

Let me begin with some declarations. I am not a scientist and do not seek to write as a scientist. I have no scientific capacity to defend evolution. I do not know how old the earth is. I cannot explain instantaneous creation out of nothing, nor can I walk you through the intricacies of evolutionary development. But I am a biblical scholar and a Wesleyan theologian and will write toward a position that may allow holy conversation to occur between people who occupy pews and those who sit in university classrooms.

As I have listened, I have heard a fear emerge about the interpretation of the Genesis account of creation. The reasoning claims, "If we give in here and say it is a poem or a story or a myth, what's to say the virgin birth or resurrection won't be next? And if this part of the Bible is fiction, how do we know that other parts aren't as well? We must defend the Bible." It's as if the creation account of Gen. 1 is where conservative Christians have determined to make a Custer's last stand.

Recently, I came across an excellent book by John H. Walton, professor of Old Testament at Wheaton College. His interpretation of the creation narrative is carefully articulated in *The Lost World of Genesis One: Ancient Cosmology and the Origins Debate*. Walton expresses an understanding of Genesis that has captivated me for years.[2]

He suggests that Gen. 1 is the account of God coming to dwell in his creation with his creatures. While the pagan stories of creation seem to imply that creation exists for the gods and humans are meant to placate the gods, our story is quite different. God moves in a way to cause creation to function for the sake of his creatures. The biblical account narrates the activity of God on behalf of his creatures rather than forcing the creatures to appease their creator or suffer the consequences.

The major contribution of Walton is his insistence that this text, Gen. 1, is not about the creation of the material universe but rather about God making the world function for his purposes. The text is in keeping with the dominant strain of theology throughout Scripture--God has come to dwell among us. Could it be that Gen. 1 is not a story about the creation of the material world but about God making the world he created into his dwelling place?

Sadly, we have determined that Gen. 1 is the factual story of the creation of the world. We have taken our scientific theories to it and have superimposed them on it, looking for proof of the correct theory. We wish to prove that God created the world, not some random forces of chaos. But the people to whom the text is written could not have imagined a world that God did not create. They did not need to be convinced that God created the world. It was already assumed. What they did not understand was how God had come to dwell among them as a people for his purposes in the world. The story of Abraham and his family will flesh out how the God of the universe intends to do that.

So while we believe God to be the Creator of all things, Gen. 1 is not necessarily the story of material creation. When we force scientific creation theories on Gen. 1, we are asking the text to answer a question that is not being asked. Genesis 1 is not about the time periods over which the material universe came into existence but about a time when God created a functioning world, ordered according to his purposes, and came to take his Sabbath rest in the cosmic temple of creation. This train of thought is heard throughout the Bible:

> Thus says the LORD: Heaven is my throne and the earth is my footstool; what is the house that you would build for me, and what is my resting place? All these things my hand has made, and so all these things are mine, says the LORD. But this is the one to whom I will look, to the humble and contrite in spirit, who trembles at my word (Isa. 66:1-2, NRSV).

"Viewing Genesis 1 as an account of functional origins of the cosmos as temple does not in any way suggest or imply that God was uninvolved in material origins--it only contends that Genesis 1 is not that story."[3] We have plenty of Scripture that does declare God the Creator of all: Col. 1:16-17, Heb. 1:2, Ps. 100. If we allow a scientific debate to interpret Gen. 1, we have given modern science more weight than the human author of the text and the community to whom it was written. Biblical scholars across the centuries have seen the biblical story as a rich and complex text with many interpretations. Putting modern scientific ideas into this ancient story distorts the meaning of the text, which is clearly about God's faithful and caring relation to the world, not the details of how that world came to be.

Another concern is the development of a much-too-small doctrine of creation. The doctrine of creation must not be narrowed to a beginning. God continues to create because creation is rooted in God's future purposes. If Gen. 1 is to be read literally, I prefer to read it as the story of God interacting with his already-in-existence, chaotic, death-bound, disordered creation--which may have been materially existing for billions of years in some form--and bringing order out of chaos for the sake of dwelling with his people. In this reading, Adam and Eve are historical beings, whose names are part of a Hebrew genealogy, who experience God as their Creator, but even more so, who now understand their role within creation. They are privileged to function as obedient creatures of God, subduing and ruling creation as his partners. One does not have to explain how the material world came to be to understand how the text works to tell the community this story.

Or, in other words, Gen. 1 takes no position on the age of the earth or the method by which it came into existence. Thus, we need not pass a faith verdict on young-earth, old-earth, evolution, or any other theory of the origin of the material universe. We can enter the world of science with our eyes open wide. When science offers substantial evidence of a process or pattern in the universe, we simply thank God that his ways are becoming clearer to us than before. Christians have no fear of scientific discoveries of the origins of the universe. Our belief is not rooted in the how, because Scripture has not chosen to reveal the how. Our faith is rooted in the reality and experience of the God who came to dwell, who has a purpose to redeem and restore all of his creation, and who stubbornly continues to create that future until Rev. 21 is realized--a new Jerusalem come down, all things made new, death forever done, and God's dwelling with his people forever. Interestingly, the last chapters of the Revelation picture the temple made by God in which the Lamb is its light, and all creation celebrates.

So how does the Christian enter the conversation with science?

We are free to discover. But when science crosses the line of exploration and observation and begins to suggest that there is no meaning or function intended in creation, we have a problem. Science cannot fathom the mind and purpose of God in creation. There is no evidentiary way for this to be proved. When theories of evolution go beyond how species evolved to the purpose behind this evolution, they have entered a realm that is not science. They have become either philosophers or theologians. Our faith interprets the findings of science as the activity of a loving God.

What we learn from science need not shake our faith in God. Our line of defense is not a scientific model for Gen. 1 but confidence in the Creator God, who has a loving purpose for his creation, and intends to dwell with his creatures and redeem us. The greatest act of creation is yet to come--God making all things new.

ENDNOTES AND SUGGESTED READING

1 The following is an excerpt from *A Charitable Discourse: Talking About the Things that Divide Us* (Kansas City, Beacon Hill Press 2010). My experience with this book and its readers convinces me that the time is right for the discussion on evolution.

2 John H. Walton, *The Lost World of Genesis One: Ancient Cosmology and the Origins Debate* (Downers Grove, IL: IVP Academic, 2009).

3 Walton, p. 96.

6

ROBUST CONVERSATION AND COLLECTIVE DISCERNMENT

Eric Vail

Eric Vail is a Professor of Theology at Mount Vernon Nazarene University.

I recall a conversation I had with one of my junior high friends one hot Sunday afternoon, in the church parking lot, while we were waiting for our families. He wanted to understand how dinosaurs could fit in the whole sequence of the world when they were not mentioned in the Bible. I have no memory of where or when I had learned my answer to him, but in my sophisticated junior high way I told him that the "days" in Genesis 1 could be any length of time. Thus, the Genesis 1 story could actually have taken place over billions of years (very, very long "days"). Furthermore, there is no detailed listing of every species God created in Genesis 1, so there could have been time for God to create dinosaurs, for them to die, and God to create more land creatures.

What strikes me about that memory (among many things) is that there was never a time when my Nazarene family members or my Nazarene church tried to indoctrinate me to believe I had to pick between my Christian faith and the discoveries of science. It was possible to be a Christian and a scholar, no matter the academic discipline.

Perhaps my experience was abnormal; many of my relatives and I have loved learning and have shared that love at some point in our Nazarene colleges and universities by teaching in the fields of education, physics, athletics, mathematics, biology, computer science, and religion.

Perhaps my experience was abnormal given that my childhood church (College Church of the Nazarene in Bourbonnais, IL) was full of people who gave their lives to study and teach in so many fields of inquiry. No matter the reason, "Nazarene" never meant anything different to me than generation after generation of people wholly devoted to the doctrine of entire sanctification and higher education. To hear my grandparents' generation talk, the faculty and students at our Nazarene colleges and universities were seeking the highest level of excellence in their studies in the same way they were unwavering in seeking the highest reaches of holiness in the Lord. Piety and scholarship both were to be conducted wholly unto the Lord, with integrity and excellence.

Just because I do not remember experiencing a disconnect between the realms of piety and scholarship does not mean I have not struggled to understand the relationship. One of the first papers I remember being assigned as an undergraduate at NNU was on the relationship between faith and reason. Thanks to rigorous professors, I was made painfully aware of how much reflecting I still needed to do!

When talking to my junior high friend in the church parking lot, I had tried to listen to the voices of academic study and then make the Bible follow details of science. Thus, I was reading Genesis 1 as having really long "days" so that the story could be saying the same thing that scholarship about the Big Bang and the processes of evolution was saying. In wanting the Bible and science to say the same thing, I was allowing that thing to be dictated by science.

When I began taking biblical studies courses in college, I realized some important issues that changed my approach. First, the ancient worlds of Israel and the early Church were very strange compared to the customs, beliefs, and understandings of today. Until college, I had never read the Old and New Testaments as a cross-cultural experience. I had been understanding Scripture according to my worldview. Second, while God had certainly used biblical texts in formative ways in my life, I had been reading them with the sound of my own voice. It was as though the words were an extension of me (my world) through which God would touch me. When the world of the texts became foreign to me, the text itself became distinct from me and my own voice. Whatever the texts were saying, it was different from me and my categories. Third, the more I understood that the worldviews of the ancient world were not mine, the more I struggled to do what I had done in junior high. I could not just make the Bible fit my categories by saying, "The Bible says 'A'. That must mean it is claiming what I heard in my interpersonal communications class, my science class, or business class." Fourth, I had to get to know the Bible anew, on its own terms. It has its own voice (or, more accurately, voices). I had to understand its claims in the realm of its own time and location. Only after getting to know what it said in its own world could I begin to imagine what those kinds of claims would look like in my own world. That means that in the radical way God's self-disclosure disturbed people across time, it must disrupt me now (in the same Spirit), in ways peculiar to my own context.

In coming to respect the voices of Scripture, I could no longer mold them to my world. At the same time, I could not force my world—informed by centuries of scientific discovery—back thousands of years to take on ancient customs and worldviews. One option I tried was letting the worlds of faith and reason—Scripture and modern scholarship—have their own separate realms of authority. If Scripture is revelatory of "all things necessary to our salvation," I could let it govern matters of the soul and let scholarship speak authoritatively on matters of living in the world. Yet, that kind of dualism is dangerous (as I soon enough began to learn). It is exactly what the radical Enlightenment thinkers wanted. They wanted to split "the facts of life" from questions of religion and morality. Rational arguments about politics, economics, law, technological advance, or any other public issue were the only arguments that came to matter in the West; religion increasingly became an interior private matter. That way religion would get out of the way by having jurisdiction over only invisible spiritual matters and let non-theistic human reason govern our everyday affairs.

Scripture and science (or any other academic discipline), religion and reason cannot just separate from each other and have separate realms of authority. God's self-revelation and redemptive work has significance in our everyday engagement within the world (beyond much more than in our inner spiritual life). Yet, people who are going to do the scholarship to hear and reflect on the Church's canon are likely not trained to be scholars in the array of other academic disciplines. If our best readings of Scripture and theological reflections on the Christian faith are going to speak into everyday living, they have to be in conversation with the front-edge of our present world. But *conversation* from the biblical-theological side does not mean dictating what other scholars must say in their disciplines. It means hearing and reflecting together where the living God, revealed preeminently in Christ Jesus, might continually be discerned in these experiences and discoveries of God's creation.

At the same time, it is not up to other disciplines to dictate "the facts of life" upon which religion must append itself in order to help us cope and be good people in that world. Data does not interpret itself and give itself a name. Human beings give names and meaning to what we discover. Our Nazarene scholars, in the full spectrum of academic disciplines, should be in conversation with the people in the theological disciplines regarding naming and theologizing about the data with which they are working, in light of the triune God revealed to us. Robust conversation and discernment within the entire Body, across the spectrum of specializations, is the only way for us to proceed with a non-dualistic witness of and participation with God's creative-redemptive engagement in the world. Our vision of and cooperation in full-salvation and holiness, as New Creation is begun and awaited, may hinge on this interdisciplinary dialogue more than we have yet come to acknowledge.

7

TAKING SCRIPTURE SERIOUSLY

Shea Zellweger

Shea Zellweger serves as a ministerial intern at Overland Park Church of the Nazarene.

"You don't take Scripture seriously."

I was a junior in college when I heard those words spoken by my favorite professor in a class on some of my favorite books of the Bible, and I was instantly offended. *I* didn't take Scripture seriously? How anyone could say such a thing was beyond me. This man clearly knew nothing about me. Come to think of it, neither do you.

I was raised in a Christian home, where the Bible was a part of daily life. My family was very committed (probably over-committed) to our local church, my father read the Bible aloud every night, and in a given year I probably went to half a dozen Bible-centered events. The only test I ever failed was in 7th grade. Every question on the test was about evolution, and every answer I gave was from the Bible. I wasn't a scientist but knew what Scripture said was sufficient for me. By the time I graduated high school, I had memorized more Scripture than most people do in a lifetime, and along the way I had read dozens, probably hundreds, of books about spiritual warfare, the end times, and the mountains of evidence which proved the Genesis creation account was absolute fact. And in my sophomore year of college, I had made the ultimate sacrifice: I had given up on my intended lucrative career in psychiatry to pursue the thankless, penniless life of a minister, because I was certain that's what

God was calling me to do.

So there I sat in a class on the prophets, giving a brilliant (in my estimation) explanation of how Daniel's 70th week and Revelation fit together, when my professor leveled that unforgivable charge, "You don't take Scripture seriously." Perhaps you can understand now why the very thought offended me. He asked me to turn to 2 Timothy 3 and read verses 16 and 17. I did him one better and quoted them without hesitation.

> *"All Scripture is God-breathed and is useful for teaching, rebuking, correcting and training in righteousness, so that the man of God may be thoroughly equipped for every good work."*

He was not impressed by my instant recall, and pressed on making his point.

"Can you tell me where in the Bible it says Scripture is useful for telling the future?"

I could not.

"Where does it say Scripture is a primer on the end times?"

It doesn't.

"How about Math, or history, or geography, or science?"

No, I didn't know those passages either. He continued.

"The problem, Shea, is that you are asking Scripture questions it's not meant to answer, and not bothering with the questions it does. How does your analysis of these prophecies equip people to do good works? How does it teach, rebuke, correct, or train them in such a way that they can be righteous? If your interpretations can't do any of these things, then what's the point in having them?"

I couldn't bring myself to say it at the time, but my professor was completely right. I had spent so much time using the Bible as evidence to prove my point that I hadn't bothered to consider its intended purpose. It was as if I had been given a nice new pair of shoes, but instead of wearing them and letting them take me where I needed to go, I had been using them to kill bugs, prop open doors, and fix wobbly table legs. Shoes can be made to do all of those things, but that's not their purpose. There are other items out there that do those jobs a whole lot better. I hated to admit it, but I knew that I had to reconsider everything I thought I knew about Scripture.

So I began studying in earnest once more, but this time instead of trying to gather facts and evidence, I would ask myself "what is there about this passage that helps me to be prepared for good works?" Sometimes it changed my understanding a little, sometimes a lot, and sometimes not at all. But when I finally decided to tackle Genesis, everything changed. I half-read, half-remembered the seven day creation account. As I read, asking how this passage fulfilled the purpose of Scripture, I was amazed. This was the story about a God who cared about everything in the universe. It was a story about a God who looks at the world, at living things, and even at humans, and calls them "good." But they weren't just good. Those humans were a reflection of who God was. They bore in themselves an image of the Divine. It was a beautiful, intimate story about God's special love for and relationship with humans, which included me. It was then that I realized I could no longer read this, one of the greatest love poems ever written, as though it were a list of facts whose only use was to prove others wrong.

I am still not a scientist. I have read a lot on the subject, but I can't really tell you with absolute certainty the age of the earth or the timeline of how humans came into being. What I can tell you is what I learned the hard way: to really take Scripture seriously, we have to let Scripture do what it was meant to do. Scientists may find indisputable evidence tomorrow that this or that story in the Bible didn't happen as written, but that won't matter one bit for those who take Scripture seriously. We need not plug our ears or drown out the voice of the scientists because we know the right question to ask of Scripture, and it is not "did that really happen?" Scientists will do what they do best, proving and disproving this or that theory. We will be able to accept that with ease because we take Scripture, and its purpose, seriously.

8
CREATIVE LOVE

Deanna Hayden

Deanna Hayden is Pastor at Southwood Church of the Nazarene in Raytown, MO.

It was a bright and beautiful day outside, but my gaze was focused on my feet as I shuffled away from class that afternoon, kicking pebbles as I carried on a mental conversation with my Creator.

"You know, God, you have a lot of explaining to do. You told me to transfer to this school, and then you told me to switch to this crazy theology major. So if you're going to throw this curve-ball at me now, then we are going to have a serious problem."

Frustration, confusion, even anger filled my being as I struggled through the mess of issues that threatened to demolish the foundation of my faith. The Bible was holy. It was perfect. It was the place to which I went whenever I had a question for God. But new questions were hovering above, like a huge wrecking ball aimed at my belief system, and I feared it would leave me with nothing.

That day as I walked back to my dorm room, I didn't have much hope. All I could do was pray—that is, if what I was doing could actually be called "prayer"--streams of accusatory statements for God was more like it. But I continued on anyway for days and weeks, arguing with myself and with God, trying to make sense of it all. Finally the day came when I drew the line.

"Can I believe anything anymore? What is there to believe, God?"

The voice of my Redeemer echoed back to my heart: *I love you, child. You can believe that.* The chaos of questions within me suddenly became silent. My soul pondered that word for a while. God loves me. I could believe that. And if I could believe that, then there were some other things of which I could be certain. The Scriptures began to flow through my heart in a new way:

Hear, O Israel...love the Lord your God...[1]

This is the first and greatest commandment...[2]

And now these three remain: faith, hope and love. But the greatest of these...[3]

And so began the building of a new foundation of faith in my life. A faith not grounded in words on a page, but on the Word; a renewed faith founded on the God who is the very essence of Love. It is the foundation on which God has been rebuilding ever since.

That foundation has held fast through some pretty big ordeals, too. It held through the rest of that time of questioning in my life, more than 15 years ago now. (I say that as though the questioning is over, but I don't think it ever will be!) It held fast through the challenges of being a woman who felt a call to the ministry. And it continues to hold fast as I journey with people, inside the Church and outside, who struggle with their own faith.

There are a variety of struggles we seem to have. One of them, which is relevant to this conversation, is the issue regarding the Bible's account of Creation. I am not a scientist, so there's a lot I don't know about the discussion of evolution. I am a pastor. I am a student of the Scriptures. As I've discussed with other people things relevant to the Creation account and other biblical texts, I've learned the underlying value of the discussion usually has less to do with the intellectual argument itself. It has much more to do with the love and grace in which we approach each other in discussion. This is not to say there is no value in having a strong intellectual argument. I still have the responsibility of continuing to learn and grow as a student. But if I "can fathom all mysteries and all knowledge...but have not love, I am nothing."[4]

When I converse with my atheist friends, it is certainly important that I have a knowledge and understanding of the Bible and science. (Truth be told, I need to do a lot more scientific reading!) But if all I am interested in is stumping them and seeming to have all the answers, I will get nowhere. After all, that is what they are trying to do to me! It would make me no different from them. But if I have knowledge and understanding which is built on a foundation of Love, what amazing doors are opened for the Holy Spirit to work through! What awesome and miraculous victories can be accomplished through the labor of love. Thanks be to God!

It grieves me when Love is not the foundation on which our conversations take place. Especially when discussions between brothers and sisters in Christ take on a purpose of arguing, debating and "winning." What kind of witness is it to the world when we cannot speak to each other with love and respect? *Lord, have mercy on me for the times I've contributed to more tearing down than building up.*

The Bible is, first and foremost, the Story of God. And as God is Love, the Bible is the Story of Love. Let us not use it as a book of science or of history. Let us not use it as a tool to manipulate others, or destroy our relationship with people and in turn destroy their relationship with God. And let us not make it into an idol. The Bible is not God. Only God is God. As we journey together with others, inside and outside the Church, let us allow the foundational theology from which we speak be a Theology of Love. Let the words of our mouth and the meditations of our heart be pleasing in the sight of our Redeemer. And by the grace of God, let our loving openness to discussions like this one compel others to probe the unfathomable depths of their relationship with such an amazing and creative Love.

ENDNOTES

1 Deut. 6:4-5, New International Version.

2 Matt. 22:38, NIV.

3 1 Cor. 13:13, NIV.

4 1 Cor. 13:2, NIV.

9

EVOLUTION:

A STUMBLING BLOCK FOR EVANGELICALS

John W. Dally

John W. Dally is a chaplain at Pikes Peak Hospice and Palliative Care in Colorado.

Present day Evangelicals are being bombarded with scientific information that does not fit well into their theological model. While evangelicals are more than willing to spend time dealing with matters of humanity and God, they often fail to deal with the discoveries of science.

One subject that is a hot button for evangelicals is the subject of evolution. While 97 percent of scientists and 61 percent of the public believe that humans and other life forms have evolved over time,[1] many evangelicals will use any approach they can to discredit the model. Evangelicals have accepted significant numbers of discoveries by the very same scientific community, but when it comes to evolution they will look for potential flaws or even dismiss it altogether. Why is this the case?

It has been my experience that the reason for the rejection of evolution is twofold: Foundationalism and Anthropocentrism.

FOUNDATIONALISM

What is meant by the term evolution?
Evolution: Change in the gene pool of a population from generation to generation by such processes as mutation, natural selec-

tion, and genetic drift.[2]

From my experience, most evangelicals do not have difficulty with natural selection. Anyone who has watched a nature program can see with their own eyes that natural selection is a fact of life. Nor do evangelicals have a problem with adaptation. Even humans can adapt to different climates and conditions. The problem comes when it is applied to divergence of species, especially the human species because this is in conflict with the evangelical Biblical view. This is where we come up against Foundationalism. Foundationalism is defined as:

> *any theory in epistemology (typically, theories of justification, but also of knowledge) that holds that beliefs are justified (known, etc.) based on what are called basic beliefs (also commonly called foundational beliefs). Basic beliefs are beliefs that give justificatory support to other beliefs, and more derivative beliefs are based on those more basic beliefs. The basic beliefs are said to be self-justifying or self-evident, that is, they enjoy a non-inferential warrant (or justification), i.e., they are not justified by other beliefs.* [3]

In evangelical circles that basic belief from which all other beliefs are derived is the Bible.

To the Foundationalist, the Bible is the single foundation from which all other beliefs are derived. If anything comes along that brings questions or doubts to the Bible, it makes the whole structure of belief unstable. This brings a level of anxiety.

The awareness of Foundationalism is used by many preachers and theologians to afford them the authority to derive different beliefs and refute findings that do not agree with their model. As long as they cite the Bible as the foundation of their position, they are justified. A good example is the creationists. Years ago, I listened to a tape by a creationist center in San Diego. The speaker began his lecture by stating, "If we question a seven day creation model, we must question the entire Bible and therefore salvation itself." Then he went on to make his argument for a creationist model of earth. He was using Foundationalism to cause anxiety among his listeners and then laid out his arguments knowing that his audience would accept his model out of fear of losing their salvation.

The problem with Foundationalism, as applied to Christian faith, is that it is more in theory then reality. While evangelicals will say they affiliate with a church because it is Bible-centered (*sola scriptura*), in reality there are many sources for their affiliation– among them fellowship, acceptance, theology, worship style, programs and the like. Affiliation with a church may be by heritage. "My grandfather was a Nazarene, my father was a Nazarene, and I will be a Nazarene." Even the Wesleyan churches draw from four sources for doctrine: Scripture, tradition, reason, and experience. Where people may say it is the Bible that is the foundation of their faith model, they are relying on more of a web, with many points for stability. However, as long as a person "believes" they are founded on the Bible only, any assault on that foundation brings anxiety.

When confronted with an argument that shakes the foundation of the Foundationalist, he or she must shore up the foundation. To discredit an assault, a Foundationalist will sometimes develop irrational arguments. I knew a person who said that the things science has discovered are there to "test the faith" of the believer. God has made things "appear" the way they are to see if God's people will believe the Bible– God's word, or science– the work of Satan! I pointed out that this would make God a deceiver. However, he casually and thoughtlessly disagreed. I knew another person who knew that the stars are known to be millions and billions of years old. Yet he believed the Bible to say that the stars were created after the earth. His answer was that God created the beams of light before he created the star! Foundationalists will grasp at anything to shore up their foundation even if their answer is irrational. To alleviate the anxiety, they will put aside their own reason.

The strange reality about Foundationalists is that they themselves believe things that are contrary to the Biblical account. An unbiased look at Genesis 1 reveals that such people have already accommodated views that are counter to the account. To just name a few, these include:

1. The universe is vast and made of billions of stars with a vacuum of space.
2. Light comes from stars and the sun.

3. There is nothing over head but empty space and celestial bodies.

4. Dry land comes from the rise of continents caused by plate tectonics and continental drift.

5. Sunlight is necessary for vegetation to exist.

6. The sun was created from the nebula that gave birth to it through gravity. The remaining debris accreted to become the planets, including the earth.

7. With Hubble images we can see stars from 13.4 billion years ago. The naked eye galaxy, Andromeda, is 2.4 million light years away. That means that its light has been traveling at 186,000 miles/sec for 2.4 million years.

8. Reptiles came before mammals.

All of these are accepted by Foundationalists, even though they are counter to the Genesis 1 account.

Why do Foundationalists have no problem accommodating these points but will refuse to accept ideas like evolution? The reason is simple. We have irrefutable evidence of these observations. What choice does a Foundationalist have when confronted with such overwhelming evidence but to accommodate and accept it as fact, even if it is counter to Genesis 1?

As demonstrated, Foundationalism is more of a theory than a reality. Therefore, why will evangelicals accommodate a myriad of findings that contradict the biblical account, yet insist that life could not have evolved even though there is as much evidence to support evolution as to accept the accommodations mentioned above?

ANTHROPOCENTRISM

This is where anthropocentric forces come in. Anthropocentric means:

1. *regarding the human being as the central fact of the universe.*
2. *assuming human beings to be the final aim and end of the universe.*
3. *viewing and interpreting everything in terms of human experience and values.*[4]

Humans think they are special. Humans see themselves as the top of the food chain. Evangelicals consider humanity the pinnacle of God's creative act. The thought that humans may be no different from other animal species is abhorrent. The common feeling is that humanity is so special that it is outside the animal kingdom. The thought that humans evolved, that is they came from lower life forms, is anathema.

The anthropocentric view has led to severe problems. Refusing to see humanity's place in the natural order has led to abuses. It has led to the extinction of species, to cruelty visited upon other species, and to seeing other creatures as a source of gain. It has led to destruction of resources at the cost of the environment. In a word, anthropocentrism has led to exploitation.

It does not stop with the earth or animals. It has also been a source of strife within humanity. Deciding which races are more "human" than other races has led to abuse, from exploitation to slavery to war to genocide. However, for this discussion, I want to focus on the concept that the human race is better than any other species, that it is unique, and therefore, cannot be linked to the animal kingdom as portrayed in evolution.

If the human race is unique, it should be easy to distinguish differences between animals and humans. However, animals and humans do share traits. Some of those traits include culture, emotions, language, humor, use of tools, memory, self-awareness, intelligence, farming, and building.[5]

We share genetic traits as well,

> *The Human Genome Project is revealing many dramatic examples of how genes have been "conserved" throughout evolution -- that is, genes that perform certain functions in lower animals have been maintained even in the human DNA script, though sometimes the genes have been modified for more complex functions.*

> *This thread of genetic similarity connects us and the rough*

million other species in the modern world to the entire history of life, back to a single common ancestor more than 3.5 billion years ago. And the evolutionary view of a single (and very ancient) origin of life is supported at the deepest level imaginable: the very nature of the DNA code in which the instructions of genes and chromosomes are written. In all living organisms, the instructions for reproducing and operating the individual is encoded in a chemical language with four letters -- A, C, T, and G, the initials of four chemicals. Combinations of three of these letters specify each of the amino acids that the cell uses in building proteins. [6]

What makes humanity special is the higher thought processes that has allowed humans to comprehend the infinite, to understand the concept of a relationship, to create. However, this may make the human species advanced, but it does not make it unique and outside of the animal kingdom. It is not surprising that God "gives" man dominion and authority over nature. It is not intrinsic; it is assigned to the species (Gen. 1:28). For this we are blessed and should be grateful, but not anthropocentric. We are part of the animal kingdom. In fact, we are part of the cosmos.

There is a process that began with the Big Bang. In that event, everything necessary for the development of a species capable of comprehending God was in place. It has been determined that all stars find their origin in the Big Bang. All elements come from stars. All matter and life is made up from this multitude of elements. From primordial life, other forms evolved. Eventually, a species was successful enough and survived to become modern man. However, any significant event could have changed everything. If the asteroid had not crashed on the Yucatan peninsula, maybe a descent of the dinosaur would have filled the niche that humans have in the cosmos.

This leads to an interesting observation. Humanity is part of the cosmos. Humanity is part of the animal kingdom. Humanity is the only species we know of that can comprehend God and come into relationship with God. Therefore, we are the link between God and God's creation. We play the role of priests, between God and Creation. We represent creation to God, and as servants of God, we tend to creation and are put in charge of it. (Gen. 2:15)

The model of evolution is here to stay. We must confront it and deal with it from a rational and biblical approach. If we can reject the flawed concept of Foundationalism and the arrogance of anthropocentric thinking, we can explore the model of evolution and may find our rightful place in God's creation.

ENDNOTES AND SUGGESTED READING

1 Research Center for the People & the Press, http://www.people-press.org/2009/07/09/section-5-evolution-climate-change-and-other-issues/ Accessed 2/11/13.

2 Dictionary.com, http://dictionary.reference.com/browse/evolution. Accessed 2/11/13.

3 Reference.com, http://www.reference.com/browse/wiki/Foundationalism.

4 Dictionary.com, http://dictionary.reference.com/browse/anthropocentric Accessed 2/12/13.

5 Ultimate Listverse,http://listverse.com/2012/02/24/10-human-attributes-found-in-animals/ Accessed 2/14/13.

6 The Common Genetic Code, http://www.pbs.org/wgbh/evolution/library/04/4/l_044_02.html Accessed 2/14/13.

10

ALL CREATION SINGS

Mark Winslow

Mark Winslow is the Dean of the College of Natural, Social, and Health Sciences at Southern Nazarene University.

Praise God, from whom all blessings flow; praise Him, all creatures here below; praise Him above, ye heavenly host; praise Father, Son, and Holy Ghost.

"The Doxology" is an inseparable part of my memories growing up in the church. We always sang this anthem of praise following the offering, as a testament to God's blessing in our lives. More recently in my life, I have revisited this song often in my mind to ponder its affirmation that all of creation, the whole of the cosmos, the Earth and all the creatures therein – give glory to God as Creator. I have begun to contemplate more deeply what God's intent for the Earth and *all* its inhabitants is, and how our roles as stewards of the "Garden" are a part of His plans.

Clearly, my introduction hints of a different track than that taken by the writers of other fine essays in this compendium. My story is similar to those who have written about the process of examining the evidence for evolution and eventually accommodating evolution with faith. In so doing, I've had to reorient my views about the Bible and the traditions in which I was raised. I grew up as a Free Methodist missionary kid in Asia, attended a Christian college, and for the last 20 years have been a member of the Church of the Nazarene. It's only been in the last ten years that I have seriously considered the implications of biological evolution. I'll be the first to say that the evolutionary story of the cosmos and of life has profound implications. Entire books have been dedicated to addressing the issues. In this essay, my goal is to explore my relationship to animals within the larger story of evolution, and how that relationship fits within God's intent for goodness in creation.

As a Christian and a scientist, my beliefs about God and my place in His story rest on scriptural understanding – yet my theology should not occur in isolation from my knowledge about nature and the cosmos. Our Wesleyan heritage affirms that reason and experience (both inextricably linked to scientific understanding) shape and lend credence to our understanding of Scripture and accompanying tradition. For example, Genesis 1 advances the proposition of a created order and God's declaration of the goodness of Creation. I choose to uphold this proposition while acknowledging Earth's rugged history in which untold numbers of animal species have come and gone prior to the advent of human beings. Genetics and paleontology also reveal that human beings share an indelible connection with animals.[1] Science simply informs us that these things are plausible. What we as Christians choose to do with that knowledge should be guided by scriptural understanding and the work of the Holy Spirit to "open our lives to His truth and the truth about the world" so that we may "become better persons, not just people with more information."[2]

I can't pretend to fully comprehend God's declaration that all of created order was at one time good when I sift through the geological evidence, which suggests death and destruction is the dominant storyline within the annals of Earth's history. Yet personally, I maintain that God's intent for creation was and continues to be goodness. Further, I believe that in the final eschaton God will redeem all of creation to Himself. The bookends of the Bible, the first two chapters of Genesis and the last chapters of Revelation, attest to God's intention of shalom for creation. It's just that everything in-between – including the time and place in which I find myself – is so messy.

Thus, I find myself pondering what role I play in bringing about God's intent for a restored creation. God commands us to exercise dominion over all the creatures of the Earth (Gen. 1:28). The Hebrew word for dominion (*rādâ*) fits the portrait of a king who executes justice for the oppressed, delivers the needy, helps the poor, and embodies righteousness in all he does (Psalms 72).[3] Our relationship to the Earth and its creatures is to be the same. As Tom Regan writes, "We are expressly chosen by God to be God's vice-regents [divine imaging] in our day-to-day affairs of the world; we are chosen by God, that is, to be as loving in our day-to-day dealings with the created order as God was in creating that order in the first place."[4]

Our work as vice-regents is not exclusive to human beings but includes those aspects of creation in which we can play a part in God's redemptive plan. While we as Christians endeavor to live in ways that help others to know the transformative grace of Christ and restore them to right relationship with God, self, and one another – I would also hope that we want our lives to be marked by right relationship with the rest of God's creation, including His creatures. However, our relationship with animals has been marked by disregard and abuse. The rise of factory farming in the last half century in which chickens, pigs, and cows are crowded into concentrated animal feeding operations (known as CAFOs) force billions of animals to live in confined spaces that severely limit their movement and natural behaviors.[5] Jonathan Safran-Foer uses the term "war" to describe our "technologies and techniques brought to bear... and the spirit of domination" we bring against animals.[6]

Our society's disregard for animals stems largely from viewing them as commodities, and as such, their pain and suffering is secondary to the bottom line: profit. Yet, in the extended view of history, animals predated humankind – surely there was God-ordained purpose to their existence long before human beings arrived on the scene. Howard Synder writes that "life forms have their own 'right to exist' because they come from God's hand." Animals have intrinsic worth regardless of their association with humankind.[7]

John Wesley was keen to note that the capacity to be in relationship with God "distinguishes men from beasts, — that they [humans] are creatures capable of God, capable of knowing and loving and enjoying him."[8] Despite this theological assertion, biological evolution has revealed that we share more in common with animals than once thought. In recent years, neurobiologists have begun to better understand the neural networks through which many animals experience consciousness and affective states – in ways similar to humans.[9] We should not be surprised then to learn that "farm animals feel pleasure and sadness, excitement and resentment, depression, fear, and pain. They are far more aware and intelligent than we ever imagined … they are individuals in their own right."[10] Yet, as Wesley acknowledged, much of the suffering of animals is due to the "violence and cruelty of him that is now their common enemy, — man." Surely this is not part of God's original intent and eventual hope for creation.

My purpose here in writing about creation in a theological construct, and informed somewhat by biological evolution, is not to advocate for any particular change in lifestyle. However, I would hope that we would pause to reflect that since God cares for creatures, we also should care for them. In the end, we recognize that it is only through Jesus Christ that "all the broken and dislocated pieces of the universe—people and things, animals and atoms—get properly fixed and fit together in vibrant harmonies, all because of his death, his blood that poured down from the cross" (see Col. 1:18-20, MSG). But in the meantime, may each of us intention ourselves through Christ to be part of God's redemptive plan for creation – and even if metaphorically so – sing with all of creation a song of praise to God, the Creator and Sustainer of life.

ENDNOTES AND SUGGESTED READING

1 Darrel R. Falk, *Coming to Peace with Science: Bridging the Worlds Between Faith and Biology* (Downers Grove, IL: Intervarsity Press, 2004).

2 Timothy J. Crutcher, "Wesleyan Ways of Knowing and Doing," *Telos: The Destination For Nazarene Higher Education*, G. Chenoweth and B. Ragan (eds.) (Bourbonnais, IL, 2011).

3 Steven Bouma-Prediger, *For the Beauty of the Earth: A Christian Vision for Creation Care* (Grand Rapids, MI: Baker Academic, 2010).

4 Tom Regan, "Christianity and Animal Rights: The Challenge and Promise," *Liberating Life: Contemporary Approaches in Ecological Theology*, C.Birch, W. Eaken, and J. McDaniel (eds.) (Maryknoll, NY: Orbis Books, 1990) 80.

5 See for example, the *Pew Commission on Industrial Farm Animal Production* at http://www.ncifap.org/.

6 Jonathan Safran-Foer, *Eating Animals* (New York, NY: Back Bay Books, 2009) 33.

7 Howard Synder, *Salvation Means Creation Healed: The Ecology of Sin and Grace* (Eugene, OR: Cascade Books, 2011) 45.

8 See http://wesley.nnu.edu/john-wesley/the-sermons-of-john-wesley-1872-edition/sermon-60-the-general-deliverance/.

9 e.g. http://fcmconference.org/.

10 Jane Goodall, in her introduction to Amy Hatkoff's *The Inner World of Farm Animals: Their Amazing Social, Emotional, and Intellectual Capacities* (Stewart, Tabori & Chang, 2009).

11

REGARDING THE VIRTUE
OF A FULL DIET

Henry Spaulding

Henry Spaulding is University President at Mount Vernon Nazarene University.

Living on a university campus requires a multi-lingual approach to intellectual discourse. The process of engendering a healthy conversation surrounding theology and evolution necessitates just such a capacity. Ludwig Wittgenstein provocatively writes, "A main cause of philosophical disease – a one-sided diet: one nourishes one's thinking with only one kind of example."[1] My experience has taught me that it is very easy to find nourishment in discussions like theology and evolution on one side of the issue. The lines are drawn and the enemies are identified, so that the mind can be settled and life can go on.

Many years ago, I had a student who drank from only one well. Everything was clear, and questions were rarely allowed to confuse his self-imposed clarity. One day I leaned over toward him and said, "You have concluded entirely too much for an eighteen-year-old." I suppose this merely confirmed his suspicions about me! I have found that the challenges presented by the theology and evolution dialogue encourage many to drink from one well. It is a temptation that I feel very keenly.

My path has been in the so-called "soft sciences": theology, philosophy, and the humanities. I enjoy the banter in the *Platonic Dialogues* or even the *Dialogues Concerning Natural Religion* (Hume). There is something interminable about such discussions, and it is relatively safe to roam with these texts, ideas, and themes. It has been an easy place for me to remain for more than thirty years of university/seminary teaching. This does not feel much like a disease, but then Wittgenstein may have a point.

On the other hand, science has a language and culture all its own. I am personally intimidated by this network of ideas, theories, and explanations. I know several scientists, i.e. biologists and physicists, who are people of faith and can travel the pathways of evolution with ease and even enjoyment. This reminds me of another thought expressed by Wittgenstein, "If a lion could talk, we could not understand him."[2] Clearly, understanding requires more than a dictionary; it requires a form of life. This is precisely where I am trying to learn how to be attentive to the importance of avoiding a one-sided diet. Perhaps, the most important lesson for me has been to listen and learn as much as I can.

There are several reasons why a "full" intellectual diet is essential for greater understanding. First, the Scripture indicates that God created the heavens and the earth. This event was not "private" in any way. It was a very "public" event, even though no one was there to witness it. For this reason, it is a legitimate concern for people of faith and science. There is no reason to fear the empirical study of the universe. Augustine, the fifth-century theologian, referred to this as the "vestiges of the Trinity." We should expect to see the fingerprints of God in creation. Admittedly, Augustine had much less suspicion regarding nature than we Protestants often exhibit.

This leads to my second observation. The theology-and-evolution-intersection should point us theology-types to think more about nature and graced-reason. Luther and Calvin cast some measure of doubt in this area, and it has led many to a one-sided example. The disease Wittgenstein seems to be pointing toward runs the risk of diminishing the capacity for engaging the world in an open and honest manner. Wesley opens the door toward a fuller engagement of the world. While it is clear that Wesley understands the primacy of the Scripture for theology, he allows for reason to play an essential role. Graced-reason points to a fuller diet and allows for a robust discussion. The multi-lingual requirement for engaging faith and evolution seems to be allowed by Wesley's approach. On the way to engaging a full-diet, I have found insight in this methodology.

Understanding evolution in its purely naturalistic form does not appeal to me, but neither do the views that refuse an honest engagement with empirical science. Many of my colleagues in the natural sciences struggle with these very questions. Bringing science into conversation with the Christian faith is difficult, but a full diet requires it.

Finally, the conversation is an expression of faith. When we take theological work seriously, it leads to a disciplined reflection on the world through the lens of the sources of wisdom found in the Christian tradition. I know that such a path is fraught with danger and the possibility of misunderstanding, but it can be the source of an intellectual diet worthy of a reflective Christian.

Admittedly, talking about evolution and theology has never been on the top shelf of my agenda, but this says little about its true significance. Contemplating such a full diet suggests the need for intellectual humility. I see entirely too much hubris these days on issues like this. Learning to listen with an open mind seems necessary for anyone who intends to think fully, to learn from those who we may not always agree, and think through issues in community. This leads to a certain fearlessness borne of intellectual honesty.

Talking about evolution and theology requires a fearlessness of character. Forces at work in the church and society tempt me to timidity. It is not possible to engage in this conversation while looking over our shoulders. In fact, I cannot lead a university or teach theology with an attitude of self-protection and safety. This is a great deal like engaging the intersection of evolution and theology. Since I am a native Southerner, let me put it this way – *You can stay on the front porch, but you miss entirely too much if you do.*

ENDNOTES AND SUGGESTED READING

1 Ludwig Wittgenstein, *Philosophical Investigations*, G.E.M. Anscombe Trans (Englewood Cliffs: Prentice Hall, 1953, 1958) 255.

2 Ibid, 223.

12

EVOLUTION, THE BIBLE, AND HUMAN INTELLECT

Jim Edlin

Jim Edlin is Professor of Biblical Literature and Languages at Mid-America Nazarene University.

The surgeon's words sent a chill through my body. Our family gathered in a small room while a man of great skill and knowledge announced that he could not save my father's life. The surgery was a fairly simple procedure. However, the doctor discovered that radiation treatments from twenty years before made surgical repair impossible. Science failed my father and it cost him his life.

The best scientific knowledge twenty years before told my father that his cancer would be best treated by the use of surgery, medication, and radiation. Yet some people with the same cancer chose only surgery. As it turned out, that group faired better than those who opted to follow the best medical advice of the time. They tended to live longer with fewer complications.

MARRED REASON

My father's story illustrates an important biblical truth: human intellect is marred. Sin has skewed our reason. We do not have to read far into the Bible to get the point. Genesis 3 tells us that sin makes us think wrongly about ourselves, others, and God. We, who once were in perfect harmony with our social and physical environments, found ourselves alienated from them because of our rebellion against God.

According to Genesis, we began to think that we could no longer be entirely honest with those around us. We felt ashamed, that we must hide from our Creator, blame fellow human beings, and distance ourselves from both of them. We were no longer comfortable in our world. How foolish. How unreasonable. How misdirected. Why would humans think like that? Because of sin. A disrupted relationship with God mars human reason.

SKEWED SCHOLARSHIP

If we have understood the Bible correctly on this point, then it is possible that current evolutionary theory may be wrong. Our best scientific understandings could be skewed. There are many gaps in our knowledge, many questions yet unanswered, and many biases to overcome. We are working with finite, underdeveloped, sin corrupted minds and hearts.

It is also likely that some of our best biblical understandings are wrong. During the 19th century, our brightest biblical scholars told us that Daniel was confused historically. Several issues suggested this, but what was so blatantly obvious is the story in Daniel 5. It indicates that Belshazzar ruled Babylon when it fell on October 12, 539 BC to the Persians. Of course scholars knew from other ancient texts that Nabonidus was Babylon's final king. That is, they knew this incontrovertible fact until additional texts became known that proved Daniel correct and embarrassed biblical scholars. Belshazzar actually did ruled Babylon in its final days while the eccentric Nabonidus remained absent.

The history of both science and biblical scholarship is littered with misunderstandings, twisted facts, corrupted data, false premises, and inaccurate conclusions. In spite of this, much has been achieved in these fields. Human knowledge has advanced in some incredible ways. My father undoubtedly lived an additional twenty years because of developments in medical knowledge at the time. Biblical scholars understand the setting of the Bible far better than they did centuries ago. Yet much has been distorted, missed, and misused as well.

While we celebrate advances in human knowledge, we must remain fully aware of just how vulnerable it is. We may not have all the information we need. We may be misreading the information that we have. We may be biased. We may be too emotionally attached. We may arrive at the wrong conclusion. Truth may elude us. The "assured results" of biblical scholarship and of scientific knowledge simply may not be true.

SAVING GRACE

Such a situation might be cause for despair, if not for the Author of All Truth. Our fragile and imperfect reasoning leads us to one place and one place only. It throws us back upon the grace of God. We are entirely at God's mercy. We have no other place to go. If we ever come to truth, it will only be because the Spirit of Truth enables us to perceive it. Truth belongs to God alone. It is his gift to give. "He gives wisdom to the wise and knowledge to the discerning. He reveals deep and hidden things; he knows what lies in darkness, and light dwells with him" (Daniel 2:21-22).

All truth is revealed truth. It is God's gift to humans. Often it comes to those who seek it earnestly, discipline their minds, spend hours analyzing, and otherwise work very hard at discovering. This is where we become confused. We think that somehow we achieved this knowledge because of our perseverance and developed analytical abilities. We become enamored with our own brilliance and fortitude. In the end, however, we know nothing apart from what God allows us to know. We are clueless unless God gives us a clue.

A POSTURE OF HUMILITY

As we pursue a discussion about the interface of evolution and theology, I propose a posture of humility for theologian and scientist alike. I recommend frankly confessing that we do not possess all the data nor do we fully understand what we do have. May we offer our thoughts and listen to others without insisting that we possess the inside scoop. We are simply fellow pilgrims on this journey for truth.

Let us remind ourselves frequently, as the Scriptures do, that God hates arrogance and loves humility. "He mocks proud mockers but gives grace to the humble" (Proverbs 3:34). May we seek God's grace and freely acknowledge that any insight we gain into truth is purely a gift from heaven.

Surely God would be pleased with such a posture on all sides of the discussion. In fact, God may be more likely to lead us toward the truth about evolution and theology from just such a place.

13
PREFACE TO THE DIALOGUE

Dee Kelley

Dee Kelley is Senior Pastor of San Diego First Church of the Nazarene.

In the northern United States, a driver must become adept at navigating a car in the snow. Winter driving requires additional skills and attention to issues that are not part of normal driving conditions. In the winter, the freedom and joy of "making donuts" in a wide-open, snow-covered parking lot gives way to the intensity of driving on a highway in a heavy snowfall. On the open road, the large snowflakes fly right at the windshield and are mysteriously captivating in their unique shape and rhythm. It is easy to become so focused on the snowflakes that one loses sight of the road and the other cars. Mesmerized by the snowflakes three feet away, a driver can completely miss the circumstances that lie ahead.

The focus of this dialogue is evolution and faith. It is a topic worthy of attention and has produced some outstanding essays, as you certainly have noticed. My concern is for the people in my congregation. I don't want them to think that a person's view on evolution has become, on one side of the debate, the litmus test for faithful Christianity and, on the other side of the debate, the litmus test for reasonable Christianity. When someone is in the middle of the stormy debate, it is easy to become solely focused on the beauty, shape and rhythm of the arguments yet forget what it is that defines us as the body of Christ. Our faith is built on Jesus. Very simply, we worship the Christ that Scripture reveals.

In John 13 and 14, the disciples (specifically Peter and Thomas) ask Jesus to tell them where He is going. It appears they want a map for their journey, a list of instructions. Jesus doesn't give them a list of instructions on how to stay faithful. Instead He says, "I am the way." They ask for a map, and He offers them the Map-Maker. The present dialogue or debate remains beautiful as long as it gives way to that which is essential–relationship with Christ. In regard to this debate, if I received indisputable evidence that my position on this issue is wrong, would that destroy my faith? If so, then maybe I am not ready to engage in the conversation. On the other hand, if my faith is anchored to my relationship to Christ, then I can listen attentively, consider open-mindedly, and participate graciously.

THE PATH OR THE DESTINATION

There are at least five different ways to get from my home to a great shopping and eating area called the Gaslamp District. One route will give you fewer traffic lights, one route is better during heavy traffic, one route is more scenic, and another will allow you to stop by a few other important spots on the way. I'm not sure I can say which route is the best; it probably depends on the traveler. That's not to say that any route is okay because not every route takes a person to the Gaslamp District. However, it does imply that someone else's path will probably not mirror my own. Similarly, regarding faith, I enthusiastically recommend a relationship with Jesus to everyone, but I'm not sure I would recommend the path I have taken to anyone. Sadly, I often forget that fact and assume others are on my same pathway. So, when we are in a debate on a subject like evolution, please forgive me when I am yelling instructions to you and the instructions don't make sense. I have forgotten that we may be on different roads. And when you offer sage instructions to me and I give you that blank stare that implies I have no idea how you came to that conclusion, please know that what I see through my windshield may not look exactly like what you see through your windshield. Even though our roads may be headed to the same destination, the landscape and turning points may be vastly different.

When my daughter was a toddler I gave her very specific instructions about crossing the street. She was never to step off the curb without first taking hold of her mom or dad's hand. This was an important rule, and we reiterated it time and again. My daughter is now 25 and living 1500 miles away. She doesn't wait at an intersection for me to show up to take her hand. She is fully capable of crossing the street by herself. It's not that the rule we established so many years ago is wrong. It's just that the rule is no longer adequate for the current conditions. I contend that the stakes are still high when my daughter crosses the street, and caution is still merited. However, for her, and for me in this current dialogue, some arguments no longer seem adequate for the roads we are trying to cross. And it may be that the new conclusions we reach will prove to be inadequate for the landscape my daughter's child faces.

As you read this book, I think you will be challenged by a reverence for Scripture, a call to civility, and an adherence to an orthodox Christology. You will read personal testimonies of faith, descriptions of the body of Christ, and confessions of uncertainty. You will not find essayists who defend a young-earth approach. I do hope that those who have taken up the challenge to engage in this conversation will have the courage and opportunity to apply their same methodology and insight to other issues where science and Scripture cross paths. We are in need of greater reflection and dialogue on significant social issues where Scripture offers even fewer texts than it does on the creation story. This includes, but is certainly not limited to, abortion, same-sex attraction, and euthanasia.

The truth of the matter is that there are wonderful, God-fearing, Christ-following, Spirit-led people on different sides of the debate. I am sure that I have something I can learn from all of them. My hope is that you and I don't get lost in the minutia or lose fellowship as we split hairs. Instead, I pray that the dialogue leads to inspiring moments that celebrate God's creation, humble moments that reveal how much we have to learn from each other, insightful moments when we catch a fresh glimpse of God's truth, reflective moments when we contemplate new ideas, and eternal moments when we set the book down and go walk in nature instead of debating the nature of nature. So, I hope you enjoy the essays as much as I have, but I have to confess that they don't hold a candle to the joy of spinning a car in circles on a snow-covered parking lot.

14

LOOKING FORWARD:

HOW MILLENNIAL VOICES WILL SHAPE THE "SCIENCE-RELIGION" DEBATE

Grant Miller

Grant Miller is Associate Pastor for Young Adults at Nampa First Church of the Nazarene in Nampa, ID. He also works as Web Content Specialist at Northwest Nazarene University.

For me, it all began with the stars.

I was serving as a counselor at a Young Life camp in a remote part of British Columbia. Every night, after my cabin was asleep, I would leave them under the watch of my co-counselor and settle into the camp's main office for a few hours, where I could access an astronomy course I was taking online through a satellite internet connection.

One evening in the middle of the week, I exited the office well after midnight. The campground is built on a small peninsula that stretches out into a coastal inlet, and in the evenings it is usually very cool by virtue of its proximity to the water and frequent cloud-cover.

However, that night the clouds were absent, and as I glanced up at the open sky my stomach flipped. Above me, free from light pollution, was a brilliant display of stars. The dazzling panoramic magnitude of the heavens was everywhere, and I was awestruck.

If I have ever come close to a legitimate crisis of faith, it was at this moment. For weeks I had been studying the vastness of the universe:

things like black holes, planet formation, and the Hubble Deep Field. My mind was full of the immensity and intensity of the universe. To put it plainly, I freaked.

I grew up in an amazing Christian home. I'm an example of a dwindling group of Millennials who have never had a strong issue with the church and believe in its general organization and mission. I grew up in Christian schools, the son of Christian educators. I used biology textbooks in high school that discredited modern scientific theories about the origins of life and was taught to understand Genesis 1 in a fairly literal way. I remember studying with fervor concepts like the gap theory and how the firmament played a key role in the flood of Genesis 6 as well as the reduction of the human lifespan.

I don't bring up my scientific education or those topics because I think they were improper. I received an excellent education that was highly developed in all areas, and I attended Bible classes where different styles of interpretation and theology were common fare. While I know some had a different experience, my education was much more about making me a critical thinker than about making me a good fundamental evangelical (though there's nothing wrong with that, either).

However, I think the feelings I experienced at the camp that night are part of an experience that most members of my generation have undergone. Many of us attended schools where evolution was taught as fact; some, like I, were taught it as theory. All of us, however, if we attended a typical church, have probably had to come to grips with the cognitive dissonance that arises from the confrontation between science and common evangelical thought on the topic of origins.

Standing there, staring up at the sky, I had an epiphany that those bright shiny things up in the sky were *actually real*. They occupied physical space. I realized that photons that were produced millions (and billions) of years ago via nuclear fission in the hearts of distant burning suns were striking my corneas for the first and last time, and I was deeply terrified of what it meant for my identity as a human being.

I was afraid because at the core of my young evangelical Christian heart was the notion that the human race (and I, by proxy) is the pinnacle of the created order. I suppose the more descriptive way to describe one of the central tenets of my faith to that point was a misguided anthropocentrism. My story of salvation and relationship with Jesus had a core that was built on the fact that human beings were created on their own special day, in their own special way.

That seems to also be one of the central issues for many people in the discussion of origins. It's hard to imagine some of the ideas presented by evolutionary theory as being true because it seems to threaten the role of humanity. If all life is fundamentally interconnected at a genetic and chemical level, what does that mean about the role of humankind as caretaker of the Earth? What about sin nature? What about Christology? What about *imago Dei*? The list could go on for quite some time.

These are incredibly important questions, and proponents of a reconciliation of origin theory and the Christian faith need to be willing to deal with them in a more honest and direct way. However, in my experience, many members of my generation are just too tired of the whole debate to feel up to the task. Study after study of millennial attitudes about religion report that we don't believe the church to be a place where safe and honest dialogues about religion and science can occur. I find that desperately sad; if there were ever a generation most capable of shaping doctrine on this issue for centuries to come, it would be such as this.

I belong to a generation that has plenty of room in its margins for gray areas like this topic, because most Millennial Christians—at least those of us who are staying in the church—are finding that origin theories that do not line up with literal 6-day creationism are not necessarily at odds with our relationships with Jesus Christ. In fact, most of us don't seem to feel you must pick one or the other, as long as you authentically believe that your place in God's hands is not threatened by your opinion about the complexity, enormity, or age of the universe; instead, your place is actually made all the more significant *because* of those things.

Are these topics worth the debate and development of opinions?

Of course, as long as they lead us to a better relationship with God and others. Should we be teaching young people to ask deep and hard questions about science and theology, perhaps even questioning what they have been taught in both Sunday school and sophomore biology? Indeed. Is this discussion worth bringing into our churches as a central point of conversation and charitable discourse? If the church wants to survive this first representation of a truly postmodern generation, then the answer must be a resounding and oft-repeated "yes."

In fact, if any generation were best equipped to successfully bridge this divide, it would be the Millennials. Some sociologists have seen fit to call Millennials the first truly post-modern generation, giving rise to all of that room for gray-area processing. Growing up in a world that is filled with a constant stream of technological innovations that change the way humanity exchanges ideas and uncovers information, it's hard to imagine that this generation would not have perspectives and beliefs that differ drastically from those of their parents and grandparents. I think there are a few reasons that these emerging differences in thinking might be priming Millennials for reconciliation of the religion/science discussion.

First, Millennials have the most exposure to recent scientific thinking because of the ongoing progression within the scientific community that recognizes evolutionary theory as being a non-debatable issue. Be it high school biology class or graduate-level research, Millennials are presently distributed across every level of formative scientific experience, and they are learning that they must come to reconcile whatever religious perspectives they hold with an overwhelming amount of evidence for theories concerning the origins of life and the universe that conflict with a hardline conservative/literalist theological stance.

Second; Millennials, if they are indeed the first truly post-modern generation, naturally have the most room for reconciliation and integration of beliefs within different conceptual systems. A postmodern generation is going to be more naturally inclined to look for connections and accept potentially conflicting ideas between scientific and religious worlds than the more black-and-white epistemological tendencies of Enlightenment-influenced generations.

Finally, Millennials have demonstrated and reported repeatedly the desire to discuss the religion/science debate within the church and have also iterated dissatisfaction with the church's current efforts in this arena. Faced with the choice between ignoring the topic and losing a generation or embracing the discussion, the church is poised to begin and perpetuate a reframing of its stance. Millennials will likely compose a major part of the leading voices in that discussion.

I, like most members of the Millennial group, am not interested in living or dying for the cause of propagating evolutionary theory or attacking it, but like most of my generation's Christians, I feel that the worlds of science and religion are very capable of working together. We know and believe that God has created the universe and is involved in constantly sustaining it, but the path that we took to get here is a cursory detail next to the call to holiness that is a direct result of salvation. I hope that in recognizing this black-and-white truth, we can engage civilly with one another on scientific and theological topics, seeking above all the ways that "since the creation of the world, God's eternal qualities—his eternal power and divine nature—have been clearly seen, so that all are without excuse" (Romans 1:20).

15

I'VE EVOLVED TOO

Stan Ingersol

Stan Ingersol is Denominational Archivist for the Church of the Nazarene.

"The evolutionary idea is certainly compatible with Christianity; but not so long as it claims to be the supreme idea, to which Christianity must be shaped. Evolution is within Christianity, but Christianity is not within evolution." – P. T. Forsyth

I was raised by a zoologist. That has been one of my life's greatest blessings, for to paraphrase Charles Darwin, "There is grandeur in [their] view of life." Biologists look at the natural world with a sense of wonder. With artists, they share a sense of awe.

As a young science teacher, Dad introduced the science fair to Ponca City High School in Oklahoma in the mid-1950s and served as its faculty sponsor for three years. Then, in 1959, his work took us to Ethiopia for seven years. He taught at an agriculture college that Oklahoma State University was fostering in Harar Province. Other staff biologists were Bill Burger, later curator of the botanical collections at the Field Museum of Natural History in Chicago and author of *Perfect Planet, Clever Species* (2003); and entomologist Bob Hill. The three biologists were intrepid researchers, and on weekends Dad plotted the stratification of mammals in Ethiopia's Chercher Highlands and adjacent areas, going to rain forests, rock valleys, and desert plains. He added hundreds of specimens to the collections at the College of Agriculture and established a zoo at the college.

Dad took evolution seriously. One morning at the breakfast table, he asked my brother and me, "What is Darwin famous for?" We both replied, "The theory of evolution." "No," Dad answered, "the theory of evolution was around long before Darwin. What he contributed were two plausible explanations for what drives evolution: natural selection and sexual selection." Dad taught science even at breakfast.

My brother inherited Dad's science gene. He, too, is a zoologist. Dad's sisters married agricultural scientists who taught at Oklahoma State University. I've known scientists all my life. I've loved scientists and been loved by them. These relationships shape my life-long interest in how to understand science in the context of our Christian faith.

Likewise, my professional interests shape my understanding, especially Church history. My particular affection is for the history of the Victorian Church in England and America, when nineteenth-century science brought new understandings to the Christian Faith. And church history shows that churches and individuals grappled with these challenges in various ways. Owen Chadwick notes in *The Victorian Church* that the new science had little influence on the rise of unbelief, which was largely based on philosophical grounds, not scientific ones. James Moore's *The Post-Darwinian Controversies* demonstrated that some of Darwin's most intense intellectual foes had no real antennae for the Christian faith, while, conversely, some of his most convinced supporters were drawn from the ranks of committed and fully orthodox Christian believers.

When I first learned about evolution in science class, the concept conflicted with what I believed the Bible taught, and yet I suspected that it had to be true in some way. After all, my father was a scientist whom I knew, loved, and respected. I also respected his colleagues in the science department, whom I knew to be honest and honorable. On the other hand, no one really helped me to think through how to square this with the first eleven chapters of Genesis. As a result, I compartmentalized my thinking. Four years of study at a Nazarene college didn't help. All of the biologists at Bethany Nazarene College were evolutionists when I arrived there as a freshman in 1968. In fact, all of the professors who taught science were, except one, who soon retired. Still, there was reluctance to talk about evolution and the Christian Faith. There was similar reluctance on the part of the religion faculty, so I put Genesis 1-11 in a little box and ignored it.

This compartmentalization wasn't that uncommon for my generation. But eventually I had to take the issue out of that little box and deal with it.

I have a strong visceral reaction against the whole notion of "myth" in the Bible. No matter how the term is qualified or explained, I can't get past that visceral reaction to a word that will always connote "not true" in my mind.

On the other hand, I have no visceral reaction to thinking of Genesis' early chapters as theology, pure and simple, that is expressed in narrative form. There are, after all, many different ways that Biblical writers "do" theology. In the Gospels, Jesus is portrayed as doing theology through teaching and parable. The Gospel-writers themselves theologize through writing the passion narratives. Other New Testament writers wrote theology by means of epistle and apocalypse. And in the Old Testament there are yet other methods of theologizing: psalm, proverb, prophecy, and the editorialized history found in Kings and Chronicles.

Theology is also done through narratives. Narratives, in fact, are a great way to teach theology. Preachers do it in sermons all the time. Jesus did it. And once I accepted Genesis 1-11 on this basis, there came peace of mind and the removal of some residual intellectual clutter.

There also came greater appreciation for the great affirmations of the early chapters of Genesis, such as the cycle of stories about sin in chapters 3-11 that collectively probe this sorry dimension of human experience: sin as eating from the Tree of the Knowledge of Good and Evil (in other words, experiencing in one's own person the distinction between good and evil); sin as jealousy and fratricide; sin as hubris that leads to babble; and the towering story of Noah that depicts God's wrath toward sin and the Divine judgment upon it.

Like anyone else, I still have to face the most important question that arises from this literature: where do I stand on its affirmations? Is Israel's faith in the One God also my faith? Can I affirm with Israel that God is the creator of heaven and earth? And as an earth creature (a'dam literally means earthling), will I accept my place in the ecology of embodied existence and do my part to tend this garden into which God has placed me?

As God is my witness, I do and I will.

SECTION 2

A
SCIENTIFIC
PERSPECTIVE

16
ON THIS WE ALL AGREE...
IN THE BEGINNING GOD

Nancy Halliday

Nancy Halliday is Associate Professor of Cell Biology at the University of Oklahoma College of Medicine.

It was in a General Zoology course at Southern Nazarene University where I encountered a Christian perspective on evolution that I had never heard before. I was shocked and yet relieved when the professor declared, "There is no need for your faith to be in conflict with your understanding of science." I was shocked because I did not expect a person of deep faith to hold that perspective. I was relieved because my family held science as an important shaping factor in our worldview. From the pulpit, I heard regularly that evolution was an evil lie. But my increasing understanding of the biological world conflicted with this view. So I did what most of my contemporaries did, I compartmentalized science and faith – not allowing one to dialogue with the other. This is a common story for students entering Christian institutions of higher learning, including our Nazarene universities. But I believe that faith and sound science need not deny one another; God is the author of both forms of revelation, the natural world and the written Word. Science and faith ask and answer very different questions, and as a person of faith, I look through both lenses to get a more complete understanding of God.

I don't plan to make scientific arguments that support evolutionary biology in this essay. There are many wonderful resources on evolutionary biology written by scientists, some of whom are true believers in

Christ.[1] The scientific community –including myself and most scientists who are Christian – strongly supports evolution as the only explanation that can fully account for observations in many fields including biology, paleontology, molecular biology, geology, astronomy and many others. Evolution is also pervasive as a foundation of modern medicine. What I want to emphasize in this essay are these three points: 1) There are fruitful approaches to the controversy that can transform one's faith; 2) Dogmatic views produce an unnecessary and harmful dichotomy; and 3) I believe it is sinful to divide the church on this issue. We need to be tolerant and respectful of views that differ from our own when discussing origins.

As a new faculty member in the Department of Biology at Southern Nazarene University (SNU), I hesitated to deal with the complexities of science and faith in the classroom. I even told the chair of my department that I was going to evade the controversy by not discussing evolution in my courses. I was taken aback when the chair responded adamantly that it was my *duty* as a biologist who is Christian to deal with this issue head-on. In hindsight, I deeply appreciate that challenge and charge. I gradually incorporated a Christian perspective on evolution into most of my courses, culminating with the "Origins" course I team-taught during my last years at SNU. I observed a developmental transformation in our students as they moved through their years of biological study from compartmentalization to an integrative reconciliation of science and faith. I have learned a few lessons on how to approach the presentation of the perceived conflicts along the way.

In the classroom, I introduced the scientific views on evolution early and gently. I waited until the end of the fall freshman Biology course, in order to develop a relationship of trust with my students. It is important for students to observe the professor's authentic Christian faith before the introduction of something that holds so much controversy. Students respond in a variety of ways, from complete denial (foreclosure) to "ah ha" moments such as I experienced. My primary message was that deeply committed Christians hold a continuum of perspectives on origins – but these perspectives should not be used to judge someone's orthodoxy. I describe dividing the church over this issue as sin.

Transformation (if it happens) takes years – so give students a safe, tolerant environment in which they can explore freely and ask the tough questions. (What does an evolutionary perspective say about the character of God? What does it say about the Bible?) It is essential for students to see Christian biology professors dealing openly and honestly with faith and evolutionary biology. The Church of the Nazarene has an inclusive stance on interpretations of the Genesis accounts of creation – so allow students to reconcile the issues in a way that makes sense to them without judgment. Present them with the continuum of Christian perspectives on origins. Disclose personal stances humbly. Respect each student's current position on the issue. Expect the students to support their views with academic rigor and integrity. Move them beyond a superficial view to synthesize their own perspectives on science and faith. They must have a well-examined faith in order to navigate through the challenges that will come if they remain in the sciences.

My own story reveals how resolution of science and faith has aided my Christian walk. My graduate studies took me deep into the inner workings of the cell. In the study of cell biology or biochemistry, one risks becoming excessively reductionistic. In fact, a majority (70%) of scientists in these areas of study become agnostic or atheist as they assume that all can be explained in scientific terms, leaving no necessity for God in biological processes.[2] I experienced precisely the opposite outcome as I studied cells through the lens of a believer. As I understood more about the cell, my sense of awe for the Creator increased in magnitude. But I, also, faced significant challenges to my faith in graduate school. I recall one specific experience with my openly atheistic doctoral advisor. As we looked at some fascinating data regarding cytoskeletal order and regulation, he asked, "Nancy, why is it that as your understanding of biological systems grows, you don't see the absurdity of your faith?" I looked up in astonishment and replied, "Jim! How can you look at the complexity and elegance of biological systems and claim that there is no Creator?" Jim challenged my faith every week. If I had not already found resolution of the perceived dichotomy between faith and science (which strengthened my faith), I'm not certain I would have finished graduate school with my faith intact. For this, I thank my undergraduate professors who journeyed patiently with me as I worked to reconcile science and faith.

I currently teach at the University of Oklahoma College of Medicine. Many medical students actively seek an integrative perspective on faith and science. Just as youth in the Nazarene denomination, medical students are walking away from the church. As they progress through their medical training, they come to believe that science and faith are mutually exclusive. They are students of science, and science wins this war. Without Christian mentors to guide them through the journey from conflict to a satisfying resolution, they fall prey to this false dichotomy. I find this tragic. We need to recognize that this unholy false dichotomy is not only impacting our Nazarene youth, but also drives a deep wedge between science and faith in a broader population. We need to appreciate that by holding a dogmatic perspective of origins, the American Protestant church is forcing a whole segment of society to perceive they have to choose faith *or* science.

Much of the perceived conflict between science and faith arises from a literal interpretation of the Scriptures. Interestingly, if one approaches the first two chapters of Genesis as a scientific account of creation, a major problem arises, for two, quite different, creation stories are found here! For example, the order in which things are created do not align in these accounts. Perhaps God was accommodating the ancient level of understanding held by the writers. Using the "science of the day," in Genesis 1 He delivers the life-changing message that He is the Creator of all things. In Genesis 2, God reveals how intimately He was involved in the creation of humanity and seeks relationship with us. Today, those timeless truths need to be separated from the ancient science.[3] Historically, the Church of the Nazarene believes in plenary inspiration of the Scriptures rather than inspiration-by-dictation. Nazarenes have the freedom to approach the perceived conflict with tolerance and respect for all positions held on the beginnings of things. We can believe in Creation by a divine Creator and thank God for that faith, but avoid posing creation and evolution as intrinsically antithetical alternatives.

Dividing the church on the issue of origins is wrong. Belief in a literal six 24-hour day creation is not essential to one's salvation; with this, as with all "non-essentials," it behooves us to allow one another liberty! The Church, including the Church of the Nazarene, would benefit from a more inclusive approach that allows for a God ordained and sustained evolutionary process that is strongly supported by sound science. If all truth is God's truth, and it is, then there need not be conflict. Because God is the author of both special (the Bible) and natural revelation (created nature), we need not fear the two contradicting one another. This position affords the believer scientist with a freedom to pose questions to nature about how the creation works. The Biblical perspective then provides rich answers regarding meaning, purpose, and all things pertaining to salvation, which are outside the scope of scientific inquiry. The result can be a more complete understanding of Truth.

The topic of origins is one on which sincere Christians hold different views. Christians who have not studied the natural world in detail would naturally find the process of evolution incredible. There should be tolerance and respect for the whole spectrum of views within the Church of the Nazarene, so long as all recognize God as the Creator. Dividing the church over this issue is where I believe sin enters the dialogue.

ENDNOTES AND SUGGESTED READING

1 A few of those resources include: Darrell Falk, *Coming to Peace with Science: Bridging the Worlds Between Faith and Biology* (Downers Grove, Ill.: Intervarsity Press, 2004). Francis Collins, *The Language of God: A Scientist Presents Evidence for Belief* (New York: Free Press, 2006). National Academy of Sciences, *Science, Evolution, and Creationism* (Washington, DC: The National Academies Press, 2008). Karl Giberson and Francis Collins, *The Language of Science and Faith: Straight Answer to Genuine Question* (Downers Grove, Ill.: InterVarsity Press, 2011).

2 Ecklund and Scheitle, "Religion Among Academic Scientists: Distinctions, Disciplines, and Demographics" *Social Problems*, Vol. 54, Issue 2, pp.289-307.

3 Denis O. Lamoureux, *I Love Jesus & I Accept Evolution* (Eugene: Wipf and Stock Publishers, 2009).

17

EXPLORING EVOLUTION THROUGH THE REPRODUCTIVE PROCESS

Jennifer Chase

Jennifer Chase is Professor of Biology at Northwest Nazarene University.

Growing up, I never imagined there was a perceived incompatibility between faith in the Creator God and the biological descriptions of the mechanisms of evolution. Now, I am not so naive about these perspectives. Some people do feel that Creator God's sovereignty is threatened by treating evolutionary changes as just another process that He ordered. I agree, wholeheartedly, with the Church of the Nazarene in "opposing any Godless view of creation." From where I sit, evolution is as God-filled an explanation of a process as the concepts of reproduction and genetics.

I was raised in a Christian family of Nazarenes, the daughter of a high school biology teacher. We were raised to look at God's world through a Christian lens as well as the lens of the biology of an earth that had been around for a long time. When our family traveled to Dinosaur National Monument, we considered how those long-extinct organisms were forerunners of birds and mammals. Irritating weeds in the yard showed us the amazing ability of life to adapt in order to fill a void in the natural world. For my middle school Africa project, I chose to look at the human fossil record starting with the Leakeys' discovery of Australopithecus africanus in the Rift Valley. In those changes, you could see the physical shift from animal to man. In my home and childhood, change of species through time was treated as simply another process in God's universe. It still seems to me to look a lot like a long-term extension of reproduction.

The act of conception or creation of an individual is devoid of a stated role for the Creator. Not only do we not state that God picks out the sperm to start the process, we don't have any speculation about how God does the "knitting." (Psalm 139:13) We do not buy specifically Christian books of "what to expect when you're expecting," telling new moms specifically what God is doing as the baby grows. Rather, there is a purely biological description of the processes, e.g., the spine "knows" where to form, and it has blocks of cells (somites) migrating from back to front in the formation of muscle and cartilage. While there is some mystery left to exactly which genes are "on" when and their chemical mechanisms, I believe that the biological descriptions of embryonic development describe how God is daily creating new human lives.

The process of copying cells and genes is a remarkable biological success. The offspring cells are nearly identical to parent cells. However, none are identical. Each time DNA is copied by chemical machines, a few mismatches occur and alter the code for proteins. This is easiest to see in bacteria who have very simple reproductive lives: they divide in half. In graduate school, I did a short project using tens of millions of bacteria from a single family. Because the process of DNA copying is only nearly perfect, there were sure to be many genetic differences in the millions of bacteria. I spread this family of related bacteria onto media with toxic levels of heavy metals. Most, but not all, were killed. The offspring of survivors, also, were not harmed by high levels of the toxic metals. Some genetic change made it possible for the survivors to pass the toxic test, since genes can only be passed on through dozens of generations.

I took for granted that the process of evolution, a change in a species through generations of random genetic changes, would take place in my experiment. It was simply an inexpensive way to generate thousands of organisms with a few changes in their DNA. The only question for the experiment was if any of those helpful changes took place in the protein we were studying. Random changes had taken place and my toxicity test made those changes a matter of life and death for my bacteria.

The process of sexual reproduction gives an individual even more options for diversity by receiving a unique combination of parental genes. Because both of my parents were members of Eastern Nazarene College's gene pool from the 1960s, there was little chance I was going to get gene versions more prevalent in New Guinea tribes. In a population, some gene versions are so protective that offspring people will survive better, like my surviving bacteria. One example of a protective gene is the sickle-cell trait found predominantly in Africans, which confers protection to malaria. It's not hard to look around the world to see populations of people that have clearly different traits from other groups (e.g., Nordic and Mbuti). Some would call this trait differentiation process "microevolution," describing how species have changed since their creation.

Biologists do not have a simple definition for "species." It might be said that different species are two genetically similar populations that are just different enough not to be able to breed and produce fertile offspring. For example, horses and donkeys are different species because their offspring is an infertile mule.

I have heard from Nazarenes who are able to accept that God uses the process of evolution within a species but do not accept it as a mechanism for the development of new species. Are they suggesting that the process of genetic drift is God-full, but it would never, even after generations of inbreeding, lead to two groups of genetically similar organisms that are unable to breed and produce viable offspring? I hope we would not argue over this arbitrary limitation of God's processes.

If the argument is actually, "The earth has not been around long enough for evolution to make species," then that is not an argument with the theory of the process of evolution but about cosmology.

I may not know how God's hand reaches in to reproduction, genetics, evolution, or even how He holds atoms together. But, I know Christ became a living embryo who grew into a baby, then a man. God uses processes in creating us all.

18

DARWIN AND THE FARMBOY

Dennis Williams

Dennis Williams has served as a Professor of History at Southern Nazarene University since 1994, where he currently serves as Dean of Teaching and Learning.

I had an advantage over many who grew up evangelical when it comes to thinking about God, creation and evolution. Growing up on a southern Great Plains farm, I observed evolution happening in all kinds of venues. My family grew both milo and cotton until the Russian Grain Embargo and the OPEC-induced Oil Crisis shifted the business model of south plains farmers to a cotton-centric monoculture.

Before this shift, farmers across the area worked closely with seed companies to produce greenbug resistant varieties of milo. I recall hearing my father and grandfather discuss the toll greenbugs were taking on the current variety and their hope that next year's new varieties would be more resistant. If they were, within a few short years, the greenbugs adapted to whatever it bred into the plant's genetics that had provided resistance. It was biological warfare on the genetic level - survival of the fittest in operation.

With that awareness, when high school biology presented Darwinian evolution, my classmates and I understood what Darwin was talking about. In our agriculture classes we learned about breeding livestock to enhance desirable characteristics - more meat, more fat, larger litters, easier birthing and on and on. We saw slides of stock bred in the 1930s, 1950s, and 1970s, the same lines of stock, and noted how their body shapes changed through time as particular individuals were selected by breeders and other individuals were sent to market. I was amazed by how different an animal could look after just a few generations of selective breeding, and how color and markings could change as other varieties were bred into the line to get this or that particular quality. While some might say that this is only microevolution not the trans-species evolution most folks think of when discussing evolution, it was easy for me to imagine God doing much the same thing with elephants descending from Ice Age mammoths and mastodons.

When I later delved into how Darwin came to his conclusions, I noticed that while his voyage around the world got him thinking about the problem of variation and speciation, it was through his study of advances made by nineteenth-century livestock and pigeon breeders that he came to understand more precisely what he had observed among the Galapagos finches.

One might argue that "agricultural varieties are not the same as wild species." While true, agricultural varieties often show far greater differences in look (phenotype) than many species in the same genus do. It was easy for me, as had Darwin over a century earlier, to take what I knew about how farmers manipulate genes through selective breeding and to imagine the same kinds of operations at work in the wild.

My Galapagos was a canyon looking out over a mesquite and juniper strewn landscape where we hunted quail and deer during the lull between summer work and harvest. In our area there were, according to taxonomists two distinct species of deer (genus Odocoileus), white-tailed deer and mule deer. They are easily distinguished by their ears and tails. White-tailed deer have long bushy white tails, while mule deer have short black tipped tails and long big ears.

Commonly, the rules related to defining different species suggest that distinct species cannot successfully interbreed or, if they do, the resulting hybrid is typically sterile (think horse + ass = sterile mule). Yet, sitting on the edge of that canyon under a one-seeded juniper tree I witnessed many a doe with long muley ears and bushy white tails trailing fawns. I knew what I was seeing and I was aware of the rules related to inter-species breeding. Rather than finding a problem with the Bible, I watched brangus cows and calves walking around in the same pasture and saw a parallel. The only difference was that one was "wild" bred and the other domestic.

Someone might object, "But that's not the same thing, cows are just one species and humans have been breeding them successfully for millennia." To which I reply, then what was going on with those deer? Aren't the same God-designed processes of genetic variation and breeding at work in wild nature and tame. Until very recently, humans only had what God gave nature to work with to do their own agrarian work. We couldn't do anything God isn't/wasn't already doing naturally all over the hills in his global pasture.

This observation did beg the question of what a species is. My answer to that question came through my work as a historian.

After graduating from Southern Nazarene University, I went to graduate school to study history. In particular I found the history of science, particularly the history of ecology, fascinating. Reflecting on my youthful experiences, I suppose it's easy enough to see why. I distinctly remember one "Aha!" moment when I was studying the way taxonomists worked in the 19th century.

The 1800s were heady days for taxonomists. At just as European explorers made their way, along with European merchants, soldiers and colonists to the far reaches of the planet, Carl Linnaeus gave life scientists a structure to classify and name all the creatures being discovered around the world. He created a structure, first used for plants and later adapted to other forms of life, in which living things were carefully examined for similarities to other known creatures. Creatures that looked alike were lumped together into family groups. The ones that look quite a lot alike were segregated into groups called genera (meaning race or kin). Then the taxonomists examined creatures within the genus and further segregated them by ways they did not look alike - a little bushier hair here, an extra joint in an antennae there, and assigned those to separate subgroups called species. The groups can even get sorted into smaller subgroups - subspecies and varieties.

In those days, naturalists, the young Darwin among them, were rampaging across the globe collecting specimens of most every new thing they saw and bringing back or sending in samples by the box and barrel of pressed plants, salted fish, pelts and skins and skeletons. Taxonomists, such as Harvard ichthyologist (fish scientist) Louis Agassiz, would open the assorted collections, lay out the samples, sort them by similarity, compare them to species that already had names(discarding the ones that did), and then attend carefully to analyzing those with variations in color, patterns or shape. They would sketch them in fine detail and take meticulous notes on those parts that were used to identify one species from the other. If they found a group that didn't fit with already known others, they would write up their findings, name the group a new name according to Linnean convention and publish it for all the other taxonomists to see. New species were identified and named almost every year in every category of life. Some were so obviously distinct that even non-scientists could tell them apart, and those had different common names to show for it. Others were only different in the eyes of the trained observer.

Since science is a discipline where discovering new things is a goal, it is not surprising that there were numerous fights over who first found a new species and received the prestige and the right to give it its new Latin name. Some argued over whether the organism in question was a new species or just an old, already named one with slight, insignificant observable variation. In an effort to bring order to the chaos, taxonomists worked on defining the terms and rules, such as the sterile hybrid rule to try to sort things out.

This is where the interbreeding of white tailed deer and mule deer on the Texas plains comes in. While it is obvious that they are in the same genus, it also seems obvious that they are different species. But they can interbreed and when they do, their offspring are not sterile. Thus, they do not meet the definition of a hybrid. Let their populations mingle and let a population of those crosses build up and voila, we seem to have a new species.

Likewise, if we did not have good historical records of the crosses made by pigeon breeders starting with rock doves to create magnificently different varieties of pigeons shown, raced, and eaten around the world, each would be classified as a different species, if not a different genus.

So where does this take us? First, it is important to note that people name species and create the rules for how groups of similar creatures get their names. So the question of whether or not small changes over a long time from a distant ancestor to the current one lead to something so different that it gets its own special name is something only people think are important. It seems that God turned that job over to people without interference.

Second, as God created the genetic foundations of life, he filled the DNA toolbox chock full of survival tools that could get turned on and maximized under the right conditions. Most of the time that happens "naturally" without human interference, but for the last 5000 or more years humans have taken advantage of that toolbox and have been working diligently to manipulate it to our advantage. Our penchant for efficiency and satisfaction with working in the slower reproductive time frame of the natural order has led us to the point that we we've dispensed with sexual reproduction and gone to moving genetic material between organisms that could never transmit it naturally. Those new genes are now part of the tool box of the recipient species and future offspring.

This then raises the question - do we have a new species? We do if taxonomists were to organize and name organisms by genetic similarities and differences, which they can see now directly using technologies that did not exist in the 19th century. Then they relied on the shape of body parts, colors and the like to hint at genetic the breadth of genetic distinctions. And when we spray herbicides on our genetically modified, herbicide resistant crops and the weeds get resistant to the herbicides, because of the ability God designed into his creation for adaptation to life threatening environmental changes, will the offspring of the survivor weeds have evolved to in response to natural selection of a harsh environment? Indeed. Evolution, change over time, happens - in the wild, on the farm, in the lab, and in culture (compare a neolithic village to a modern city or popular music in the 19th century with that of today).

For me, the question is not did the world as we know it evolve naturally from a different looking world long ago. The evidence is clear on that. How it happened is not a big deal either. The gradual or rapid transmutation of species through genetic variation and selection is inherent in the system God designed.

The critical issue for us in the 21st century is, what will we big brained tool users do with it? Can we use our moral reasoning skills to use our tools wisely? When asking about matters concerning God and the world, the questions of morality and ethics are paramount. Over thousands of years, we have learned how to tap into the genetic system and can now quickly bend it to our will in potentially frightening new ways. Will our morality and wisdom catch up? Will we use genetic modification to violate God's decree that the Tree of Life is off limits to us? Or will we blindly pursue such goals as infinite longevity through genetic or technological enhancement with little regard for what it means for the system of life that sustains the planet and all the rest of God's good and pleasing world?

19

BREAKING AWAY FROM A FALSE DILEMMA

Steven Smith

Steven Smith is a Mineral Exploration Geochemist and Environmental Geochemist for the U.S. Geological Survey.

False dilemma - a logical fallacy which involves presenting two opposing views, options or outcomes in such a way that they seem to be the only possibilities: that is, if one is true, the other must be false, or, more typically, if you do not accept one then the other must be accepted.[1]

Despite having been raised since birth in the Church of the Nazarene, I never encountered the ideas of Young Earth Creationism until I was almost 17. That's not to say that my church teachers accepted evolution, but none of them seemed to have a problem with the age of the earth. Much has changed in our church during the last 40 years.

I first encountered Creationist thought during high school in 1974 when I read the book *Scientific Creationism*[2] by Henry Morris, the acknowledged father of the modern Creationist movement. This book explained how the earth was created about 6,000 years ago during six 24-hour days, how all of the fossil-bearing rock layers were deposited during Noah's Flood, how biological evolution was impossible, how scientists had conspired to make up theories that denied the evidence of Creation, and how true science confirmed a literal reading of the book of Genesis.

Each chapter addressed an issue as a simple choice with only two answers (e.g., *Evolution or Creation?, Accident or Plan?, Old or Young?, Apes or Men?*), and those choices were summarized in the conclusion with the following statement.

"There seems to be no possible way to avoid the conclusion that, if the Bible and Christianity are true at all, the geological ages must be rejected altogether."[3]

With a high-school level understanding of science and theology, I was convinced by this "either science or God" argument and, to my knowledge, became the first Young Earth Creationist in my local Nazarene church. I knew the enemy and the enemy had a name. It was Evolution.[4]

After high school, I enrolled at Olivet Nazarene University. Initially, I had no goal in mind other than possibly studying science. I was placed in the Chemistry program and spent the first year getting required courses out of the way. One of those required courses was Old Testament Bible, during which I frequently argued with the professor whenever ideas were presented that didn't support a literal reading of Genesis or a Creation event only 6,000 years ago. By the end of my freshman year, I felt led to change my major to a combined Geology-Chemistry degree. I had always loved collecting minerals, rocks, and fossils and dreamed of a career where I could travel to remote mountains and wild places. But geology also presented another challenge. I had heard that the geology professor didn't necessarily believe the earth was young.

I remember going to that first Geology class armed with every available Creation Science argument, ready to do battle for the faith. Yet despite my preparation, it was for naught. I found myself walking the same path as the earliest geologists, who starting from a perspective of a Biblical Creation about 6,000-years in the past modified later by Noah's Flood saw evidence in the rocks for sequences of many different events and environments that could not be explained within the accepted Biblical time frame or by the Flood. Long before we ever talked about radiometric age determinations, the evidence that the earth was much older than a few thousand years became overwhelming. I also saw how rock layers could be grouped into larger "geologic ages" based on their depositional environment and fossil content with boundaries defined by major environmental changes or an extinction event. I was shocked to discover that these geologic ages had been identified and named, not by God-denying Evolutionists as I had been taught, but mostly by Christians and even ministers who saw their work as glorifying to God. Not only were the geologic ages real and the earth older than 6,000 years but the fossils within them told a story of change: starting in the oldest rocks with strange creatures unlike anything seen today, followed in order by the earliest appearances of fish, amphibians, reptiles, mammal-like reptiles, dinosaurs, birds, and placental mammals and with the youngest rocks containing fossils of extinct animals that closely resemble those extant. Thus, the rocks even supported one of the lines of evidence used by Charles Darwin in his argument for descent by modification (now called evolution).

Although I was fascinated by geology and had found a scientific field that I loved, my faith was in shambles. Based on what I had believed and read in the Young Earth Creationist literature, if the geologic ages were real, if the earth was old, if evolution had happened then the Bible was false, Christianity wasn't true, and Christ's death on the cross was meaningless. So what was left? I felt betrayed and seriously considered leaving the church as an agnostic to seek truth in science alone.

In retrospect, two factors kept me from leaving: (1) the support of a strong Christian family (and a young lady soon to be my wife) that gave me the freedom to question without condemnation; and (2) the strong witness of my Olivet geology professor, who had not only faced all of the same scientific evidence but was one of the most Christ-like men I had ever met. But before I could move on, I had to recognize that I had been snared by a false dilemma and that the Bible didn't need to be read as a scientific treatise on how to create a world. That was a time of turmoil and what I needed most was theological support that would allow me to reconcile what I read in the Bible with what I saw in the rocks.

Yet, in another way, I was fortunate. I had only lived with this false dilemma for three years before having to deal with scientific evidence that shook my faith. Unlike my own youth, today many young people in our churches have been inculcated since birth with these either "science or God" statements through Sunday School, VBS, homeschool textbooks, and church-sponsored schools. How much harder is it for these students to study sciences like geology, astronomy, anthropology, paleontology, or biology and still preserve a faith that has been supported by a false dilemma? I have seen students break down into tears as they stood on an outcrop of rock and saw evidence that contradicted what their church had taught them. I have comforted my own daughter when she was told by a Sunday School teacher that she couldn't be a Christian if she accepted evidence for evolution. I have talked with scientists who were once raised in a church and are now bitter agnostics because the church had "lied to them" about science. They had been asked to make a choice – either science or God – and they had chosen science.

Many Christians strongly hold theological positions that are incompatible with evidence for a 4.54 billion-year-old earth, common ancestry of all earth-based life, and speciation through random genetic variations winnowed by non-random natural selection. I once stood in those shoes. During that time, I felt the fear and anxiety that comes when scientific progress threatened to upset the certainty of my faith. In anger, I lashed out at those Christians who had "compromised" the Bible with the enemy of "Evolution." I confess that I also used the false dilemma to support my arguments. "Choose God and live; choose science and perish!" May God forgive my arrogance. For despite the side of the issue you identify with, is it worth winning the argument if it means that someone else loses their soul?

The science-or-God false dilemma is especially pernicious for at least four reasons. First, even though it is meant as a defense of the faith, it has the potential to drive our youth from the church. Whenever we boil down our argument to "take it or leave it," some will inevitably choose to depart. We need to be real sure that an issue is absolutely critical before we lay down ultimatums. Second, the false dilemma argument concedes to science the authority to judge the veracity of the Bible or even the existence of God. Science is a very useful way of understanding the Creation, but it is not the right tool for determining the motives or will of the Creator. I would even go so far as to say that when Christians attempt to use science to prove God or the Bible, they have succumbed to the philosophy of scientism – the naturalistic idea that science has the authority to answer and judge all issues. Third, there really are people who delight in destroying the faith of Christians. When we teach our children to base their faith on a false dilemma then we have given those who wish them harm a very potent weapon. All they need to do is to show the actual evidence that science has discovered and then modify our own statements to "since science is true, then the Bible, God, and Christianity is false." Finally, the false dilemma considers all middle ground to be part of the war zone between two or more opposing sides. Those who are not for us are against us – even if they are also followers of the same Christ. We have divided the body of Christ into several warring camps and the battles are acrimonious. Polls suggest that the endless debates are a significant reason that young people today are leaving the church.[5]

The issues of science and faith are among the most critical ones facing the church today. We live in an age of science. To ignore or deny modern science is to become irrelevant in our culture. But as a church, as a denomination, we cannot make any progress until we can discuss these problems among ourselves in a spirit of respect and charity – even when we disagree. My hope in these discussions is not that we all come to the same scientific or theological understanding of evolution or age-of-the-earth issues but that we can move away from the false dilemmas forced by an exclusive and rigid mode of Biblical interpretation. God is too great and majestic to be confined in man's theology. We have to allow Him to inspire and even surprise us from all of his Creation and not just from the Bible.

ENDNOTES AND SUGGESTED READING

1 http://rationalwiki.org/wiki/False_dilemma. Last accessed Aug. 29, 2013.

2 Henry M. Morris, *Scientific Creationism* (General Edition) (San Diego, CA: Creation-Life Publishers, 1974).

3 Morris, p. 255.

4 For many Christians today, the term evolution doesn't just refer to the concepts of common ancestry, descent with modification, or natural selection, it has been expanded to include issues with the age of the earth, geology, cosmology, nuclear physics, paleoanthropology, and a host of other scientific ideas that are perceived to be in opposition to Young Earth Creationism. As one put it, "Evolution is all the science I don't believe in."

5 Barna Group, September 28, 2011, *Six Reasons Young Christians Leave Church*, https://www.barna.org/barna-update/teens-nextgen/528-six-reasons-young-christians-leave-church. Last accessed Aug. 29, 2013.

20

NOTHING MAKES SENSE IN HERPETOLOGY EXCEPT IN THE LIGHT OF EVOLUTION

John Cossel

John Cossel Jr is a Professor and Chair for the Biology Department at Northwest Nazarene University.

I fear that in following the great essays that have preceded mine, I will have little to offer. But I take hope as I remember Sunday evening testimonies at the small country church I attended as a teenager. I recall being moved and inspired by the various believers as they shared the same story but each from their own personal perspectives. It is with that in mind that I would like to share with you my personal journey, and how both faith and science inform my view of creation. Fellow Christian biologist Theodosius Dobzhansky originally stated "Nothing makes sense in **biology** except in the light of evolution."[1] I would argue the same holds true for my area of study, herpetology.

I am a herpetologist...that is I study amphibians and reptiles. To say that I have always been fascinated with these animals sounds a little cliché. But one of my earliest memories is of chasing frogs, followed by many fond recollections of slithering snakes, tadpoles in jars, lizards in pockets and other herpetological delights. By high school, I was taking an independent study on herpetology, working my way through a college textbook on the subject.[2] All this time, I had no conflict between my childhood faith and science. I don't recall being taught explicitly that the Genesis account was literal...that is just how it was read from the pulpit, in Sunday school, and in my private devotions. The notion of God creating all species of amphibians and reptiles ~10,000 years ago did not seem problematic.

I continued my pursuit of herpetology by majoring in biology at Northwest Nazarene University. However, in contrast to Dr. Nancy Halliday's experience as an undergraduate at a Nazarene college, my experience was not one of spiritually safe explorations of evolution.[3] Rather, my experience was more like the U. S. Army's stance of "don't ask, don't tell." The topic of evolution was largely ignored in the curriculum. As I recall, when it did come up, it was left hanging as if some vague shadow that seemed no more menacing to my faith than the boogey man. Don't get me wrong. My professors were wonderful, godly men, and I still strive to be like them in many ways. But regarding the topic of origins, while some of my professors made it clear that they were young Earth creationists, others only left me guessing. In fairness, I understand what may have been some of the reason for this ambiguity. The college did not want to cause any perceived animosity with the sponsoring Church, and if evolution wasn't listed specifically as an issue of heresy, its treatment left that message implied. After teaching high school biology for 6 years, I also understood the notion of respecting the beliefs of my students and their parents and not abusing my position of influence by making strong personal stances of where I stood on the issue of evolution. Regardless of the reasons, while at NNU, the theory of evolution proved no threat to my faith, nor affected my appreciation of amphibians and reptiles.

As a high school biology teacher, I avoided much of the evolution controversy as had my teachers before me. However, I was exposed to the ideas of evolution as a cohesive theme throughout the biology text. Even at that simplistic level, the theory seemed to make sense. While I was still teaching, I started a master's program at Oregon State University. Here I was exposed to even more evolutionary theory. And again, it seemed to make sense. Finally, I left my high school teaching position to pursue a doctorate at Idaho State University. Evolution was a pervasive concept in all of my classes, and an upper division course in evolutionary theory left no doubt in my mind that while aspects of the theory are likely to change as new data are made available, the basic tenets were true. Species share a common ancestry and the variation we see today is due to the processes of evolution–yes, even my beloved amphibians and reptiles.

Although I do not recall anyone telling me I had to choose between my faith and evolution, the issue seemed naturally polarized. I experienced feelings of doubt and shame for choosing science. This led to the feared "spiral of doubt" about other issues of faith. Until, in the end, I wondered about my own Christianity. But that is not where the story ends. Thankfully, some time later, I was asked if I was a Christian (on a herpetology camping trip of all places). Without rationalizing, or over-thinking, I affirmed verbally what my heart knew all along. *Yes, I believe in Jesus Christ as the Messiah, and I have assurance that I am saved by His gift of salvation.* From that point on, I came to the realization that I can accept science and faith as compatible ways of knowing the universe and its Creator...even if the Creator uses natural processes to continually produce biological diversity.

I know there is not sufficient space here to provide detailed support for evolution. But I will provide a series of evolutionary predictions and observations that offer a glimpse of why nothing in [herpetology] makes sense except in the light of evolution.

My students and I study frogs in Costa Rica–a jewel of God's creation. Among the many kinds of frogs found there are two frog species that appear very similar but are separated by an inhospitable mountain range. Geologic evidence indicates that this mountain range is less than 2 million years old but old enough to allow the isolated frog populations to have evolved into 2 different species. Genetic data support this prediction; evolution helps make sense of this observation.

These two frog species are from a group known as poison dart frogs. The term comes from the practice of indigenous hunters using secretions from the skin of some of these frogs to coat the tips of their darts or arrows. One species is so toxic that a single frog has the ability to kill several adult humans. Evolutionary theory predicts that the glands responsible for producing this poison would occur in other species that are not as dangerous. Further, the glands would be expected to occur in the ancestors of this species. As it turns out, all extant (non-extinct) frogs have these glands in their skin. I have heard it argued that all thorns, diseases and poisonous animals etc. are the consequence of the fall of mankind in the garden. A more satisfying answer for me is that these frog toxins are a consequence of intense predation pressure. The ancestral species that had even mildly poisonous secretions would a have a slight advantage over other individuals that were not poisonous. As generations passed, every slight modification to the structure of the toxin molecule that made it a stronger poison was selected for and inherited by subsequent generations. It is a much greater God that facilitates the amazing diversity of life we see today, as a result of the forces of life rather than consequences of sin.

This group of colorful frogs provides further examples of how evolution provides explanations for what we observe. Geologic data suggest that Africa and South America separated from each other ~200 million years ago. In addition to the poison dart frogs found in South and Central America, there are also brightly colored, poisonous frogs found off the east coast of Africa in Madagascar. Evolutionary theory would predict that in spite of their superficial similarity, the species occurring on Madagascar should be more closely related to each other than to the group of dart frogs from the Americas. Genetic data support this prediction and the resulting "family trees" that can be constructed make sense in the light of evolution. They each evolved from their own common ancestor after the continents separated.

Going further back in geologic time, the theory of evolution predicted that the unique shape of frogs (short torso, no tail, etc.) evolved from a more primitive ancestor that had more vertebrae and a tail. For some time, this missing link was, well, missing. But, in 2008, a new fossil was described.[4] It had distinctly frog features but also had a longer torso and a tail. Why would there be a fossil with mixed features? This does not make sense, except in the light of evolution. The list could go on, but these examples should give you an idea of why I accept evolution as the explanatory theory for making sense of so many things observed in herpetology.

When I verbally affirmed my belief in Jesus Christ, I didn't have a functioning schema of how my faith and science could be compatible. However, as I walk the path of faith and science an earlier realization grows stronger. Just as I will never know all there is to understand about biology, likewise, I can never fully comprehend the mysteries of God. The more I learn about herpetology (and all of science), the more I realize I don't know. This realization has grown more acute with every graduate degree and every year of teaching. Does this fact keep me from wanting to learn more? Quite the opposite... it is thrilling to know that the miracle of each living organism holds untold volumes to be discovered. Similarly, I now realize that when I "knew all the spiritual answers"; both my faith and my view of God were too simplistic.

As my faith journey continues and my knowledge of God deepens, my realization of his mystery has also increased. But, it is OK to not know every detail of "how" in science or faith. My approach to each is similar... I operate on the underlying principles that 1) science is a reliable way to gain an understanding of the physical universe; 2) the Holy Bible is a trustworthy way to learn more about the nature of God and his plan of salvation. Both provide valuable ways to learn about God and nature. More importantly they both allow us to make predictions about either the physical universe or the character of our Lord and Savior. The exciting thing for me is that science and faith are not mutually exclusive, and that God's creation is the very thing that as we understand it more fully, we should have an even clearer idea of God's nature. "For since the creation of the world God's invisible qualities—his eternal power and divine nature—have been clearly seen, being understood from what has been made, so that people are without excuse" (Romans 1:20).[5] Thanks to both my science *and* my faith I grow more in awe of God and His creation daily.

My main hope for Nazarenes Exploring Evolution is that those coming from a conservative perspective will realize that promoting a false incompatibility between evolution and faith is damaging. I feel that exploring, rather than ignoring, the issue would have saved me much heartache as a young biologist. I also hope that those who accept evolution as God's mechanism for continual creation would extend patience, yet resolution to stand up for a position of faith and evolution. Heeding the message of Matthew 18:6 "If anyone causes one of these little ones—those who believe in me—to stumble, it would be better for them to have a large millstone hung around their neck and to be drowned in the depths of the sea."[5] To me, stumbling can best be minimized by walking in the light and examining the path with eyes wide open. I am always prayerful about my role as a professor. I covet your prayers as I now attempt to expose a new generation of biology majors to the theory of evolution while helping them grow in their personal faith in Jesus Christ.

ENDNOTES AND SUGGESTED READING

1 Theodosius Dobzhansky, "Nothing in Biology Makes Sense Except in Light of Evolution," in *The American Biology Teacher*, Volume 35 (1973), 125-129.

2 CJ Goin, OB Goin, GR Zug, *Introduction to Herpetology*, 3rd ed. (WH Freeman & Co., 1978) 378.

3 Nancy Halliday, "On This We All Agree– In The Beginning God." Nazarenes Exploring Evolution, 2013. http://exploringevolution.com/essays/2013/03/27/in-the-beginning-god/

4 JS Anderson, et al., "A stem batrachian from the Early Permian of Texas and the origin of frogs and salamanders," in *Nature*, Volume 453 (May 2008), 515-518.

5 New International Version (NIV) THE HOLY BIBLE, NEW INTERNATIONAL VERSION®, NIV® Copyright © 1973, 1978, 1984, 2011 by Biblica, Inc.®

21
PERMISSION TO EXPLORE EVOLUTION

Dianne Anderson

Dianne Anderson is Professor of Biology and Director of the Graduate Program in General Biology at Point Loma Nazarene University.

Permission to explore evolution. That is what I wanted deep down, but it is not what I heard from pastors, teachers, or my family. I remember being kept away from the human evolution section of natural history museums and being told that scientists were just out to prove that God didn't have anything to do with creating the world. The overall message was that it was wrong to even explore the evidence for evolution because none of it was true.

Even as a young child, I was drawn to biology. On our farm, I would make up my own backyard experiments, trying to figure out how plants and animals worked. While most other kids spent their free time reading novels or watching TV, I was reading biology-related sections of *The Worldbook Encyclopedia*. I would ignore any reference to evolution in what I read because at my Christian school, and my church, evolution was cast in a negative, avoid-at-all-cost manner. We even sang anti-evolution songs during chapel. I remember singing a song with the words "I'm no kin to the monkey, and the monkey's no kin to me..." I accepted what my teachers and family told me. I didn't do drugs or smoke, and I *certainly* didn't explore evolution. After all, I was a Christian, and I wanted to remain one.

I went off to a Nazarene college to study biology. In those four years, I remember only one occasion when the evidence for evolution was even brought up in class. Our professor talked about the fossil record and the dinosaurs, but the message that I left with was that we really don't know what to make of this data, since we know that the earth is less than 10,000 years old. I remember trying to figure out how all of the animals could have possibly fit on the ark; it just didn't pencil out. None of it made sense, and I wasn't really comfortable just ignoring an issue that didn't seem to have a satisfactory conclusion. I really wanted to make it work.

For my next step in life, I intentionally chose a master's degree in microbiology, with the assumption that evolutionary concepts wouldn't really impact that topic area, and thus I could avoid the entire issue. The public university faculty and students accepted evolution as a given, so there was no need to discuss it. Therefore, I again didn't learn about it in classes or seminars. With my master's degree in hand, I was hired by a public community college as a biology professor. The course objectives required that I teach evolutionary theory and the mechanism of natural selection as part of the assigned curriculum. It felt awkward, uncomfortable, and dishonest. Since I had never learned the concepts, or examined the evidence for it, I felt like I knew about as much as my students, maybe even less. My heart would race as I presented the concepts to a full classroom. It all seemed to make sense on paper, but my spiritual side was squirming. Students would sometimes come to my office to talk about not accepting evolution. I would tell them that I was struggling with it as well, but that it was a concept they needed to know about, just like the cell theory and photosynthesis. I had nothing else to offer them. I had never met a Christian who accepted evolutionary theory, so I certainly couldn't.

About fifteen years ago, something fascinating happened, and the two parts of my world intertwined in a way that I would have never anticipated. My husband and I started attending a different Nazarene church. Our small group gave me the permission and support to explore what I had secretly wanted to understand for so long. We read through *Battle of Beginnings* by Del Ratzsch, and we talked about various ways to read and understand Genesis. I developed trusting relationships with both theologians and scientists in our church, including Darrel Falk. My theologian friends helped me to see that a literal interpretation of the

Bible as a science text was not necessary and may, in fact, cloud the true meaning of the Scriptures. The purpose of the Bible seemed to be much more about love, grace, and forgiveness than it was about science. In addition, the concept of the Bible not being one book, but rather a collection of texts written in different genres and with different purposes was particularly helpful to me. My biologist friends helped me gain confidence in my hope that the Christian part of my world could actually coexist with the biological part of my world. These committed Christians were experts in molecular biology and developmental biology, areas of biology in which I had had no formal training. The confidence they expressed in the idea that God has used biological processes to create organisms was a powerful influence on my journey. I had attended Nazarene churches since I was twelve, but had never experienced this sense of spiritual and intellectual freedom before.

During this same time period, I started a PhD program in math and science education. As I considered various dissertation topics, my advisor presented an idea that would radically change the course of my teaching, as well as my understanding of biology. She invited me to work on a project focused on how college students learn the theory of natural selection. This was my chance, my excuse, to explore. I accepted the offer and spent the next four years studying the evidence for, and the mechanisms of, evolution, as well as conducting research on how to help students learn the theory of natural selection. My intellectual and spiritual worlds had been joined in a fascinating new way.

Permission to explore evolution. This is what I provide for students in my current role as a biology professor at Point Loma Nazarene University. I share my passion for my faith and for science with my students, and I talk about how the two can complement each other. When our students encounter overwhelming genetic, developmental, and fossil evidence for evolution, I don't want them to feel like they are in an either/or situation.

Accepting and understanding evolutionary theory as a way to explain how God created gradually has caused me to adopt this framework in every class that I teach because it weaves the details of biology into a coherent story. Finally, it makes sense. I still have questions, but I feel so fortunate that I have permission to explore and to learn, and most importantly, to encourage and support my students as they do the same. This includes making it very clear to my students that their personal relationship with Christ as Savior is so much more important to me than what they believe about creation/evolution issues. As their professor, I just want them to feel supported in their journey to explore all of biology. What a privilege. What an honor. What a responsibility.

22

ANXIETY, COGNITIVE BIASES, AND THE NEED FOR EMBODIED CHARITY AND HOSPITALITY:

THE DIFFICULT PROCESS OF EXPLORATION AND DIALOGUE ON ORIGINS

Ronald W. Wright

Ronald Wright is Professor and Chair of the Department of Psychology and Counseling at Southern Nazarene University.

"Beware you be not swallowed up in books! An ounce of love is worth a pound of knowledge." ~ John Wesley

"The issue isn't whether there can be a conversation about faith and science; the issue is whether the Body of Christ has the requisite virtues to sustain such a conversation." ~ James K.A. Smith

As a psychology professor and psychotherapist I have learned that the type of listening that allows for dialogue to occur is a truly difficult process. Listening is an act of love that opens one up to risk. To listen means one must first attempt to hear the other and to understand them from within their context. Setting oneself aside in this manner is difficult! This is also risky because it means one might be attacked, misunderstood or, perhaps even more threatening, one might be changed in the process. Many of the conversations on origins seem to involve people talking past each other and trying to get the other side to concede to the rational or rhetorical power of either a scientific or biblical argument. In my experience, there has been very little real listening in this conversation; hence the above quotes from John Wesley and James Smith remind us that our character and motivations matter as we enter into this conversation. So rather than making this an essay on my journey or perspectives on the issue of origins, I would like to lay out what I see as some of the psychological dynamics that make exploration and dialogue difficult in this area. I do this with the confession that I, too, struggle with these dynamics, but also with the hope that as we become aware of some of the barriers to listening, we can move towards embodying in this dialogue a humble, hospitable, and loving manner.

ANXIETY

The first dynamic that makes listening difficult is the experience and effects of anxiety. We live in an age of anxiety. On a daily basis there are reminders of the threats to our safety and physical well-being. Economic hardships and fears have been central to our concerns for the past several years. Adding to these anxieties is the manner in which modernity leads to the social reality called plurality. Plurality refers to the situation in which diverse human groups live together in environments of peace and interaction.[1] With urbanization, ease of movement around the globe, mass education, and technological mediums that allow instant access to events happening around the world, we live in a time where diverse ideas can easily come into contact with our own. In this context, much of what has been "taken-for-granted" and been in the background of our assumptions and worldviews comes under scrutiny and reflection and is moved to the foreground.[2] One can respond to this potential "cognitive contamination" in a manner that shuts down all other ideas, openly embraces all other ideas, or dialogues with other ideas while humbly holding on to key ideas.[3]

What this means for the origins dialogue is that it is easier than ever to see neither Christianity nor even the Church of the Nazarene as monolithic; there is variability in biblical interpretation (e.g. literal, contextual, poetic, historical, metaphorical, etc.), as well as other major differences in emphasis across denominations and even within our own denomination. Evolutionary science is likewise not monolithic (at least in biology and psychology), as there is variability in interpretation of the data on whether gene selection takes place at the level of the individual, group, or on multiple levels or whether natural selection is driven by selfishness or cooperation. For Christianity, the Church of the Nazarene, and evolutionary science, the "of course" taken-for-granted background assumptions have seemingly shrunk and individuals are faced with lots of complexity to sift through in a reflective and conscious manner. Add the challenges of an interdisciplinary conversation into this mix and an individual is faced with what can seem to be an overwhelming and anxiety-provoking task! In the face of this anxiety, it can be tempting to move to an exclusivist position that shut downs all other ideas and promises absolute truth and certainty. While this allows one to talk, it hinders one's ability to really listen.

For a better understanding of how you may experience anxiety in this context, I encourage you to engage in some critical self-examination with these questions: do I feel anxious, angry, or defensive about alternative understandings when it comes to the origins debate? If so, why? What is that about?

"US AND THEM" BIAS

A second, related dynamic, which makes listening difficult, is the work of in-group/out-group biases. The need to belong is a strong motivation and when coupled with anxiety or a sense of threat, this can form strong and reactionary in-group/out-group dynamics. For example, if a group is expecting bias from another group they are much more likely to strongly criticize and belittle the other group.[4] This can assist in the formation of unhelpful stereotypes (e.g. evolutionary scientists are atheists, creationists are fundamentalists, etc.), which can lead to prejudice and guide our behavior in exclusivist ways when in contact with "them."

There is also a tendency to automatically view one's own group as "better" than an out-group (this is such a strong tendency that it occurs even when people are randomly assigned to a group and know they have been randomly assigned!). "We" begin to classify our differences from "them" according to important properties or ideas that separate us and, of course, "we" are right! This is a very strong dynamic because it couples with a self-serving bias called the false consensus effect whereby we tend to overestimate the commonality of our or our group's opinions (e.g. "Surely most everyone else agrees with me on this"). Obviously, these in-group/out-group dynamics can make dialoguing and listening to "them" difficult wherever one is located within the origins conversation.

Some questions for critical self-examination here are, how do I portray people who hold positions different from me in the origins debate? What kind of stereotypes and/or prejudice am I guilty of when addressing "those" people?

COGNITIVE BIASES

A final dynamic, which makes it difficult to listen, is a suite of cognitive biases–used to help us perceive and make judgments about the world and people around us–that are often used in an automatic and non-reflective manner.[5] I will briefly mention three of these biases and their potential for errors.

The first is the confirmation bias, which is the tendency to only look for information that confirms one's positions and to not attempt to search for evidence that disproves those beliefs. In my General Psychology class I write "2, 4, 6" on the white board and ask students to give me a series of three numbers they think meet the rule I have in mind. Students typically provide three to five sets of numbers that ascend by "twos" before they tell me they are confident that they know the rule I have in mind (also displaying the overconfidence phenomenon which is described below). It is only after I tell them their rule is incorrect that they begin to actively attempt to disprove the rule on which they are thinking (the rule I have in mind is "any three ascending numbers"). Actively attempting to disprove what we believe to be true is a difficult and seemingly counterintuitive process. Much of the conversation on origins seems to display this type of bias as folks present only research or Scripture that supports their position. This, of course, makes listening quite difficult.

The second cognitive bias is the overconfidence phenomenon whereby we overestimate the accuracy of our beliefs; that is, we are often more confident than accurate in our beliefs. I fall prey to this all the time as I grade students' papers. My wife will ask me when I will be done, and I consistently am overconfident in my belief that I can grade the papers in a shorter amount of time than it does. This also can be seen in students' confidence that they are prepared to make a good grade on the test before an examination. The overconfidence phenomenon can affect the origins dialogue through coupling with in-group/out-group dynamics and creating a sense of surety that "they" are wrong and most people believe like "us" or through a false sense of confidence that we "know" all of the ins-and-outs of the theology and science involved in the conversation.

The final cognitive bias is belief perseverance and the manner in which once we provide an explanation for a belief, the more difficult it is for that belief to be discredited. An interesting finding related to this is that having people provide an explanation for the position opposite of their own can combat belief perseverance. I wonder if this might have some utility for our ability to listen within the origins conversation? When these three cognitive biases are in operation together, it is easy to see how peoples' beliefs become impenetrable to outside influence, which in turn makes true listening and conversation where there is the potential for change to occur more difficult.

Some final questions for critical self-examination here are, am I only looking to "prove" my position or am I actively attempting to look for evidence that might disprove my beliefs? Might I be too confident about my belief system? How might I go about trying to explain other positions in order to help me listen with charity and humility?

I understand the ultimate purpose of "reading" Scripture and nature to be the same. That is, the goal of both is to lead me towards love of God, neighbor, and the created order. My hope is as we become aware of some of the barriers to listening and begin to practice listening with charity and humility (and the practices within the Church and within science that encourage these virtues!) we will also learn how to love God, our brothers and sisters in Christ, and the created order more deeply.

ENDNOTES AND SUGGESTED READING

1 Peter Berger & Anton Zijderveld. *In Praise of Doubt: How to Have Convictions Without Becoming a Fanatic.* (New York: HarperOne, 2009) 7.

2 Ibid

3 Ibid. Berger & Zijderveld refer to these three positions as the exclusivist, pluralist, and inclusivist, respectively.

4 Vivian, J.E. & Berkowitz, N.H. Anticipated outgroup evaluations and intergroup bias. *European Journal of Social Psychology,* 23, 513-524. 1993

5 These biases, the confirmation bias, the overconfidence phenomenon, and belief perseverance are common terms in the research and literature of social psychology. One can find more information and research on them in any social psychology textbook, such as David Myers, *Social Psychology (10th Edition)*, New York: McGraw-Hill, 2010).

23

ECHOES FROM MY
JOURNEY OF FAITH

Lowell H. Hall

Lowell H. Hall is Professor of Chemistry at Eastern Nazarene College.

"So, how could anyone believe the earth is more than 8,000 years old?" "Do you really believe that humans came from monkeys?" "Doesn't the Bible give us direct answers to these important questions?" Perhaps questions like these come my way because I am a professional chemist and an Evangelical Christian. That last question seems like the necessary place to start in any dialog about science and religion – what do the Biblical writers reveal about their understanding of our world?

My family gave me a Christ-centered home and love of Scripture; experiences which I cherish. For a young man in a Nazarene home, ideas about an ancient age for the earth and the evolutionary development of human beings seemed opposed to Holy Scripture. However, when I began to meet highly knowledgeable Christians who talked in understandable terms about those topics, I determined that I must become more knowledgeable.

I

As a professional chemist, I wanted to know how to confront those issues. Furthermore, I wanted to know which Scripture passages might be related to my professional interests. So I began to read about the way Christians over the centuries dealt with new developments in our understanding of the world from both scientific and non-scientific sources. A significant controversy in the 17th-18th centuries caught my attention because many Christians opposed a new development from astronomy, which stated that the earth is not the center of the universe but is a planet orbiting the sun.[1] Their opposition was based primarily on interpretation of Scripture like Josh 10:12-13, I Sam 2:8, I Chr 16:30, Job 38:4-6, Ps 75:3, Ps 96:10, Ps 104:5, Ecc 1:5.[1] I am sure our current familiarity with the solar system concept makes it very difficult for us to recognize the world view of the Biblical writers and also to understand these Scriptures as Christians did centuries ago.

Those Protestant Christians wrote extensively about their Scripture-based opposition to the earth-in-motion idea. A typical commentary on those Scriptures comes from The Reverend Fanciscus Ridderus, a pastor in The Dutch Reformed Church (1680),

"Scripture records Joshua saying, 'Sun, stand still'. Joshua should be understood by God and by the church, which cannot understand him in any other way but by his clear historical words which attested that the sun interrupted its course and stood still. If we cannot believe what Holy Scripture says about these events, then we cannot accept Holy Scripture on any matters." [2a]

He expresses complete support for the stationary earth.

Consider also Rev. Jacob Du Bois (1650):

"We have to submit and give ourselves as captives to divine Authority, and not depart from the proper sense of the text because of some human 'it seems so': for, if this were accepted, one could have no truth, not even in matters of faith, from Holy Scriptures." [2b]

Both Du Bois and Ridderus expressed a strong fear that all meaning in Holy Scripture is lost unless the method of literal interpretation is followed for every word. However, their fears proved unfounded. Christians came to accept the motion of the earth around the sun without decreasing their faith in Scriptural integrity.

And yet these very strongly stated positions have an uncomfortably familiar ring in the 20th and 21st centuries. For example, South Carolina Pastor Richard Phillips wrote,

"Can the Bible's theology be true if the historical events on which the theology is based are false? . . . The hermeneutics behind theistic evolution are a Trojan horse that, once inside our gates, must cause the entire Fortress of Christian belief to fall."[3]

These illustrations are powerful historical and contemporary lessons, cautioning us not to take Scriptural references to our world as God's science lessons, thus allowing us to consider new concepts from the sciences without fear.

However, some Christians today continue to support a young earth or dispute that evolutionary creation is God's method, using the same Scripture-based approach as those who opposed the earth-in-motion concept centuries ago. In this opposition, I sense a shrinking back from Holy Spirit guided examination of new information. By contrast, on my faith journey I am hearing songs of joy, celebrating our Father's world, revealed through both science and Scripture – even when open questions remain.

II

As I continued to think about that historical event in astronomy, I began to consider many other Biblical references to our world, the realm I investigate as a scientist. In nearly 2750 Scriptural references, the earth is not described as spherical although Hebrew and Greek have specific words for that shape.[4] If one purpose of Scripture is to reveal scientific concepts, then we might expect some of those many passages would make earth's spherical shape clear. The Biblical writers also believed that thinking takes place in the heart and other organs such as the liver and intestines: "As a man thinks in his heart ..."[5] Today we know that thinking occurs in the human brain. More than 25 times the Bible refers to the earth having foundations and pillars of support, structures which we know do not exist.[6] Furthermore, in his powerful kenosis passage Apostle Paul writes in Phil 2:10, ". . . that at the name of Jesus every knee should bow, in heaven and on earth and under the earth . . ." – three distinct levels, including a place below the earth, which is consistent with concepts of Apostle Paul's time but which we know are incorrect.[7] Apostle Paul is enunciating the Lordship of Jesus over all creation, not the structure of the world. In all these references to our world we read the world view of Biblical writers. Although God could have revealed the actual workings of His universe in Scripture, it appears He did not.

Christians came to accept the 'solar system concept'. No new interpretation of Holy Scripture revealed the motion of earth around the sun (solar system). That concept came entirely from the science of astronomy. So, when we consider questions such as the age of earth or biological evolution, let us keep in mind that the Bible is not a repository of scientific information, as John Calvin put it.[8] Put succinctly, knowledge of our world has come from the sciences but God's love and plan of redemption are revealed in The Bible.

So in all of this, we see the importance of accepting that the Biblical writers wrote from their contemporary understanding of God's creation. Therefore, we need the guidance of the Holy Spirit to discern the actual message, although those passages make use of their ancient view of our world. For example, these passages reveal and proclaim God as creator, His Lordship over all creation, and His care and provision for us in establishing a stable place in the universe for us.

In all the many, many passages in which their ancient world views are used, God did not inspire the Biblical writers to revise those views of the world. God accommodated to the writers to present critical truths about God and His creation, even in their own terms about the world. Whatever anyone may think about current science, there is no disagreement about the motion of the earth around the sun; there are no foundations of the earth with pillars; thinking takes place in the brain and not in other places, etc. To me it appears that if God intended to inspire Biblical writers about the nature and operation of His creation, he could have done it in literally thousands of Biblical passages. But He did not. I believe that sends us a strong proclamation from God that His word is not intended as a source of revelation about how He created and how His creation functions.

Most important is the actual message that God inspired in the Biblical writers. One way to think about this is to consider the beliefs of the people who were contemporaries of the Biblical writers. Most cultures believed in many gods and worshiped idols. Those gods included the sun, the moon, and the planets among others. Ancient literature is filled with battles among gods. Also human beings were seen as servants and, indeed, slaves to those gods. However, Holy Scripture reveals what was very startling to the contemporaries of Moses, David, and the Apostles: There is one God. The one God created everything else – out of His love, not from battles with other gods. The sun and moon are revealed as serving humans and not as gods, serving as light and energy for life on earth. Love is at the center of God's nature: God so loved that He gave . . . You shall love the Lord your God . . . and your neighbor as yourself . . . God came into this world in the person of Jesus – God in human form! - teaching that we should even love our enemies. Those ideas were completely the opposite of the beliefs of the contemporaries of the Biblical writers – and many today. The centrality of love was the bold and astonishing message of the creation and the cross – and still is today.

An important point here is that the non-believing contemporaries of the Biblical writers shared the same view of the nature and function of the world as did those inspired Biblical authors. God did not inspire any correction of their views. However, the central message of Holy Scripture was a radical correction to the prevailing views of the nature of God – as it is today. What a strong contrast!

So when I read Scripture I am not looking for what we today call science. The central Biblical message sounds out like a trumpet, telling us the true nature of God and our relationship to Him. That astonishing message was carried to us through the understandings of the Biblical writers – earthen vessels containing the awesome message. I am deeply concerned that the strong disagreement over Scripture interpretation is diverting our attention and efforts from our mission in this world – spreading the gospel of salvation from Jesus Christ, loving our neighbor and not hating our enemies – as Paul put it, bless but not curse.[9]

III

So how do we understand the creation story in Genesis? I accept it as deeply true but not a literal account of what God did and how He did it – in the same way that I do not accept the world view of the many Biblical passages that talk of the sun going around the earth, foundations of the earth using pillars of support, etc. In the preceding paragraphs I briefly illustrate that the Biblical message is very different from a technical account of God's creation. Even as a professional scientist, a chemist, I would find such an account to have very little meaning compared to the incomparable, colossal, and astonishing message about one God and His love and care for us. As a scientist, I can work on understanding the nature of God's creation and how it functions. I believe that because we are created in the image of God, He has given us His gracious gifts of curiosity about His creation and abilities to comprehend His creation, at least in part. However, the history of humankind is clear: we humans do not know how to find God on our own. So God inspired Biblical writers and, most of all, sent His Son into our world to show the way, bringing us salvation and showing us how to relate to God and our neighbors through love.

More and more on my faith journey, I believe that current scientific references to our world only appear in conflict with the Bible.[10] Through the sciences we can develop a richer understanding of God's creation without conflicting with historic Christian theology. God came all the way down to our human level to inspire Biblical writers. He used their language and concepts to communicate a far greater message: His Lordship over creation and His love for us. God revealed His love in human flesh as Jesus. "Down from His glory, ever living story . . . What condescension, giving us redemption . . ."[11]

Also on my journey this understanding of Scripture interpretation came to me as a new and helpful insight. However, I also discovered that my insight was not new at all. The position of The Church of the Nazarene refers to Holy Scripture ". . . inerrantly revealing the will of God concerning us in all things necessary to our salvation . . ."[12] This position on interpretation of Holy Scripture is a long standing view in Christianity, including John Wesley.

So on our journey together in community let us celebrate the light shining from the Logos throughout Scripture, revealing God's love in all its power and mystery. In community let us also celebrate the knowledge God reveals to us through science about His universe, revealing its wonders beyond our imaginations.

My ongoing journey is also showing me that many Christians have not shared the same experiences I have. The Holy Spirit reminds me of important words often quoted by John Wesley, "In essentials, unity. In non-essentials, liberty. In all things, charity."[13] The Holy Spirit continues to teach the professor.

ENDNOTES AND SUGGESTED READING

1. See several sources, including Rienk Vermij, *The Calvinist Copernicans* (Royal Netherlands Academy of Arts and Sciences, 2002); Charles Hummel, *The Galileo Connection* (Downers Grove, Ill.: InterVarsity Press,1986); Jerome J. Langford, *Galileo, Science and the Church*, (The University of Michigan Press,1971).

2. a. Rev. Franciscus Ridderus, *Scriptural Light*, (1680).

b. Rev. Jacob Du Bois, *Astronomical Theological Dialogue*, Leiden (1650). For these and other quotes as well as an extensive discussion, see Vermij (p254, p328).

3. Richard N. Ostling, "The Search for Historical Adam", *Christianity Today* (June 2011), 27.

4. Denis Lamoureux, *Evolutionary Creation: A Christian Approach to Evolution* (Eugene: Wipf & Stock, 2008) 106.

5. Proverbs 23:7. See also John Walton, *The Lost World of Genesis One: Ancient Cosmology and the Origins Debate* (Downers Grove, Ill.:InterVarsity Press, 2009) Chapter One; Lamoureux, Chapter Four.

6. For example, Job 9:6; 38:4 and Ps 75:3. See also Lamoureux, Chapter Four, and Walton, Chapter One.

7. Lamoureux, 107-110 and Walton, Chapter One.

8. See Alister McGrath, *The Foundations of Dialogue in Science and Religion* (Oxford: Blackwell, 1998) 124, and Darrel R. Falk, *Coming to Peace with Science* (Downers Grove, Ill.: InterVarsity Press, 2004) 34-25.

9. Romans 12:14.

10. For example, the Principles of Biological Evolution make no statement about God. Only atheists state that evolution claims there is no God.

11. Quoted from the opening two lines of the first and second verses of "Down from His Glory", William Emmanuel Booth Clibborn (1921).

12. *Manual*, The Church of the Nazarene, Article IV. See also II Timothy 3:16-17.

13. The source of this phrase is uncertain and several web sites have been devoted to searching for a source. Suffice to say, this expression was often used by John Wesley and probably originates from an earlier time. Some attribute the phrase to Moravians about a century before Wesley.

24

PROVIDENCE AND EVOLUTION

Burton Webb

Burton Webb is Vice President for Academic Affairs at Northwest Nazarene University.

Type *providence* into Google and see what you get -

Noun:
1. The protective care of God or of nature as a spiritual power.
2. God or nature as providing such care.
Synonyms:
foresight - forethought - prudence

Over the last 15 years I have developed a close friendship with a man who has been a mentor, guide, colleague, pal, and rescuer at various times in my life. Keith Drury and I have been setting out on adventures together that have spanned the United States and taken us to corners of the country seldom traveled by humans. Along the way, we have talked for hours, days, and weeks about God, science, theology, and the nature of everything. To say our relationship is expansive barely begins to cover it. In one such conversation, Keith said to me, "You know, perhaps the greatest contribution you could make to theology as a biologist is in developing our understanding of divine providence." I don't know how great the contribution will be, but in the paragraphs to come I will attempt to follow Keith's lead once again.

For me, divine providence starts with the beginning. "In the beginning, God created the heavens and the earth..." Think about the providential planning that act took! God had to envision all that would be and prepare for every eventuality that might exist. Stars, oceans, land, and air - all of the big things we see around us and marvel at when we go on vacation. But there's more. God also had to think about all the plants, birds, fish, reptiles, amphibians, and mammals that we see less frequently. There are some incredible plants and animals in the world. Hold on, there's still more. We are surrounded every day by all manner of microorganisms: bacteria, viruses, phages, zoo and phytoplankton, rotifera, all manner of parasites. They are incredible to behold, and the vast, vast majority are not disease causing but beneficial to the world around them.

Just the existence of all these things is incredible! Then, God also needed to provide a way for them to survive, things for them to eat, niches for them to inhabit, environmental currents to bring them new resources, instincts for them to use for survival. Most important, God needed to create a star that was just close enough to warm them but not so far away that the atmosphere would filter out its energy and light. That star would produce all sorts of energy that would power weather, build clouds, drive the wind, empower the waves, and most important, begin the process of energy conversion. You see, without chlorophyll, the phytoplankton and plants would not be able to convert the energy from sunlight into sugar and later into protein, fat, and nucleic acid. All animals depend on plants' ability to make this conversion. We owe our existence to the providence of God, from the moment of creative thought.

The same sunlight that provides warmth and energy also triggers change in the fundamental building blocks of life. Here again, we see the providence of God. As organisms began to flourish and fill the earth, they encountered strange and unknown environmental conditions in the world around them. Providence came to the rescue again, in the form of energy from the sun that was capable of altering the very structure of the building blocks of life itself. We rail against mutation when we have a loved one with cancer or a child with birth defects, but the ability of DNA to mutate allows organisms to adapt to changing conditions in the world around them. This isn't something that happened in the ancient past and has stopped now; it happens now all around us. God's providence continues to be at work in the laboratory of the world.

I've just given one example of the providence of God that appears to be two-sided. Mutations are valued as either bad or good, depending on where they happen. God's providence is evident in the creation of an adapting system, but that mechanism of providence also has a downside in human health. Another example that might be a little easier to understand is the relationship that exists between the red-tail hawk and the field mouse. The hawk circles high above the sage fields outside my front door until he sees the fast food God has provided- the mouse. From the point of view of the hawk, the mouse represents God's providence of food; from the point of view of the mouse, God's providence looks like evil.

Take a step back from both the mutation and the mouse. We live in a relatively closed system here on planet earth. We have limited resources that must be continually recycled and renewed. What if everything that has ever lived were still alive today? What would our world look like? The answer is easy really. We would be buried under meters and meters of insects, swimming in our own waste, fighting for the limited surface area that the sun warms. The very fact that we have limited lifespans, disease, and circles of predator/prey is part of the providence of God.

Wait a minute, you say, I thought this project was about evolution?!?

It is. You see, a providential God would not only need to create everything, he would need to build into his creation the ability to adapt; he would need to build the ability to respond to changing conditions in the environment caused by meteors, asteroids, tectonic movements, polar shifts and climate change. Without the providential ability to evolve, life on the planet would not survive. Change, in any context, is messy, fraught with the potential for error and outright failure. That's probably why we fear it. Still, there are also wonderful possibilities that come along with change - new life and new ways of doing things.

Change is an ever-present reality. It is built into the very fabric of our universe. Living organisms must change. God, in his providence, gives all of creation the ability to adapt, and he gives us (humans) the added ability to choose. How amazing, how incredible is our providential God! God could have created an "as is" world where everything was static and unchangeable, but that's not the world we have. Our world has evolved and continues to evolve to the everlasting glory of God! From a theological perspective, the world we have meshes well with a Wesleyan understanding of God. If God desired his creation to love Him in freedom, he had to create a system where freedom existed, where change and variation were part of the fabric laid down from the beginning of time. We see evidence of providential (but not absolute) freedom in quarks, bosons, strings, electrons, molecules, DNA, proteins, weather, meteors, comets, critters and yes, in humans too. By giving humans the ability to choose, there is an upside (service to God) and a downside (sin). The world we have – a world where systems evolve – bears witness to the provision of God.

25

EVOLUTIONARY BATTLE FATIGUE

Donald A. Yerxa

Donald A. Yerxa is Emeritus Professor of History at Eastern Nazarene College and director of ENC's Honors Scholar Program.

Perhaps my experience is not the norm for a lifelong Nazarene, but evolution has never been terribly problematic for me. I cannot say the same, of course, for reductionistic naturalism. Not surprisingly, I have always viewed materialistic thinking as fundamentally incompatible with my Christian faith, as well as good sense. Despite having written a number of essays and co-authored a book on the origins debate, in recent years I have checked out of the conversation suffering from what one might call "evolutionary battle fatigue." With this essay, I step back into the conversation briefly to reflect on why the tone and content of much of the contemporary origins debate is disappointing.

My first exposure to evolutionary thinking was in 1964–65, when as a high school freshman I took a biology class shaped by the fairly new Biological Sciences Curriculum Study (BSCS). I can still recall terms from the BSCS textbook like *coacervates* and *amino acid soup*. Although the BSCS's naturalistic perspective on origins was not lost on me, I had far more pressing matters with which to contend. In those days, the big issues for a good Nazarene teen were smoking and drinking with sexual immorality not far behind, lurking in the moral swamplands of "lewd and lascivious" rock-and-roll music and Hollywood movies. Endtimes preaching and fears of world communism dominated my "larger" intellectual horizons. As I reflect on those days, I don't recall having difficulty compartmentalizing what I learned in school from the more immediate demands of my local church, with its weekly ritual of confronting me with fearsome questions of eternal destiny.

I shall always be grateful to Clayton Dyer. He was a biology teacher at my high school, though he was not assigned to the BSCS class. Dyer was also a Sunday School teacher at my church, and I recall vividly how he told the class one Sunday that we could "believe in" evolution and remain good Christians, as long as we steadfastly held to God as the Creator. Evolution, he maintained, was our best understanding of the processes God employed to bring about life. That was good enough for me then, and the framework of theistic evolution has guided my thinking ever since. It must be noted that I am not a scientist—far from it! I majored in history at Eastern Nazarene College (ENC) and went on for an M.A. and Ph.D. in American history (with an emphasis on naval history—of all things!) at the University of Maine. So, my understanding of evolution has decidedly been that of an amateur. But I never encountered a persuasive argument to challenge the basic stance of theistic evolution that Dyer presented to me back in a Church of the Nazarene Sunday School class. In retrospect, I view this as a great intellectual gift.

Fast forward to the mid-1990s. A group of ENC faculty members launched an interdisciplinary book club, and in that setting, I became exposed to the emerging science and religion dialogue that the Templeton Foundation had spawned with an enormous financial investment that trickled down to evangelical Christian colleges like ENC. In 2002—after a series of improbable events for a naval historian that included interviewing Sir John Polkinghorne (with Karl Giberson and Kent Hill) for *Books & Culture* and engaging in postdoctoral study in science and religion at Wycliffe Hall, Oxford—I co-authored a book with Giberson on the origins debate. We intended our *Species of Origins: America's Search for a Creation Story* to be a non-polemical tour d'horizon of the debate over evolution in North America.

When I co-wrote *Species of Origins*, I harbored some sympathy for the intelligent design (ID) project. I freely admit that I lacked the expertise—and continue to do so—to reach an independent assessment of the science behind evolution and ID. But the design theorists (as they liked to be called) struck me as being eloquent critics of the ontological materialism that many science writers smuggled into their books. And while I had no quarrel with evolution as a God-created mechanism, at a gut level of intuition it did seem implausible that evolution alone could account for the astounding organized complexity of life on the planet. Now ID spokespersons, with seemingly solid academic credentials and without the baggage of a literalist reading of Genesis, were arguing that my intuitions of design could be confirmed empirically. I knew that the overwhelming majority of scientists, including many with very strong Christian beliefs, considered the ID camp's claims to be hyperbolic. And ID's talk about "theistic science" troubled me. What would that look like methodologically? But I was willing to suspend judgment, and let the IDers make their case. If empirical evidence of design could be provided, wouldn't science have to salute?

Unfortunately, the design camp did not advance much beyond its initial assertion that evolutionary thinking cannot adequately account for the manifest complexity surrounding us in nature. Moreover, its claims seemed to be increasingly based on philosophical and theological assumptions, not science. And as critics of design became shriller (something I have written about elsewhere), key people in the design camp made increasingly pretentious, even preposterous, claims and predictions. Without a body of scientific literature to support them, ID apologists, for example, confidently predicted that intelligent design would replace Darwinism as a thriving scientific research program. Undoubtedly, the most disconcerting assertion coming out of the ID camp was that it was ushering in a "design revolution" that promised to alter fundamentally the entire scientific enterprise. From ID's infancy, its advocates saw themselves as actors in a Kuhnian drama against the normal science of evolution. In 2004, however, William Dembski made the extraordinary claim that ID "fits the bill as a full-scale scientific revolution" because it challenges not only evolutionary biology, but also "the *rules by which the natural sciences are conducted* [emphasis added]."[1] This assertion was very troubling. Any substantive alteration to the rules of science—its requirements of evidence and avoidance of private knowledge—moves us beyond science to something else. Science is science. It has limits. But it has been a wildly successful enterprise, and talk of revolutionizing its methods is, in my view, ill conceived.

So the shrillness and venom of ID's critics and the hyperbole of Dembski and company soured me to the whole origins debate. Both sides were talking past each other, hoping to "win" the debate rather than seeking to understand. I once thought that ID might take the long-standing intuition of design and, according to Dembski, "cash... [it] out as a scientific research program."[2] If nature is chock full of design, then surely the evidence—not merely the rhetoric—would sway the debate in that direction. To my knowledge, it hasn't come close to generating a robust scientific research program. And from where I sit on the sidelines, it seems a very remote possibility that it could ever do so.

Even more troubling for me is that the shouting match over design hijacked the conversation about reductionistic naturalism in the public sphere. I cannot prove it, but my sense is that materialism is even more the default position now among science writers and public intellectuals than it was in the 1990s when ID appeared on the scene. And the evolutionary model, far from being undermined, has become the conceptual basis for much of our thinking, not just about origins but about almost everything—morality, religion, altruism, love, etc. As one of my European colleagues has quipped sarcastically, "It's all evolution, boys and girls!"

Where does all this leave me? I no longer monitor the debate over evolution as I once did. I am confident the debate still rages in some quarters, but it is not terribly interesting to me anymore. What still does engage me—deeply—is the way extra-scientific considerations shape the narratives we offer for the cosmos and our place in it. I conclude with two very different narratives, both informed by science but by necessity going beyond it.

> *The universe has woken up. If the scientific picture we currently have is right, this was an accident, roughly speaking, and also something that happened very locally. At various places some highly organised physical systems—living organisms—have become aware of the world they are part of. In a few cases they*

have also become aware of their awareness. These living systems are products of evolution by natural selection, an undirected process that began in a fortuitous combination of chemical and physical conditions, whose course is dependent on accidents of history, and which is driven by the slight reproductive advantages some organisms enjoy over others. Even if Earth is not the only place where this has happened, the vast majority of the universe contains no awareness, no life, no reasoning. We, the awoken parts of the universe, can look around and reflect on all this, including the fact that there is no overall purpose in our being here. So the universe has "woken up," but in a local, accidental, and low-key case.[3]

§

We find ourselves in a universe that seems to have had a beginning. We find it governed by laws that have a grandeur and sublimity that bespeak design. We find many indications in those laws that we were built in from the beginning. We find that physical determinism is wrong. And we find that the deepest discoveries of modern physics and mathematics give hints, if not proofs, that the mind of man has something about it that lies beyond the power of either physics or mathematics to describe.[4]

It is not surprising that I find the former view bleak and utterly unsatisfactory and the latter, written by a Catholic physicist, highly congenial to my intellect and Christian faith. Note, by the way, that design for him is not antithetical to evolution; rather, it is linked to the laws of nature. For me at least, pondering the implications of these radically different narratives is vastly more important that being mired in the rancor of an unproductive evolution debate. Science can provide us with enormous amounts of data and many empirically informed theories that help to explain so much of what we encounter in nature. But we must not ask too much of it. It is a profound error to try to make sense of this world and our place in it holding to the view that science is the only reliable source of knowledge. Addressing the truly big questions of life's meaning takes us well beyond science into the realms of wonder and mystery. This is a hermeneutical and narrative enterprise of the highest order.

ENDNOTES AND SUGGESTED READING

1 William D. Dembski, *The Design Revolution: Answering the Toughest Questions about Intelligent Design* (Downers Grove, Ill.: InterVarsity Press, 2004) 19.

2 William D. Dembski, " The Intelligent Design Movement," Access Research Network's William A. Dembski's Files, http://www.arn.org/docs/dembski/wd_idmovement.htm (accessed 2/23/2013).

3 From Peter Godfrey-Smith's review of Thomas Nagel's *Mind and Cosmos: Why the Materialist Neo-Darwinian Conception of Nature is Almost Certainly False* in the *London Review of Books* 35:2 (January 24, 2013): 20.

4 Stephen M. Barr, "Retelling the Story of Science" *First Things* (March 2003): 17.

26

GOD IS THE CREATOR OF ALL THAT IS

Max W. Reams

Max W. Reams is Professor of Geology and Chair of the Department of Chemistry and Geosciences at Olivet Nazarene University.

God is the Author of everything. This is foundational to any Christian interpretation of Scripture and the universe. My journey through the maze of views relating science and faith is guided by this belief.

I was converted to Christ in high school. A first attempt to relate faith with my future career in geology was through a senior English essay. I attempted to cordially connect faith and science. Too bad I didn't keep that approach.

As a student at the University of Kansas, I let three things influence me. First, some professors were negative toward religion. Second, an occasional evangelist preached the evils of science. Third, Christian literature that I read did not integrate Scripture and science well. As a result, I drifted toward a negative approach to science. I was torn between observational data that screamed the Earth is old and a misguided belief that this could not be biblically valid. Evidence of evolution was all around me (I double majored in geology and zoology.) Something didn't make sense.

Then, a light came on as I sat in a zoology senior seminar. I heard a brilliant guest speaker say the Bible claimed the Earth was 6,000 years old. I knew this was incorrect, having studied the history of this view. That marked a shift in my thinking. Perhaps I, like many Christians, had placed a roadblock in the way of scientists. By avoiding integration of faith and science, we prevented them from wrestling with the essence of Christianity. I had witnessed to non-Christians, only to be sidetracked when they brought up evolution.

I began to look afresh at all I had learned. This restarted my journey toward science and faith integration. The material universe took on a different meaning. Science is not an evil force out to destroy faith; science provides a lens to see the hand of God at work. Now, instead of dreading new discoveries, I relish the amazing universe science continually reveals. Excitement replaced fear. Uncertainty gave way to increased faith in the creativity of the God of the Bible.

This remolding of my faith-science interface continues today. When I became a faculty member at Olivet Nazarene College (now University), I found President Harold Reed to be a broad-minded person who had no problem with the antiquity of the Earth.

In my teaching, I challenge students to read widely and wrestle with the many views relating faith to geology and evolution. Students come from varied backgrounds. Some have no difficulty relating faith with the findings of science. Others consider science an evil scourge to be repulsed at every turn. In order to relate to this wide range of opinions, I avoid a confrontational approach. I want students to appreciate Scripture and science and to integrate them.

I let the natural Earth speak for itself during early stages of an introductory course. Students need time to trust that their professor is a sincere believer and practitioner of the Christian faith. It is difficult to adjust head knowledge until heart trust is present.

In addition to various articles, students read Bernard Ramm's *Christian View of Science and Scripture*.[1] It is an old text, but faithful to the Scriptures and accurately presents a wide spectrum of views. Another is *Biology Through the Eyes of Faith*, by Richard Wright.[2] These books are not hard-sells, so students can work through them without emotional baggage getting in the way of thinking.

Ad hoc observations suggest this approach helps many students develop a wider appreciation for science and adopt a more integrative approach. Inspiration and relief often replace antagonism toward science. It encourages me when their eyes are opened.

When asked, "What do you believe?" I respond that I ascribe to the Church of the Nazarene statement of beliefs. Aside from those, I allow a wide range of possibilities. To "believe" in some argument about evolution or the age of the Earth, etc. is dangerous and has been disproved countless times. Faith must not hinge on some perceived gap in scientific data. Such arguments fall apart with new discoveries. I embrace discovery. That is one reason I enjoy being a geologist. Discovery is exciting!

A helpful approach is to isolate views with the fewest problems. All science-faith hypotheses present problems, since they are human constructs. I see three with the fewest religious and/or scientific difficulties:

1. <u>Ideal Time</u> states that everything was created by God to appear old or "mature." Earth's rocks look as *if* they had a history, but it is an illusion. They were made to look that way! Comparative DNA *appears* to show intricate connections between life forms. God made things to appear other than they are, for whatever reason. Ideal Time seems philosophically impossible to disprove. However, most students find it unsatisfying and an affront to their view of God. God is made to seem underhanded in His Creation.

2. <u>Progressive Creation</u> assumes that God created life forms at various moments in Earth's long history. Some forms persisted for a time and became extinct. Others persisted for extended periods. Evolutionary changes may occur but each group has a *de novo* origin (from nothing).

3. <u>Theistic Evolution</u> presumes that all changes in life forms throughout Earth's history are under the creative control of God.

Distinguishing Progressive Creation from Theistic Evolution on the basis of physical evidence seems a difficult task. If one could observe life forms present at any moment in time, either model might explain the observations. Only if a new life form suddenly appeared without genetic connections to the past could Progressive Creation be verified.

I have found the Church of the Nazarene to be inclusive, permitting a wide diversity of opinion on many issues, including evolution. However, outside influences have crept into the church to divide and polarize the denomination, attempting to make the church more restrictive. We must reclaim and celebrate our diversity. That is my prayer.

ENDNOTES AND SUGGESTED READING

1 Bernard Ramm. *The Christian View of Science and Scripture* (Grand Rapids, MI: Wm. B. Eerdmans Publishing Company, 1954).

2 Richard T Wright. *Biology Through the Eyes of Faith* (New York, NY: HarperCollins Publishers, Inc., 1989).

27

THE PERSPECTIVE FROM GEOSCIENCE

Charles W. Carrigan

Charles W. Carrigan is Professor of Geoscience and Director of the Honors Program at Olivet Nazarene University.

The billion dollar satellites that make up the Global Positioning System (GPS) have revolutionized how we relate to our place on the globe. A GPS receiver is standard in any smartphone, and a wide variety of simple, stand-alone devices can pinpoint your position to within about 12 feet on a clear day. Higher-end equipment can measure your position down to the centimeter. Latitude and Longitude have gone from somewhat obscure terms to being commonly used by the masses for navigation and to find Tupperware in the woods in the recreational activity of geocaching. But there's a funny thing about where you are in the world: it keeps changing, even if you stand perfectly still. Stand in New York and look east toward London, and the distance between the two keeps increasing, ever so slightly. Over the course of a year, that distance increases by about one inch. These changes of course are so small that they have little effect on our daily lives. Nevertheless, they are a manifestation of the slow, steady drift of the continents across the surface of the globe. But what does this have to do with evolution?

Any science & faith discussion that delves into the complicated subject of origins must take into consideration geologic context. While evidence for evolution comes from genetics, ecology, fossils, and other biological areas of study, the natural history of life forms takes place within the natural history of Earth itself. It seems important then that this conversation on evolution take place within the context of understanding Earth history.

Of primary importance here is the age of the Earth itself. Some American Evangelical Christian groups claim that the Earth is only a few thousand years young based on a literal interpretation of the days of Genesis 1 and the genealogies that follow. However, geologic studies all point to significantly greater antiquity for this third rock from the Sun. Other writers in this conversation more qualified than I have already discussed faith-affirming ways of interpreting the Genesis text other than as literal 24-hour periods of time. It is important to note that differing interpretations of the days in Genesis can be traced all the way back to Augustine in the 4th century, hundreds of years before modern science was even conceived. If there are multiple interpretations of the Genesis text by people of faith, why continue to hold on to one that is so greatly at odds with the determinations of geoscience? What is there to be gained by insisting that Scripture teaches that the Earth is but a few thousand years young? Instead, I hope to help Christian leaders better understand the claims and evidences of geoscience so that they might understand why some assertions are not reasonable in the light of observable data.

To write a short article on the evidences for the Earth's great antiquity is to sample the ocean with a straw – you aren't going to get more than a small taste, and it won't come anywhere close to describing the whole picture. The evidence, when viewed in large portion, is simply overwhelming. In this short essay, I aim to describe just a few lines of evidence that demonstrate why geoscientists conclude that it is, in fact, several billion years old. A much fuller treatment of geology and Scripture is found in a recent book by Davis Young & Ralph Stearley called *The Bible, Rocks, and Time*.[1] Both Dave and Ralph are highly competent geologists, strong Christian men, and professors at Calvin College for many years. Their work is, in my opinion, the best resource on this subject and should be on any reading list about the relationship between science and Scripture.

Returning to drifting continents, the Atlantic Ocean was born when the continents of Europe, Africa, and North and South America split apart and began moving away from one another. Between North America & Africa, the distance between these continents has reached over 4800 km (3000 mi), and continues to expand. At the current rate of expansion of 1 inch per year, the Atlantic Ocean requires nearly 200 million years to reach its current dimensions. A number of other observations demonstrate the consistency of this value. Sediments at the bottom of the ocean floor grow progressively thicker in both directions away from the center. Within those sediments, fossils of microscopic organisms gradually change from the bottom to the top of the layers. Magnetic properties of the ocean floor itself show that the Earth's magnetic field has flipped its north & south directions many times as that ocean expanded. Measurements of atomic ratios in rocks of eastern North America associated with the continental breakup yield ages of ~200 million years. All of these data and more paint a consistent and coherent picture of the history of the opening of the Atlantic. It is a long process, and yet it is less than 5% of Earth's history.

Meanwhile in the Pacific Ocean, the Hawaiian Islands leave a breadcrumb trail of volcanism that spins another tale of the Earth's past. The Pacific Plate is steadily moving to the northwest, but below it, in the Earth's mantle, is a stationary hot spot. This hot spot continues to break through and erupt lava up on to the surface of the Pacific Plate. The plate continues to move over the top of it, building the chain of the Hawaiian Islands. Only the youngest volcanoes at the south-east end of the chain where the hot spot lies are still active; the rest have gone dormant long ago. These islands are related to a series of extinct undersea volcanoes to the northwest that make up the Emperor Seamounts, some of which still breach the surface and form islands. Measurements of the radiometric ages of these rocks show a progressive increase in age farther and farther away from Kilauea, the most active volcano on the southeast end of the Big Island of Hawaii. These volcanic breadcrumbs not only track the movement of the Pacific Plate to the northwest, they also demonstrate that the movement of the Pacific Plate has remained a steady ~9 centimeters per year for at least the past 30 million years. Furthermore, those islands and seamounts to the northwest show their progressive aging. Imagine that along the breadcrumb trail, the individual crumbs start showing a bit of mold growing on them, or their edges show that mice have been nibbling at them. As the Hawaiian Islands move away from the hot spot, volcanism ceases and erosion takes over. While they are exposed above the ocean surface, erosion slowly removes the hard rock from the tops of these islands and cuts them down. Meanwhile, areas of these islands under the ocean accumulate sediments, both piles of debris from the eroded tops dumped along their flanks, and growing coral reefs of limestone reaching up to the ocean surface. Additionally, as the islands progressively cool and move away from the hot spot, their cold masses slowly sink beneath the ocean surface. As the islands sink, the corals continue to build upward to stay near the sunlight. In some areas, the eroded volcanic stump has long since descended beneath the ocean and all that remains at the surface is a ring of coral, still reaching for the sun near the surface of the water.

Both the Atlantic and Pacific Oceans record numerous events that have unfolded in Earth's past. These include volcanic eruptions, fault movements, a changing magnetic field, erosion of hard rock, clay particles settling out on the ocean floor, growing corals, the formation of soils, cold masses sinking as they cool, and more. Various rates of these geologic processes can be measured today – erosion rates, sediment deposition rates, tectonic rates, cooling rates, growth rates, etc., and all require tens of thousands of years for even the most basic geologic features to form. Complex features, such as mountain ranges or chains of volcanic islands, require tens of millions.

The fundamental problem with trying to squeeze all of this time into a few thousand years is that the Earth wasn't just spinning on its axis and revolving around the Sun with nothing else going on for those 4.5 billion years. Instead, a lengthy history of events is recorded in the rock record: volcanoes erupting; mountains rising and eroding back down; rivers moving millions of tons of silt and sand; continents colliding, pulling apart, and colliding back together again; ocean basins forming and later closing; meteors crashing into the Earth and those craters being subsequently filled with new rock layers; glaciers advancing, retreating, and advancing again; and many, many other events. Trying to compress 4.5

billion years of time into just a few thousand requires accelerating all of these processes to a million times their natural rates. To attempt to squeeze all of the events recorded into a short time span is not scientifically feasible. If that's not problematic enough, those who invoke Noah's flood as a mechanism to explain the rock record require all this geologic activity to happen in just one year! Such a scenario simply can't be entertained without requiring significant miraculous activity that is not recorded in the Genesis accounts, and is unnecessary. A flood, no matter how large, does not cause tectonic plates to shift, volcanoes to erupt, glaciers to advance and retreat, or mountains to form. Such assertions require catastrophic changes to the laws of physics. Why would God do this? Why would He create a young world that bears the marks of so many events and so much time gone by? Why would our God-given senses lead us to clearly deduce great periods of geologic time if they didn't actually happen?

Instead, I encourage people of faith to embrace the complexity, beauty, and antiquity of the Earth. There is little to be gained by continuing to hold to the view of a young Earth, as there is no geologic evidence to support this view. I do not claim to tell Biblical scholars how the Genesis text should be interpreted, as I am not qualified to do so. But we must no longer hold to the belief that all of geology can be explained by a world-wide catastrophic flood, or that its history consists of just a few thousand years. Scientific study of the Earth clearly demonstrates that these views are not tenable.

FURTHER READING:

1. Davis Young and Ralph Stearley, *The Bible, Rocks, and Time*. (Downers Grove, Illinois: IVP Academic Press, 2008).

SECTION 3

A
THEOLOGICAL
PERSPECTIVE

28

CREATIVE EVOLVING CONVERSATIONS:

REFLECTIONS ON SCRIPTURE, EVOLUTION, AND THE CHRISTIAN FAITH

Stephen Riley

Stephen Riley is Professor of Old Testament and Hebrew at Northwest Nazarene University

As I sit here holding my newborn son I admit that it is difficult to consider the theory of evolution. It is hard for me to think about things like our species evolving from something other than what we are right now. As I look at Gabriel's little hands and feet, as I listen to his breathing and smell the sweet aroma of his newborness, it is difficult for me to think that who we are now is anything but the image of God. However, I will readily admit that I am not a scientist by training. I do not fully understand the ins and outs of the theory of evolution as it pertains to biology or geology, and thus I am not sure that I am one to weigh in heavily on this. I do have a number of wonderful friends, people of faith, who tell me that the theory of evolution has explanatory power for much of their disciplines and they have a difficult time refuting the evidence they find. Though I am willing to trust their expertise, I fear too often their knowledge has little persuasive power with some people. What I am is a Hebrew scholar, Old Testament professor, and ordained elder in the Church of the Nazarene. What I think about are the wonderful texts of the Christian Old Testament and the witness they provide to the revelation of God in the world.

None of the texts of the Old Testament directly deal with the theory of evolution (that would be anachronistic), but still the issue of the theory of evolution has been continually thrust upon me. Students often will ask questions such as "How do dinosaurs fit into the creation texts of Genesis?", or "Were the seven days accounted for in Genesis 1 really 24 hours or more like years?", or the big one "Were Adam and Eve real people and did the Fall really happen?" These types of questions reflect a particular type of reading of Scripture many students have been taught, and it is emblematic of an attempt to synthesize that type of reading with what students have learned or heard elsewhere about evolutionary theory. While I understand how this type of reading makes the conversation about the theory of evolution seem to be a matter of intellectual and spiritual life or death, I do not find it to be necessary. I believe there are a number of points of contact for reflection and growth available to us if we are open to the guidance of God's Spirit when we engage in these conversations. My goal as a professor is to help my students see some of those possibilities and help them engage in the task of critically thinking about how these conversations can help us grow. Therefore, because so many of my colleagues have offered wonderful examinations of the creation texts in the Christian Old Testament in other essays, I do not feel it necessary to reconsider the particulars of the historical, literary, or cultural contexts which influenced the writing of those texts. Rather, I would like to make some observations about this matter that seem pertinent to me at this point in my journey as I continue to try to navigate this discussion amidst these texts I love while attempting to live a life of faithfulness to God.

First, the Hebrew of the very first line of Genesis can be read in at least two very distinct but equally acceptable ways. One way it can be translated is "When God began to create with the heavens and with the earth..." Another way it can be read is "In God's beginning of creating the heavens and the earth..." I like considering both possibilities. What would it mean for us to consider the possibility that God creates in conjunction with the heavens and the earth? Or, what would it mean to consider that the author of Genesis was not so much concerned with "the" beginning but rather the beginning of God's creation. I'm not entirely sure that either of those possibilities are more or less helpful for this particular conversation, but I do think it is worth considering them since the text allows such a translation. More importantly, my point here is to suggest that if the very first line of Genesis invites us as readers to make significant interpretive choices, perhaps we should have much more humility when we approach the text. I understand many people's desire for certainty. I, too, love when things are cut and dry just as much as anyone else. However, the language of our sacred text is often much more obscure than our modern translations reflect. When approaching our conversations about any issue where Scripture might be used as a weapon to end the argument, it might be helpful to remember that our readings of Scripture are just that, "readings" or better, "interpretations." I certainly hope that my interpretations are guided by God's Spirit, but I also recognize that I read from a very particular place that does not always have the wisdom and insight that a sister or brother from somewhere else around the world, or at another time in history might offer. We might be freed of the need to be exclusively right when we can be reminded that there are often inspired alternative interpretations of the same texts.

Second, I wonder why the debate about evolution often centers solely upon the issue of origins. Where do we come from? How can one reconcile the creation texts with what science is telling us? I wonder if our obsession with origins is misplaced. Sometimes I think we may focus on origins rather than dealing with our present struggles. For example, we would rather talk about the seven days of creation rather than being confronted by the repeated call that creation is good and we are tasked with caring for all of it. We would rather argue over the historicity of Adam and Eve than notice that the final (and, perhaps most important) act of the creation poem in Genesis 1 is Sabbath and God's rest. I recognize that issues of origins are present in the text and important. However, I also find it interesting that of all the issues found in the creation texts, Sabbath and care for creation get a whole lot more repetition in Scripture than do Adam and Eve or the days of creation. Therefore, if we are going to argue about the creation texts, perhaps we should allow ourselves to be confronted by some other issues than just origins and see if the theory of evolution can offer us helpful ways to think about what it means to live life here and now before God. The following are questions that I think might be helpful for generating a much more creative and robust theological conversation based on the creation texts of the Old Testament.

1. How should the truth of the theory of evolution influence our thinking about how we care for God's creation?

2. What would a serious conversation about Sabbath look like in light of what evolution says about our species?

3. How should the truth of the theory of evolution impact our thinking about what it means to be made in the image of God?

4. How should the truth of the theory of evolution impact our thinking about end of life issues?

These are just some questions that I think a little creative energy would help us flesh out the parts of the theory of evolution which are helpful and what parts we may want to reconsider theologically.

Finally, I am concerned. I am particularly concerned about the way this conversation often ends up as a zero sum game. By this, I mean that for many people it is an "either/or" "in/out" kind of conversation. Unfortunately, this is the spirit of the age, but I am not at all sure this is the correct response to God's call on our lives as followers of Christ. I rather believe that the family of God is to model something different. There are some who think that the evolution debate will be the undoing of Christianity or, even, God. Perhaps they are right. I don't know. If they are, I do not think it will be because evolution somehow unraveled God-as if God could be contained in this one conversation. However, it may be our undoing as Christians because of our inability to continue to do theology creatively in the spirit set before us in Scripture. The authors of Scripture are models for continually reinterpreting earlier texts for new contexts as a way of giving life to God's family. Unfortunately, we presently find ourselves in contexts besieged by a culture of fear where many would rather retreat into realms of safety instead of explore the possibilities of God's creative love. Our theology is best done when we have the freedom to think openly and question freely without fear of being labeled a heretic for thinking differently. If we are to offer a life-giving faith to the coming generations, we will have to face these conversations not beset by a spirit of timidity but rather by boldness and charity, undergirded by the conviction that if we are proven wrong our God is big enough and gracious enough to guide us home and love us all the same. At the end of the day, this is the place I hope to begin my inquiry into any question, such as evolutionary theory, facing the church both now and in the future.

29

MAKING THE PIECES FIT

Timothy Crutcher

Timothy Crutcher is a Professor of Church History and Theology at Southern Nazarene University.

As a Wesleyan theologian, I'm passionately committed to two things. First and foremost, I'm committed to Scripture and the truth to which it testifies about who God is, who we are, and how we relate to God. In my mind, that book must be absolutely trustworthy because without it, we'd be in the dark. No amount of thinking or searching on our part could replace God's gracious self-communication to us. So, when folks want to argue strongly for a chronological-historical reading of Scripture in order to affirm the Bible's dependability, I know exactly where they are coming from. A Bible that can't be trusted does no one any good at all.

Second, I'm committed to the idea that what Scripture says about God and us and our relationship to God has to make sense in—and make a difference in—the world of our practical, ordinary, physical existence. There are some religions—Buddhism primary among them—that make our material world less real than the abstract spiritual world, but that is not the religion of the followers of Jesus. To believe in Creation, to believe in the Incarnation, is to believe that our physical world is very real and very important to the God of Scripture. This world we encounter with our senses is the primary world God has given us to relate to one another and to God. As human beings we have both a spiritual dimension and a physical dimension. Neither animals nor angels, we live our lives at the intersection between two worlds.

So, the most useful theology and the most helpful readings of Scripture are the ones that help us live in relationship to God and others here and now. Purely spiritual debates about things that make no impact on our lives seem to me to be largely a waste of time. Like Wesley, I want "plain truth for plain people." I don't give much space in my theology to speculations we can't live out. ("How many angels can dance on the head of a pin?" I don't know, but probably less than the number of theologians it would take to count them.) I'm all for the idea of the power of the spiritual realm—after all, God is Spirit. But if it makes no difference in our workaday world to live as though God is Spirit, then I'm not sure what that statement means. I heartily hope for and believe in a trajectory for us that transcends our merely physical existence. But that trajectory only makes sense when we live our physical-for-now lives toward it.

So, for me, it is these two steadfast commitments—to Scripture and to the arena of our real world experience—that ground what it means to be a theologian in the Wesleyan tradition. All of Wesley's substantive ideas—prevenient grace, sanctification, catholicity, you-name-it—have the power that they do because they are deeply grounded in Scripture and make a real difference in how we live in this world.

Having said that, I, as a Wesleyan committed to Scripture and experience, run into immediate difficulties when I'm told that the proper way to interpret the Creation story in Genesis 1 is to say that God created the world in six literal days about six thousand years ago. Those difficulties come precisely because I hold Scripture and Creation in such high regard, not because I have a competing commitment to science or because I want to be a rebel against Church tradition. Science is important, but I don't think it has all the answers. The history of science is a history of discarding previous solutions, so we cannot expect that the way we understand things now to be the way we will understand them in 100 years. Besides, the Christian faith rests solidly on the kind of unrepeatable historical events (like the Virgin Birth or the Resurrection of Christ) that science as science cannot address.

Church tradition, too, is important, but I'm a Protestant and therefore know that Church tradition can be wrong. After all, it was common Church tradition to accept the practice of slavery for 1600 years, and I think we are all glad that this inadequate tradition is now gone. Likewise, the church fought hard against Galileo and the idea that the earth moves around the sun, but I think most of us are rather comfortable with how we feel about that issue these days. So, my problem is not an issue of dangerous science or being faithful to tradition. My problem is that my commitments to Scripture and experience both make it difficult for me to place a six-day, six-thousand-year-old creation in the context of the rest of Scripture and the rest of our experience.

SCRIPTURE

Let's start with Scripture. One problem that immediately confronts us every time we open this book is that the book itself does not tell us how to read it. We just have to make sense of it by fitting the various pieces it gives us into a coherent whole in the world in which we live. So, when the Psalmist tells us, "God is my rock," we instinctively know that he is not worshiping some stone idol because that wouldn't make any sense—despite the fact that is what his words "literally" convey. We know that is a metaphor because other places in Scripture teach us that God is Spirit, not a material thing, and that worshiping material things is actually idolatry and so that cannot be what the Psalmist meant. When we read Jotham's story of the parliament of the trees in Judges 9, a similar kind of thinking goes on. Few of us are tempted to think that this story teaches us the trees actually talk. Instead, we treat the story as a parable because it makes so much more sense that way. After all, we have far more experience with parables than we do with talking trees.

In that same way, even the most unscientific reading of Genesis 1 raises many questions about how much sense it makes if taken as a chronological account, and church fathers like Origen in the third century were wrestling with them long before Darwin. What does the word "day" mean on "days" one, two, and three if the sun—the very thing we use to define a day—does not come around until "day" four? Even the ancient Hebrews knew that plants need sunlight to survive, but again, the plants happen a whole "day" before the sun does. If we go on from Genesis 1 to Genesis 2, we find a very different story of creation, one that does not line up in any chronological-historical sense with the story before it. In Genesis 2, the whole story happens not in six days but in just one (lit. in Hebrew "On the day the LORD made the heavens and the earth," Gen. 2:4b). In Genesis 1, the plants and animals are created before human beings; in Genesis 2, they come after. In fact, the author even draws the readers' attention to this by pointing out that God didn't make any plants yet because there wasn't a human around to take care of them.

Now, we could solve these scriptural issues by importing theories or definitions that are foreign to the biblical text, like the idea of two creations or like defining "day" as "24 hours" rather than by the sun. But that move shifts authority away from Scripture and onto our own clever interpretive devices. The stories as they are written do not seem to be designed to be read historically-chronologically together. If we force them to be read so, we end up putting more faith in our pre-conceived ideas of what we want Scripture to say than in what it actually does say. If we are willing to do that, then we can make the Scripture say anything we like, and it would also lose its voice as a critical revelation from God. So, it seems—to me, at any rate—that an attentive reading of Scripture as Scripture challenges a too-easily-historical interpretation of Genesis 1.

EXPERIENCE

We run into similar problems when we try to put a six-day-six-thousand-years-ago creation into the world of our common experience. Everywhere we look in our world, we see signs of age, and great age at that. All of our experience teaches us to assume that things come together as a result of processes, and that these processes take time. Look at the Grand Canyon and imagine how long it would take for a river of water to wear away the rock like that. We've got lots of places in the world where we know that rivers have been flowing for thousands of years, and they have hardly made a dent in the earth. It sure looks as though that took a very long time. And the rock exposed at the edge of the canyon has many, many layers in it—layers that appear to have been laid down before the river had a chance to wear them away. The whole thing just looks old. You can get the same feeling by visiting just about any museum and looking at the bones of creatures that no ancient human ever wrote about or drew pictures of, bones that have over time turned into solid rock. As far as we know, that must have taken a very long time.

Look beyond our world to the stars, and the apparent age of the cosmos becomes mind-boggling. The universe doesn't look like a bubble with a radius of 6,000 light-years with us at the center, painted black in some areas but with dots of light in others. The universe looks vast. Stars move in relationship to other stars, and those background stars must be really far away for that to happen. With a simple telescope, one can see that some of those apparent pinpricks of light are actually whole galaxies, which, if they are only 6,000 light-years away instead of millions, must only have tiny stars in comparison to our sun. Just about everywhere we look, our experience tells us that our earth is old, and the time and space involved in our cosmos is staggering.

If, then, we claim that God created the world in six literal days six thousand years ago, then my impression of the world is completely unreliable. Even when I try my hardest to see the world clearly, I would have to admit that I miss it big time. Given this huge gap between the way the world appears and the way things would actually be, it would seem that the problem is worse than just saying that human beings are stupid and have no clue how to figure the world out. Rather, it would seem that the human race has actually been profoundly deceived, given every reason to think that the world is old when it really isn't. And if that's true, then only God could be the author of that deception. If the world really isn't as old as it looks, then it seems we believe in a God who has pulled off a cosmic hoax for the ages.

Confronted with that gap and its disturbing theological implications, I think to myself, *Something ain't right here.* Either I have a Bible that I can't make sense of without relying on extra-biblical cleverness and an experience of the world that I just can't trust, or Genesis 1 is doing something other than giving me a chronological account on the creation of the world in a week six-thousand years ago. Given those options, my choice isn't difficult. While I can in no way claim that I've got the "right" interpretation of Genesis, I think I can sense where another interpretation is inadequate. And while I am always open to better interpretations

195

of Scripture and experience—even if they prove me wrong—I still have to deal with that disjunction as I see it, and so this is where I find myself now.

30

FAITH SEEKING UNDERSTANDING

Robert Branson

Robert Branson retired from Olivet Nazarene University as Professor of Biblical Literature.

At the age of nine, while attending a youth camp, I first understood the claims of the Gospel and yielded my life to God. That yielding was more than an emotional experience, for it also was the recognition that God had called me into professional ministry. During my teens, this call continued to be confirmed. In high school, I was required to take courses in science: chemistry, physics, and biology. I loved the courses. One afternoon while touring the new additions being made to our church building, I discussed with my pastor what I was learning in biology, including how the dinosaurs had inhabited the earth millions of years ago. My pastor, whom I loved and appreciated, shocked me when he said, "Bob, you are going to have to believe either the Bible or science." I made no response to his statement. But inwardly, I thought, *If that is my choice, I know who wins. Science!* My second thought was, *There must be another choice.* For those readers who can remember, this was the time when Sputnik could be seen circling the earth.

During my college years, at Bethany Nazarene College (now Southern Nazarene University), my instructors urged me to continue my studies in graduate school. Upon graduation, I had a decision to make. I had been accepted at the University of Southern California in its master's in religion program, at Boston University School of Theology, and at Nazarene Theological Seminary. While seeking God's guidance, He closed the door on the first two options. I went to NTS not because God said to, but because it was the only door He left open.

While at NTS, my main interest lay in biblical studies, particularly Old Testament as taught by Dr. Harvey Findlay. At that time, I knew of only two persons who had graduate degrees in Old Testament and who were teaching in the colleges of the Church of the Nazarene. (Later I found out there were others.) It seemed to be an open field.

My theological studies on Wesley had been basic, but I did realize that this tradition maintained that the Scriptures were inerrant in their statements about faith and practice. Statements concerning dates and descriptions of the physical world, such as the sun moving and the heart being the organ of thinking and decision making, were expressions common to the culture and not to be taken as scientific fact. Later, I came to understand that God condescended to use human literary forms and culturally conditioned understanding about the world in order to clothe his message of redemption through Jesus Christ so that the common person could understand it.

After pastoring a couple of years in Atchison, Kansas, I entered Midwestern Baptist Theological Seminary and earned a master's degree in biblical studies. Upon graduation, my wife Esther, our 2-year-old daughter Jenni, and I drove to Quincy, Massachusetts, where I had been offered a part-time position at Eastern Nazarene College to teach Greek. The following year, I was hired full-time and also began a doctoral program in biblical studies at Boston University.

I served as the graduate assistant to Dr. H. Neil Richardson who also directed my program of study. Even though I maintained an almost fundamentalist view of the authorship of the Pentateuch and the Book of Isaiah, both he and Dr. Harrell Beck, the other OT professor, warmly accepted me. It was during one conversation with Dr. Richardson that I began to rethink my positions. We were discussing my stance when he stated that he did not find that conservatives dealt with the problems. In response to his statement, I decided to examine the problems and to come up with some answers.

At that time, there were two other Nazarenes in the Boston area doing graduate work in biblical studies, Sherrill Munn at BU in NT and Charles Isbell at Brandeis in OT. We would meet once a month in a free-for-all, no-holds-barred atmosphere to argue over issues. It was fun. One evening, while discussing the literary problems of Exodus, Charles commented that we have to do something with them. Both of us began to see, in the text itself, the problems posed by the claim of a single authorship. We were moved in our opinions, not by theological dogmas or traditional arguments but the Scriptures themselves, to make adjustments in our approach to understanding the text.

As I read more broadly in OT studies, I began to realize that Israel was part of the ancient Near Eastern culture that stretched from Babylon to Egypt. Israel's religion was significantly different worshiping one God, not many. In other ways, however, Israel drank deeply from the surrounding cultures. There were similarities in the sacrificial systems; Israel and the Canaanites used cognate words for the same offerings. Only the Israelites, Canaanites, and the Greeks made a whole burnt offering. Israel's wisdom sayings and psalms were cast in literary forms similar to those of the Egyptians. Solomon's court was modeled along Egyptian forms. The Temple itself was not unique in its architectural design. I began to understand firsthand how God had condescended to use human literary forms and worship practices to clothe his message of redemption. As the Word became a human being, God incarnate, so too was the Bible both truly divine and truly human.

Reading the Scripture's statements on creation (Gen. 1:1-2:4; Psalms 19:1-6; 104:1-30; Prov. 8:22-31: John 1:1-18; Col. 1:15-20) became a joy. God has not given us a blueprint of how he created the universe. The writers, moved by the Holy Spirit, employed their pre-scientific understanding of the physical world to proclaim that this one God, the only God, brought forth all that exists. It was into this same creation God entered in human form to provide redemption. Recognizing that God condescended to use human forms to clothe the messages of creation and redemption allows us to interpret the biblical story in a way that harmonizes with the findings of science. Are there problems coordinating both?

Yes, but they are not insurmountable. And as a result of properly under-standing both, we do not need to tell our young people that they have to choose which to believe.

31

CONSIDERING EVOLUTION

Carl M. Leth

Carl M. Leth is Dean of the School of Theology and Christian Ministry at Olivet Nazarene University.

CHARITABLE DISCOURSE

The first victim of many engaged conversations about evolution is charitable discourse. Conservative Christian fundamentalism marks out one position and scientific fundamentalism marks out an opposing position. Each makes an exclusive claim on the Truth (as piety or intellectual integrity), demanding surrender of any competing views as the basis of conversation. Neither of these perspectives reflects the classic understanding of the Christian Faith. In fact, both reflect a modernist assumption about the ability of human beings to master Truth that is a recent innovation of human thought. Neither reflects a spirit of hospitality or charity that are central characteristics of Christian Faith expressed in life, which have been consistently affirmed by the community of Christ across history. So, my first thought in considering evolution is a desire for frank, engaged conversation that recognizes the possibility that different folks of intellectual integrity and spiritual intention can arrive at different conclusions. Could we take one another seriously without taking one another captive?

EVOLUTION AND CHRISTIAN FAITH

Christian Faith and the theory of evolution are not necessary enemies. From the early publication of Darwin's findings there have been conservative, biblical theologians who have held that evolutionary process is not fundamentally in conflict with Christian faith. In fact, at least as early as Augustine there was discussion about the possibilities of processive development in creation. However, not every articulation of evolution will do. Christian affirmations of the acceptability of evolution have routinely been accompanied by explicit qualification of that affirmation. That is, *evolution must be understood in certain ways to be compatible with Christian faith.* The Christian affirmation of God as Creator names Him as initially creating, continually sustaining, actively interacting, and purposefully directing creation to its culmination. All things come **from** Him, exist **in** Him, and move **to** Him (Col. 1:15-17; Acts 17:24-31). Evolution may be considered as a methodology of divine creation within that context.

What is most critically at stake in this conversation is not 7-day creation, young earth or evolutionary development, but the key foundational presuppositions that shape the conversation and the implications of positions taken. Comfortable or uncomfortable, the long Christian conversation about creation extends broadly enough to allow a significant range of views (as our Manual statement affirms). There are, however, some foundational issues of authority and interpretation that are not casually "negotiable" in a classic/Wesleyan expression of Christian faith. Let's turn our attention to what those might be.

KEY ISSUES

The primary authority of Scripture - Scripture is the primary and foundational authority for what should be believed. Reason, tradition and experience are valued as supplemental or interpretive sources of authority. One unfortunate (and inaccurate) result of the use of the "Wesleyan quadrilateral" (a designation that is now regarded with reservation) is the idea that these are equal or complementary sources of authority. This is a significant misunderstanding of the classic view, which consistently affirms the foundational authority of Scripture. Certainly, Scripture must be interpreted and the interaction of these sources of authority is complex and dynamic (the early church draws on them to establish the Canon in the first place). Nevertheless, it is important to affirm the foundational authority of Scripture which means that all other sources of authority are ultimately accountable to Scripture (not the reverse).

The relation of Science and Faith - This essentially proceeds from the first point. Christianity need not be understood as adversarial to diligent science. On the contrary, many of the historically influential scientific minds in the West have been devout (orthodox) Christians. The domains of science and Christian theology do, however, intersect. The notion that they are simply different domains requires reconfiguring the Christian faith in a (spiritualized, almost gnostic) way that does not interact with natural history - clearly in conflict with central claims of the biblical Christian Faith. God's self-definition in Exodus 3 identifies his activity in history on behalf of his chosen people as his defining quality - his "name." Further, it should be no surprise that these points of intersection will pose difficulties for a discipline working from natural processes. The miraculous activity of God, ultimately demonstrated in the incarnation and resurrection, are inexplicable for science. This difficulty is anticipated in Scripture. Paul addresses this problem in I Corinthian 1:18-2:1 declaring the scandal of God's "foolishness" which transcends man's "wisdom." In the end, Science may (only) profitably and constructively help us to discover and understand (not redefine) the God of biblical Faith.

Christ, the God-Man - It is in Christology that the logic of naturalistic evolution intersects the heart of the Christian faith. Presuppositions that limit God's initiative to establishing natural laws and beginning the process of creation preclude God's intrusion into the natural world. This necessitates "natural" explanations of biblical miracles or "supernatural" phenomena. The ten plagues, manna, and the destruction of Sodom and Gomorrah are reinterpreted as primitive superstition, metaphor, cultural-linguistic word-games, etc. These are, however, the "small-fry" issues. The critical assertion of the Christian faith is that in a supra-natural event God becomes Man. The virgin birth is not about reproductive biology but divine (beyond natural) origin and the scandal of God in the flesh. The claim of the truth of the miracles of Jesus pales at the claim of the historical truth of his resurrection. Christ's incarnation and resurrection overturn the natural order (as we understand it, anyway) fundamentally. The Christian faith (classically understood) and our salvation hinge essentially on this, that God, himself, became Man. Christ revealed God to us and by his life, death and resurrection made our salvation possible.

A scientific interpretation of the Christian faith must not only make room for God. It must make a (central) place for **this** God, the incarnation of Jesus Christ as fully God and fully Man, God uniquely revealing Himself, whose life, death, and resurrection form the center of our Faith and our hope of salvation.

CONSIDERING EVOLUTION

This is a conversation we need to have. It is also a conversation we need to engage in with charity – and diligent care. There is room for this conversation in the church. The Church is not so fragile that it cannot sustain critical conversation. And, if we believe in the present, active work of the Holy Spirit, it is a conversation that God can bring to a productive end.

32

THE BIBLE CELEBRATES THE CREATOR

Marty Michelson

Marty Michelson is Professor of Old Testament at Southern Nazarene University.

Creator creates creation.[1]

This simple sentence encapsulates what every believer of Scripture discerns to be true about God.

God is creator. As creator, God has acted and continues to act with creation to shape and mold and frame the manifold complexity and beauty of the world.

Creation is the object of God's active work. From the furthest galaxies to the intricacy of the human genome, to the mystery of the unseen Higgs-Boson or the mysteries yet unfolding to our eyes from the depths of the oceans, the Creator has shaped all this in creation.

Those who believe in the testimony of the Bible testify to the reality that a Creator exists who has acted by creating the creation, which includes all things. Creator creates creation. While believers understand this to be true about the Creator and creation, it has sadly become characteristic of believers to argue about the nature and timing of how and when the Creator has created. I find this troubling.

Christians are committed to a rational world, created by the intention of a deliberate Creator. Christians do not believe that the world came into existence by chance. Christians do not believe that the Creator is arbitrary or haphazard. For these reasons, Christians can be committed to exploring in detailed and rational ways that which can be proven as observable and verifiably consistent. It is troubling for Christians to argue about the nature and timing of how the world was created when they argue for a "Biblical" worldview that is demonstrably in antagonism toward a "Scientific" worldview. Instead, Christians should explore the truth of Scripture and the truth of scientific exploration, recognizing that the Bible addresses certain issues of morality and salvation that science cannot answer, even while science addresses issues of the cosmos or geological strata that the Bible was not written to address.

Christians can commit to rational exploration of the Creator's work in creation. Christians, like all people, remain mindful of the fact that the history of exploration, hypothesis, testing, and inquiry is imperfect even while it does yield new knowledge that must be accounted for. It is troubling to find believers who argue with great fervor for specific positions on the nature and timing of creation from narrow perspectives in the Bible, because in too many instances in the past, Christians have been wrong using narrow perspectives from the Bible. It was Christian leaders who, some 600 years ago, "inquired" into the work of many scientists and mathematicians in the Inquisition, using theological grounds to imprison and kill many who were guilty of being rational thinkers in science and math. This is a troubling part of narrow Christian perspective that rejected important inquiry into life, and horribly tortured and killed people whose only crime was to seek the truth! The history of Christian intolerance should be more troubling to Christians than the history of careful inquiry into truth! It was Christian leaders who, some 400 years ago, argued wrongly for a flat earth or earth-centered solar system. While it is not now the case that every specific frame of evolutionary theory can be proven, the theory should be fully explored and openly discussed by Christians because Christians want to be committed to that which is True.

A full exploration of what science can help us evaluate and ascertain does not mean that science proves the Bible wrong nor that no Creator exists. Rather, a full exploration of what science can reveal to us about life in creation can help us more fully appreciate the complexities of creation, leaving new room to explore how believers discern the Creator's investment in creation.

Readers of the Bible are clearly mindful of the fact that the Bible makes statements about creation. Readers of the Bible are aware that both general and specific claims are made about God as creator in theological statements across the Biblical canon.

While it is true that passages from the Bible make specific claims about God as creator, the specific claims are difficult to align with precise measures, specific calculations, and detailed quantities of description! Said another way, the language of the Bible is not intentionally or narrowly scientific--with a scientific goal for objective, unbiased, and precisely measurable data.

Rather, the characteristic means by which the Bible describes the Creator and creation is in bold announcements of praise, in exuberant expressions of esteem, and exclamatory statements of grandeur! "The earth is the LORD's, and everything in it, the world, and all who live in it!" exclaims the Psalmist (24:1).[2] Where the Bible details the Creator or creation, the intent of the language is to draw our attention to God. "The heavens praise your wonders, O LORD" (Psalm 89:5). The focus of the Biblical message is to aim our attention to the quality and character of the Divine. "For since the creation of the world God's invisible qualities--his eternal power and divine nature--have been clearly seen, being understood from what has been made . . ." (Romans 1:20).

Certainly the Bible articulates positional statements about creation and the Creator, processes that take place on earth, but the Bible cannot be used as a source for all information about scientific inquiry into life on earth. The Bible talks about earthquakes (Amos 1:1, Luke 21:11) though it does not explain fault lines in tectonic plates, nor magma and the flow of material under the earth's crust. The Bible talks about the Salt Sea, but never presents for us information of value on the issues of sea levels comparing the depth of the Dead Sea to the Mediterranean. The Bible understands the lack of life in the Salt Sea (Ezekiel 47:8-11), but it does not explain the scientific make-up of the sea in terms of salinity or alkalinity. The Bible certainly does not present us with the information we need to learn that the bromine deposits from the Salt Sea are necessary and important in the electrochemistry of flow batteries. While these issues are not about evolution, they present the fact that the Bible does not explore or explain all issues that scientific inquiry can reveal for us. Science has helped and will help us expand our knowledge of how life works in the world. Scientific exploration need not be seen as a challenge to the Creator's creation and can be seen as a full exploration of all that is contained in it!

The Bible was written by persons who had a keen understanding of the world. When we read legal material in the Torah about harvest and seedtime, we know Ancient Israelites correctly observed their world! When we read Proverbial wisdom about discernment of animals (insects even!) and seasons and cycles of years, we know that early believers could learn from observable data.

The writers and collectors of the Bible understood aspects of the details of creation! Of that there is no doubt! The writers of the Bible were not focused on scientific fact, data or measure. The writers of the Bible were focused on the wonder and worship of discerning the work of the Creator!

This is by no means to discount the claim that Creator creates creation! This, by no means, is a claim that the Bible is insufficient in its task of revealing the nature of God and God's love for the world! By no means!

This is, though, a fair observation that must be made with respect to the Bible as a book read by believers. The Bible is not intended to give us everything there is to know about every subject!

The Bible addresses many water issues in various forms, including how God provides water in creation and in miraculous events. And yet, we do not expect the Bible to be the source of information on how we operate our kitchen water faucet or how to repair the lawn water sprinkler system. The Bible uses ideas about trees and fruits of trees in several passages across the Biblical canon. And yet, the Bible does not give specific advice or counsel on all trees and all fruits. The Bible provide us no advice on how to plant, harvest or eat rambutan or mangosteen, just two of hundreds of varieties of trees! Various aspects of the human body are described in numerous passages in the Bible, from eyes and ears, to a sense of internal organs in some passages. And yet, persons with a credible belief in the authority of the Bible would not want someone to use the limited information from the Bible's account of the human body as the basis upon which to perform their next surgery!

As Christians, we must think seriously about the Creator and creation. As Christians whose very identity is rooted in Jesus, the Christ, Christians need to carefully consider the view of Jesus on evolution when thinking about exploring evolution. The fact of the matter is, Jesus never addressed the issue of evolution. Jesus was aware of issues in creation. Jesus took time to consider the lilies of the field and the birds of the air. Jesus, of course, was aware of patterns in the world like seed-time and harvest (his parables and teaching demonstrate his awareness). Jesus knew that observable data yielded information about how the world functioned (he knew about wind and storms, drought and flooding, and more). Christians need to carefully consider the views of Jesus on science when thinking about scientific inquiry. The fact of the matter is that Jesus came to address issues of moral accountability of persons one with another. Jesus' proclamation understood that relationship to and with God mattered most in shaping God's intended purpose for a world of peace and harmony among living things. Jesus' life is a testimony to the fact that the Creator is committed to salvation of people and the world! And in the midst of this, Jesus' life does not attest to the need for his followers to abandon inquiry. Perhaps, in fact, one could argue that Christians are compelled to explore evolution when New Testament writers affirm that we are to "test all things" (I Thessalonians 5:21).

The Biblical vision of the heavens and the earth is rooted in a core idea, Creator creates creation.

In the shadow of that bold, core claim, there is much that the Bible does not explore that we explore through various forms of scientific inquiry.

Discerning the complexities and intricacies of the creation need not be seen as a challenge to the reign of God. And, in fact, careful consideration of scientific inquiry into the manifold aspects of creation can be engaged as an act of worship!

Exploration in the sciences can be daunting! Evidence from the scientific community suggests that we know less than 4% of all that can be known in the universe.[3] Recent discoveries in the universe challenge mathematic principles established by Albert Einstein's Cosmological Principle.[4] Increased technological capabilities allow us to "see" smaller and smaller parts of what exists, even while these same discoveries challenge what we thought we already knew, decades or centuries before![5]

In the midst of the inquiry, faithful believers can root their faith in a core Biblical idea, Creator creates creation. And from that core biblical idea, believers can explore the large, grand, magnificent perspectives that quantifiable, scientific data can provide. If theories of evolutionary processes prove demonstrably sufficient in explaining the development of life and human persons over time, the claim of belief discerned most central in the Bible need not be undermined. Evolutionary process in the formation of life does not need to be a challenge to the idea of the Creator or the existence of creation!

Believers affirm: Creator creates creation.

Exploration in science in order to better discern the mysteries of the world will continue to unravel for us new and remarkable aspects of creation. With each new progression in our discernment, we can find more precise reasons to express praise to the Creator for the complexity and grandeur of all that has happened in creation, and all that exists in creation, including our existence!

ENDNOTES AND SUGGESTED READING

1 Walter Brueggemann, *Genesis* (Atlanta: John Knox Press, 1982) 17ff.

2 Scripture here, and throughout, is New International Version (1984).

3 http://www.americanscientist.org/bookshelf/pub/exploring-the-dark-universe

4 http://www.reuters.com/article/2013/01/12/space-quasars-idUSL1E9CC08B20130112

5 http://www.theage.com.au/technology/sci-tech/after-higgs-boson-scientists-prepare-for-next-quantum-leap-20130214-2eeiu.html

33

SOME REFLECTIONS ON THE GENESIS STORY OF CREATION

Alex Varughese

Alex Varughese is Professor of Biblical Literature at Mount Vernon Nazarene University.

I confess that my method of reading and interpreting the Bible has evolved over the last forty-three years since I entered the field of Religion from the field of science. This shift was in response to a statement I heard in the setting of a theology class taught by Forrest Benner, professor of Theology at Olivet Nazarene University. The statement I heard was simply this: "The Church needs scholars who are committed to their Christian faith." After many months of struggling with this statement, I recognized that this was God's call on my life to enter into the ministry of teaching and scholarship. I was attracted to the field of Biblical Studies while at Nazarene Theological Seminary, under the influence of Harvey Finley, Ralph Earl, and Willard Taylor.

Though I was brought up in a very strict holiness church, which interpreted the Bible literally, my engagement in the field of Biology as an undergraduate student, a graduate student and later as a post-graduate research fellow challenged me to study the Scriptures methodically by utilizing all the tools of research available to me, including the study of Hebrew and Greek. My Ph.D. studies under Herbert Huffmon and Paul Riemann at Drew University involved historical-critical research and text criticism. My Wesleyan heritage challenged me to see in the text the grand theological themes that are weaved through the biblical texts. I understood that my primary teacher and guide was, and still is, the Holy Spirit; however, I also realized that the nature of Scripture as a divine-human product requires the reading of it in a responsible way. By placing the biblical text in its context, in the world of its origin, I, along with the faith community to which I belong, may faithfully hear what God is saying to us through his inspired words.

Biblical texts, as the inspired record of revelation, portray certain realities. These realities have something to do with God's relationship to creation in general and human beings in particular. Such portrayals seldom take place in a vacuum but in a world of divine-human interaction and inter-relationships. God speaks into a world of human existence, a world filled with human thoughts, hopes, concerns, and anxieties. Scripture, God's word into the human situation, not only conveys what God is saying and doing but also reflects the human crisis, the context into which God speaks his word. Scripture, therefore, is authoritative for the Christian faith, not simply because of its divine inspiration, but perhaps more importantly because it speaks into the human condition and addresses human concerns–concerns about the past, present, and future. This perspective of the biblical texts rescues them from the danger of being viewed as some ancient documents, but as the "alive and active" word of God (Heb 4:12) that continues to speak into our present human condition.

CONTEXT

The Genesis story of creation (Gen 1:1-2:4a) is not simply an ancient document that speaks about the origins but the authoritative word of God that speaks into our present human situation. Of course, this word of God first spoke into the human context of the inspired author(s) and the original recipients of this text, and it would continue to speak into the human condition for generations of those who would encounter this text.

The human context of the inspired author(s) and their original audience, though we are not certain, may have been the despair and hopelessness experienced by the Jewish exiles in Babylon in the sixth century BCE, for whom their hope for rest (their actual experience of Sabbath) was being shattered daily by their continued homelessness. If so, God the creator, who himself "rested" after bringing order and life to his creation that once existed in a "formless and void" condition (*tohu wavohu*; Gen 1:2) - an unproductive and desert like condition - speaks into the human crisis of exile with the hope-filled word of a coming Sabbath–their rest from exile,–to a community that suffered forced migration and homelessness at the hands of a cruel and monstrous political power.

Or, the author(s) of this creation account may have been inspired to create a clear, concise, and well-articulated statement of their creation faith -- an elaboration of what their ancestor Abraham confessed as his faith in God, the "creator of heaven and earth," (Gen 14:22) who called him out of his pagan world to be a source of blessing to "all the families of the earth" (Gen 12:3) -- for the Jewish community of their day that existed in a pagan world of competing claims about gods who created the world.

RESPONSE TO THEIR HUMAN SITUATION

Whatever may have been the crisis experienced by the community of the author(s) who were inspired to write this account, one thing is clear. The text clearly and without doubt speaks into that human situation by tracing everything visible (and perhaps by extension, everything invisible) to the human eye to the God whom they worship-the God of Israel. Herein we find the Israelite version of "I believe in God the Father, Almighty, Maker of heaven and earth" (the Apostles' Creed). Faith is engendered, hope is given, confession is made, blessing is received, rest is experienced, and doxology is sung by the faithful community that had first heard God's word speaking into their human context (see Ps 104, a "creation" hymn that begins and ends with the doxology, "Praise the LORD, my soul").

Out of their human situation, the author(s) and their faith community understood that whatever faith they affirm about God and creation cannot be some abstract idea but that which can be seen and experienced and be related to the physical world. So it was natural for them

215

to see in the dome-shaped sky, in the water above the sky which was the source of rain, in the water below which was the source of springs and rivers, in the varieties of plants and trees that produce varieties of fruits, in the luminaries in the sky, in the great and small creatures in the water, in the flying birds in the sky, in the animals on the land, and in themselves – the image of God in creation - the handiwork of God, the object of their praise and worship. They understood that everything that is visible to them in creation, including themselves, has a place and function to fulfill. Their theological understanding, seen in that way, was fully integrated with their secular knowledge. John Walton, appropriately argues that the account of Genesis 1 has more to do with functions of what God created and less to do with "material origins."[1]

The author(s) and their faith community acknowledged that they live in God's "good," "indeed very good," creation (Gen 1:3, 10, 12, 18, 21, 25, 31) where, however, disorderly conditions (*tohu wavohu*; 1:2) continue to exist. On the one hand, creation has order and structure. The order and structure the author(s) give to the creation narrative itself (the well-known horizontal and vertical literary pattern, and the organization of the narrative into seven paragraphs and the use of seven and multiples of the number seven) is a powerful testimony to the order and structure of creation. On the other hand, the "deep" remains; there is water above sky and water below. These elements may attempt to disrupt God's good creation, but creation is a dependable work of the creator and is safe in the hands of the creator (Ps 46:1-3). The "sea" will remain as a part of God's good creation until the appearance of the new heaven and new earth, in which there will no longer be "any sea" (Rev 21:1).

Moreover, the author(s) and their faith community understood that they, along with the rest of creation, have received a gracious invitation from the creator to participate with him in the ongoing work of creating and sustaining God's good creation. Creation continues to respond to the creator's summons, "let the water teem with…," "let the land produce…," "let them rule over…" (Gen 1: 20, 24, 26). All creation exist as recipients of the creational blessing as well as co-creators with God by bringing forth new life, by being fruitful, and by multiplying and filling the earth (Gen 1:22, 28). The disorderly waters of the sea, as well as the land God formed, bring forth life. No part of creation is exempt from the creational mandate. Creation thus continues – both as the work of the creator God and that of what he created.

Reading Genesis 1 through the lens of the author(s) context and human situation discloses something significant about how they understood their God whom they worshiped. He is an intimately relational God who is deeply involved with everything in creation, including the disorderly part of creation, who relates to his creation through speaking, doing, commanding, and blessing. His concern is not only for humans whom he created in his own image and likeness, but for all creation and their physical environment. His invitation to creation is to enjoy "rest" (Sabbath) - freedom from anxiety-filled existence- and live by trust and dependence on his good and gracious provisions for life.

A MODERN READING

We the modern readers may see the details in the Genesis story of creation as "pre-scientific" and a naïve view of the world, but to the author(s) and their community, what they discovered or experienced or observed in their physical world was an important resource for their theological thinking and faith development. They were less concerned with *how* they or their world came into being and more concerned with *who* brought them and their world into being. The knowledge of themselves and their world shaped their thinking about God; their knowledge of God shaped their understanding of themselves and their world.

Perhaps we, the modern readers of Genesis 1, would benefit from our ancient friends –ancestors of our faith traditions - who teach us through the Scriptures that we can learn more about God through our observation, experience, and knowledge of the natural world in which we live. We do not need to be anxious about or afraid of what we may discover through our capacity to observe life and the physical world through our scientific and technological advancements, which themselves are a gift from God the creator. Such advancements are a true evidence of our creation partnership with God, the source of all truth and knowledge. Such advancements also show that even in our self-proclaimed, self-sovereignty and autonomy from God, even in our less-than-image-of-God condition of existence, we humans are involved in fulfilling our creational mandate, which for the most part is a mandate to be involved in historical and cultural development, as well as scientific and technological advancements, for the sake of the well-being of creation. Our ancient friends also teach us that our knowledge of God the Creator will certainly lead us to a better and more appropriate understanding of ourselves and our physical world, which for the most part, still remains a mystery to humans, in spite of our historical and cultural progress and advanced technological and scientific achievements.

In summary, in our world of debates and controversies about evolution and creation, the author(s) of Genesis 1 invite us to reflect on the alternative: the people of God engaged in the task of doing theology by utilizing resources available to them from the discoveries of those who are faithfully engaged in the task of studying the physical world and life. These discoveries of the mysteries of our physical world and only affirm the most foundational contribution of theology – the truth about God as creator.

In the end, we members of the faith community are certain of only one thing, and we confess that as eternal truth: "I believe in God the Father, Almighty, Maker of heaven and earth" (the Apostles' Creed).

ENDNOTES AND SUGGESTED READING

1 John Walton, *The Lost World of Genesis One: Ancient Cosmology and the Origins Debate* (Downers Grove, IL: IVP Academic, 2009).

34
GENESIS AND READING THE SCRIPTURES

Hans Deventer

Hans Deventer lives in Dordrecht, The Netherlands where he is a licensed minister at Dordrecht Church of the Nazarene.

Right at the start I need to make a confession: this author was a very unlikely candidate for writing much on this topic until quite recently. It just didn't interest me. I'm not a science person and lack the fascination for how the beauty we see around us came to be. As a Nazarene, I was and still am happy to believe that God is the creator. How He did it was really not much of a concern for me.

However, through this project by Nazarenes concerning evolution, I started to realize that for many, this is no trivial matter. And truth be told, having seen and joined some not so "laid back" online discussions on the subject, I've seen how they tend to ignite a lot of heat. They also tend to frustrate me deeply. Too often, discussions were on one subject, like the theories around creation and evolution, and looked like they were purely scientific. In reality, the issue was theology and more specifically, hermeneutics. Few things are as frustrating as discussing one thing, while the issue is something totally different–the proverbial elephant in the room. In other words, we definitely have a problem on our hands here.

To delve a little deeper, my experience has quite often been that when Christians discuss evolution, the main issue is how we actually read the creation story in Genesis. Yet, the larger looming question is, *How do we read the Bible as a whole in the first place?*

I'm always encouraged by the fact that Jesus, at one point in His ministry, asked a scribe the very same question:

On one occasion an expert in the law stood up to test Jesus. "Teacher," he asked, "what must I do to inherit eternal life?" "What is written in the Law?" he replied. "How do you read it?" (Luke 10:25-26, NIV)

Of course, we know that he answered with the two great commands. The point is, however, it says nowhere in the Old Testament that these commands were actually the key commands, the main ones. That was interpretation. "'You have answered correctly,' Jesus replied." So we have it on Jesus' authority that this interpretation was correct.

Now this a fairly simple example, but it does show us how we cannot just read the Scriptures and take in the information at face value. "How do you read?" is a serious question, and we obviously can reach good or not so good conclusions and interpretations.

I won't begin to explain how the first chapters of Genesis were meant to be read. I'll gladly leave that up to the OT experts. What is way more interesting to me is why we *want* to interpret in a certain way. Now before people start to protest, allow me to stay close to home and confess that I, myself, am no stranger to this phenomenon. And as a Nazarene, I thankfully find myself in good company too! "No Scripture can mean that God is not love, or that his mercy is not over all his works" (John Wesley – sermon *Free Grace*, 26).

Why do I want to read the Scriptures in a certain way? Why would I, like Wesley, take such a principle as an *a priori*? Why would I want to read Genesis 1-3 literally? Or the book of Revelation, just to give another example? Or why not?

Again, to stay close to home, I find this question to be rather threatening but also revealing. It has everything to do with the heart of my faith, but perhaps even more, with how my faith functions and on what (or Who) it is built.

The answers to these questions are revealing and (I think) explain much of why the issue of evolution can be so explosive. There are things in the Bible that have to be true. For me, that has to do with the character of God and by extension, soteriology, or the way we can be saved. When my ultimate trust is in God, it makes every sense in the world that the character of God becomes an all controlling concern. It is THE issue. If God is not love, if He does not grant us grace and mercy, if He is a two-faced Roman god like Janus, everything collapses. I'm toast. But if He is love, if He is graceful and merciful and indeed is One, then the details don't really matter. I become free not to believe in the Scriptures, but in the God the Scriptures testify to. Hence, we Nazarenes don't believe in the Scriptures, we believe in God, in Jesus Christ and in the Holy Spirit, and in the plenary *inspiration* of the Holy Scriptures.

And still the question remains, "How do you read?" And I would add, why? Do we need a Bible like the Qu'ran, allegedly dictated by an angel? Or can we live with a book that testifies to the One whom we cannot completely comprehend, but Who has still revealed Himself, especially in Jesus Christ–"inerrantly revealing the will of God concerning us in all things necessary to our salvation"?

So what I want to leave you with is this question: How do you read, and *why* do you read this way?

I'd say these two questions are crucial in the entire debate on creation and evolution from a theological point of view. If we can be honest with ourselves and one another regarding the answers to these questions, we have gained a lot when it comes to understanding ourselves and those who might disagree with us. And as long as "we know in part and we prophesy in part" (1 Cor 13:9, NIV), this might actually be crucial to what God has called us to do in this world.

35

COMMON OBSERVATIONS ON THE CHARACTER OF THE CREATION ACCOUNT IN GENESIS 1-2

Thomas J. King

Thomas J. King is Professor of Old Testament at Nazarene Bible College.

I have no doubt that the Lord God could easily provide humanity with a detailed scientific manual which explains the creation of the universe and answers all the modern questions regarding evolution, fossils, age of the earth, dinosaurs, etc. However, that is not what we have in the case of Genesis 1-2. The creation account in Genesis is focused on communicating truth in relation to a theological message. If its main concern had been history or science, Genesis 1-2 would include much more detail and very different content. Instead, we find what commonly has been recognized as a somewhat poetic literary production expressing a divine message. This message addresses the truth regarding concerns such as God as creator, the position of humanity in creation, God's will for creation, and God's response to sin (when we include Gen 3). The creation account in Genesis reflects the general recognition that, though a great deal of history is reflected in the Bible, history is secondary to the theological message.

One example of the primacy of the theological message in the Genesis account is evident when comparing Genesis 1 with Genesis 2. In the first chapter, the order of things created on the earth is: vegetation (vv

11-12), water creatures and birds of the air (vv 20-22), land animals (vv 24-25), and finally humanity (male and female, vv 26-27). In chapter two, the order of things created is: man (v 7), vegetation (vv 8-9), land animals and birds of the air (v 19), and finally woman (vv 21-23). Scholars have presented various explanations for the differences between the two chapters, including the possibility that two different sources are represented, or that one account reflects a macro view of creation while the other reflects a narrower view of the garden. Regardless of the explanation, it is apparent that the two chapters do not present a continuous and comprehensive scientific explanation of the origins of the universe. However, the two chapters clearly express significant theological messages.

Genesis 1 (through 2:4a) is organized around seven days of creation. The repetition of certain expressions reveals a general literary pattern in relation to the creation process for each day. Elements are called into existence by means of impersonal third person jussive (expressions of will) verbs, normally translated "let there be . . ." (vv 3, 6), "let the waters be gathered . . ." (v 9), "let the earth sprout . . ." (v 11), etc. This is typically followed by the affirmation that "it was so" (vv 7, 9, 11, 15, etc.). Next, in relation to most elements, we read that "God saw that it was good" (vv 4, 10, 12, 18, etc.). Each day closes with the notice that "there was evening and there was morning" with an indication of which day has just passed (day one, day two, day three, etc.; vv 5, 8, 13, etc.). The pattern includes the qualification that living objects were created "after their kind" (vv 11, 12, 21, 24, 25), or "after its kind" (vv 21, 25). The pattern for each day is consistent enough that the reader can generally anticipate how the next day will be described. The major difference in each new day is simply the particular element of creation which is introduced. However, two aspects of this recurring pattern are dramatically broken in relation to the final creatures introduced in the account. This serves to place emphasis on these final creatures. Instead of the impersonal third person expressions used to call other elements into existence, God appears to personally intervene in the final act of creation with the first person statement, "Let us make" (v 26). While other creatures are merely called into being, these last creatures are highlighted as having been personally made by the hand of God. The second break in the pattern indicates that, unlike other creatures which are made "after their own kind," these final creatures are made *in the image and likeness of God* (vv 26, 27)! Clearly, these creatures are set apart as most significant and as the climax of creation. This communicates the message that humanity (male and female, v 27) is the most valuable element of creation in the sight of God. The text makes it clear that all of God's creation is "good" (vv 4, 10, 12, 18, 21, 25, 31). Nevertheless, the structure of the chapter accentuates humanity as most significant. *Genesis 1 emphasizes the theological truth that God is the all powerful Creator and humanity is the highlight of God's creation.*

Genesis 2 reflects a completely different literary character. Instead of being structured around seven days, the account in chapter 2 depicts a progression in terms of completion. The opening image is one of things lacking and incomplete. Verse five indicates that there was *no shrub* in the field, *no plant* had yet sprouted, the Lord had *not sent rain*, and there was *no man* to cultivate the ground. In contrast to how *good* was every step of Genesis 1 (1:4, 10, 12, 18, 21, 25, 31), Genesis 2 depicts a creation in which things are not yet good. In fact, at one point God declares that something is "not good" (2:18). In response, God begins to fill what is lacking and supply what is missing (2:7-9, 15, 19, 22). The result is a creation which operates in harmony and with interdependence. Plants and trees need ground and water in order to grow, the ground and vegetation need humans to cultivate and keep them, humanity needs the plants and trees for food to live, and the man and woman need each other so that they will not be alone. All the elements of creation depend on God for their existence and sustenance. The innocence, trust, and harmony of this image is expressed by the statement that the man and woman were both naked and not ashamed (2:25). *Genesis 2 emphasizes the theological truth that God is a caring Provider and God's intention for creation includes relationships of harmony and interdependence.*

Both Genesis 1 and 2 communicate God's intention regarding the basic position of men and women in creation. Genesis 1:27 contains three lines which are parallel in thought. This is a common feature of Hebrew poetry.

God created humanity (Adam) in *his/its* image;
in the image of God he created *it/him*;
male and female he created them.

Each line reveals additional information regarding the message being conveyed. Biblical Hebrew does not have a separate pronoun to express "it." Instead masculine (him) and feminine (her) pronouns are used to express what English speakers might consider neuter objects (it). Thus, the context of a sentence will determine whether a Hebrew pronoun should be translated "him" or "it"; or "her" or "it." The lines of Genesis 1:27 appear intentionally ambiguous until the entire verse is read. The possessive pronoun attached to "image" in line one could be taken as a reference to God or to humanity ("God's image," or "humanity's own image"). The second line immediately answers the question by stating that "in the image of God" humanity was created. However, the second line raises another ambiguity by means of the object pronoun at the end of the line which could be read as "it" or "him." This is clarified by the third line which shifts the object pronoun from singular ("it") to plural ("them"). Furthermore, the third line reveals that the object of God's creation, which is in the image of God, is actually *male and female*. This communicates the significant message that both men and women are created in the image of God. In the midst of an ancient patriarchal environment, in which women were sometimes treated as possessions on the level of domestic animals, this is a profound message. God's revelation here proclaims that *women carry the unique image of God just as men do.*

Genesis 2 also reflects a message of mutual standing between men and women. In v 18, God states that "It is not good for the man to be alone"; and God plans to "make a helper suitable for him" (NIV). The phrase translated "helper suitable for him" is made up of two Hebrew terms. The first term is commonly translated "helper." The English term "helper" can be understood in more than one sense. Often, it is used in the sense of an "assistant," "supporter," or "aide," and carries the connotation of a subordinate and inferior person. In contrast, the term can also be used to refer to assistance from a superior being in order to accomplish that which an individual or group could not achieve on their own. Various forms of this same Hebrew term are applied to God as Israel's "helper" (Exod 18:4; 1 Sam 7:12; Ps 33:20). Consequently, the term may be understood to refer to either an inferior, or to one who is vastly superior! The second Hebrew term, which the NIV translates "suitable for him," clarifies the issue. This term is a composite made up of two prepositions and a pronominal suffix. It can be literally translated "like/as in front of/ before him." The sense of the term is "corresponding to him," "equal and adequate to himself".[1] Thus, the "helper" which God made for the man was not intended to be either inferior or superior. God's "helper" for the man was intended to be one who stands before the man as an equal, who corresponds to him. *Genesis 2 includes the message that the relationship between men and women is intended to be one of mutuality and equality.*

A number of other significant messages are communicated in the opening chapters of Genesis. These messages relate to the character of God, God's desires regarding humanity, the character of sin, God's response to sin, and other theological concerns (e.g., a polemic against ancient pagan concepts regarding God and humanity). Consequently, it is evident that these accounts are not aimed at explicating the historic and scientific details of how the earth came to be. If God had intended to provide a history book or scientific manual, God certainly could have done so. However, the agenda revealed in Gen 1-2 is clearly theological. The same is true for the rest of the Bible. The Bible certainly reveals a great deal of history, but history is not its primary concern. The writer of the gospel of John illustrates this point when explaining the agenda driving the gospel account. Near the end of the gospel, it is written, "Jesus did many other miraculous signs in the presence of his disciples, which are not recorded in this book. But these are written that you may believe that Jesus is the Christ, the Son of God, and that by believing you may have life in his name" (John 20:30-31; NIV). Though the gospels certainly reveal a great deal about the history of Jesus Christ, that is not their first concern. The information provided and the literary form in which it is revealed are intentionally crafted with the purpose of persuading readers of the truth that Jesus is Lord and that by believing in Jesus they may have life! Similarly, the creation account in Gen 1-2 communicates a message of truth regarding God and God's original intentions for humanity.

ENDNOTES AND OTHER SUGGESTED READING

1. Francis Brown, S.R. Driver, and Charles A. Briggs, *A Hebrew and English Lexicon of the Old Testament* (Oxford: Clarendon, 1952) 617.

36

TWO REASONS WHY I BELIEVE THE THEORY OF EVOLUTION IS SCIENTIFICALLY TRUE

Samuel M. Powell

Samuel M. Powell is Professor of Philosophy and Religion at Point Loma Nazarene University.

I believe that the theory of biological evolution is true. Here's why:

First, I don't see the theory of evolution as a competitor with the Biblical account of origins. Some people figure that there can be just one version of the truth; since Genesis' story of origins differs from the story told by the theory of evolution, only one of these, the Biblical story, can be correct.

I don't find this view convincing because Genesis itself has two differing accounts of origins. According to Genesis 1, God created human beings last, after having created vegetation (day 3), the sun, moon and stars (day 4), birds and fish (day 5), and land animals (day 6). But according to Genesis 2, God created a male human being before any vegetation had sprung up and before the creation of animals and then created a female only after creating the animals. Even if these two narratives agree with respect to theology, we have to concede that they portray the sequence of creation in two very different and in fact incompatible ways.

Accordingly, it's not that there are two accounts of creation, one scientific and the other Biblical. It's that there are at least two Biblical accounts of creation besides the scientific account. So the issue is not science vs. the Bible. In fact, we should not think of these various narratives as competitive with each other, as though only one can be true and the others must be false. Instead we should see that any given truth can be portrayed in many ways. Like scientific accounts of origins, the biblical stories of creation describe the world. However, there is a big difference between scientific accounts and biblical accounts. Scientific accounts are interested in describing things in the world in their relation to each other. For example, a geneticist will be interested in the ways in which genes and chromosomes relate to each other and their cellular environment. Other biologists are interested in how members of a species relate to each other and their environment. Scientists, in other words, describe beings in the world in their interrelationships. Scientists are also interested in describing processes. Biologists thus seek to describe processes such as metabolism and reproduction. But whenever the Bible speaks about the world, it does so from the perspective of beings' relation to God. It describes humans as being created in the image of God and receiving the divine breath of life; it mentions animals mainly to illustrate the wisdom of God, not to provide scientific information. The Bible thus has little or no interest in describing the ways in which beings in the world relate to each other and in analyzing physical processes as scientists do. Biblical accounts and scientific accounts, therefore, really have differing purposes and, for that reason, are not rivals for the truth.

The fact that the opening chapters of Genesis contain two differing stories of creation encourages us to ask about the function of these stories. Let's focus on the first account, which extends from 1:1 to 2:4. When we read the first account in its entirety, we see that the work of creation culminates in the Sabbath. This is a clue to us that this creation story has a liturgical function–that its purpose relates to Israel's worship and not to scientific knowledge. (Another clue is the difficulty of imagining that vegetation existed before the sun was created–vegetation requires light to produce its energy. It's true that Genesis says that God created light on the first day, before the sun and stars, but it's also difficult to imagine this light just floating around the cosmos without a physical source.)

The liturgical nature of the first account is seen as well if we compare this account with the building of the tabernacle in the wilderness (Exodus 25-40). Commentators have pointed out many similarities between Genesis 1:1-2:4 and Exodus 25-40. Among the most important are 1) that God gives Moses seven instructions for the tabernacle (paralleling the seven times God's speaks in creation); 2) that the final word about the tabernacle relates to the Sabbath, as in Genesis 2:1-4; 3) that the construction of the tabernacle requires the presence of the Spirit, as in Genesis 1:2; 4) that the work on the tabernacle concludes with a blessing, as in Genesis 2:3; and 5) that the final deed of creation is the placing of God's image into the world. In the ancient world, images of gods were generally located in temples and shrines; the fact that God places God's image in the world would get ancient readers thinking about the world as a temple. What these parallels between Genesis and Exodus tell us is that the writer of Genesis 1:1-2:4 portrays the created universe as a temple that God has prepared for us, God's image, and which God has blessed for us. The divine work of creating the universe establishes an ordered reality in which human beings can worship God on the Sabbath. Genesis, in other words, describes the world from the perspective of its relation to God.

As important and as theologically powerful as Genesis' portrait of creation is, it does not constitute a scientific account of origins, and there is absolutely nothing to make us think that the writer of Genesis intended it to be a scientific account. It is a theological affirmation about God's purpose in creating the world, not a description of the interrelatedness of entities and of the physical processes by which the universe came to be.

So, to repeat my point, the theory of evolution is not competing with the biblical accounts of creation. Each is describing the created world from a distinctive perspective and for a distinctive purpose.

There is a second reason why I accept the theory of evolution: I trust the scientific community and the results of scientific research. I think that the sciences are moving toward a better and better understanding of the universe. Obviously progress in scientific knowledge does not move in a straight line. There are many zig zags and cul de sacs in the quest for knowledge; some theories turn out to be mistaken or inadequate. Nonetheless, scientific study has gradually and impressively accumulated mounds of reliable information and measurements and theories. Each of us relies on this accumulation each day in our use of computers, of medicine, of transportation and a thousand other ways. Few of us understand the science behind medicine and technology, but each of us implicitly accepts the validity of the scientific quest for understanding and the results of scientific research. We all support scientific research in the belief that scientists are gradually coming to an increasingly better understanding of things like cancer and the weather. None of us wants to return to a pre-scientific era when disease, weather, and in fact almost everything was mysterious and unknown.

Admittedly, it is difficult for many of us even to understand some scientific theories, especially modern theories. There is something intuitively obvious about the theories of gravity and electricity, even though few of us have a grasp of contemporary scientific interpretations of gravity. But most of today's theories employ complex mathematical models; others are rather speculative; a few seem counterintuitive. The theory of biological evolution is one of these counterintuitive and speculative theories, especially with respect to its most dramatic claims: that new species evolve from prior species and that living organisms have evolved from non-living compounds. These claims seem counterintuitive: how can one thing (like life) come to be from something quite different (that which is not alive)? Further, the theory seems speculative: none of us have witnessed living organisms arising from non-living compounds; none of us have seen species such as birds evolving from species such as dinosaurs. We have no experience of such processes, whereas we do have daily experience of gravity and electricity. So, resistance to the theory of biological evolution is perfectly understandable.

And yet, such resistance is wrong. There was a time when scientific research involved simple observation, such as when Galileo supposedly dropped balls of differing weights off the Tower of Pisa. We still learn this sort of science in high school. It's fairly easy because it doesn't require complex mathematics and can be illustrated with simple experiments. Several hundred years ago all science was like this. But after several centuries of development, scientific research has moved beyond matters capable of direct observation. These days, leading scientific theories rely much more on mathematical models than on direct observation. The entities that scientists study often must be matters experienced indirectly; often they cannot be seen directly. So, the fact that evolution of species is not directly observable does not bring the theory of evolution into doubt, for few questions in science today can actually be answered by direct observation.

Additionally, scientific theories today are increasingly interconnected. There was a time when Physics had nothing to do with Biology. Today, however, theories such as evolution are components of a huge structure of interconnected scientific ideas embracing genetics, geology, physiology, and many other scientific disciplines. The theory of evolution is not a single idea that biologists have devised in an intellectual vacuum. On the contrary, it is closely linked to many other theories. The question, then, is not whether anyone has seen species evolving or life emerging, but whether the theory of evolution makes the best sense of the information that we have and whether it agrees with other theories that we accept.

The scientific community, which we trust in matters of medicine, engineering, and technology, has judged that the theory of evolution does make sense of the information we have and best agrees with the other theories that we accept. This is not to say that the theory is perfect or finished. It's just to say that the theory of evolution is the one account of the origin of species that is logically connected to many well-established scientific theories and results. It is the one account of biological origins that agrees with the rest of science. And so, even though I don't understand the fine points of the theory, I accept it because it is a part of the scientific view of the world that I believe to be true.

A few closing words: Christians seem to fall roughly into two groups. There are some who believe that the church and the Christian faith are constantly under attack by godless forces and who accordingly relate to the world with a considerable measure of suspicion and resistance. Such Christians are understandably fearful of the theory of evolution. There are other Christians who, while acknowledging the difficulties that the church faces, believe that there is some degree of light and truth everywhere in God's world and that the church should join with the agents of light and truth wherever they are found. This sort of Christian usually regards the scientific community as an agent of truth and accepts scientific theories like evolution as being the result of an honest quest for truth. Although I respect and sympathize with the first group, I'm a member of the second group.

37

ORIGINS AND OUTCOMES

Randie L. Timpe

Randie L. Timpe is Assistant to the Provost for Administration at Mount Vernon Nazarene University.

Questions of human origins and humans' role in creation constituted a significant focus in my undergraduate study in religion at Southern Nazarene University in the late 1960s. These questions did not evaporate in my graduate study in psychology at state universities. Rather, they became more focused toward integrating the central truths of theology and psychology, prefaced by the foundational assumption that ultimate Truth (God determined) is a unity no matter "how" or "where" that truth (human understanding) originated. The following is a practical rapprochement between the extremes of seven day creationism and godless chaotic evolution that informs integrative scholarship, as exampled in the *Journal of Psychology and Christianity* and the *Journal of Psychology and Theology*, for which I have been a contributor and peer reviewer.

In the creation narrative humans were situated in a defined time, space, and culture such that finiteness as boundedness constitutes an original inherent quality that precedes even sin's entrance into the collective human experience. Sin exacerbates humans' inability to comprehend God fully, but it does not abrogate the impact of human finiteness on understanding origins, eventual outcomes, or the ability to dialog on fundamental issues.

Christianity understands God as the first cause of all natural and supernatural phenomena, and as first cause God exercises two roles of creator and sustainer. Not only does He create with care and love, He maintains, provides, and sustains with equal love and care on a continuing basis, a conviction detailed below.[1] Bridging the gap between radical creationism and godless evolution pivots, not only on the nature of God, but also on the nature and purpose of the biblical record. A core conviction is that the Bible is affirmation of God's existence, love and redemptive engagement in creation, and proclamation of truths central to redemption, to the end that the Bible is a history of God's love and his redemptive activity. The Bible is neither a comprehensive world history nor a science text, but presents essential truths instrumental to salvation. The biblical canon is situated in a relatively circumscribed temporal, geographic, and cultural context, and many of its admonitions reflect practical Hebraic wisdom. The canon contains multiple literary genres, but treating the Bible as a scientific text usurps its core message and purpose. The truths communicated through its literature often employ linguistic conventions rich in symbolism, myth, and parables to explain "why." This use of language should not be confused with that of modern science that is more descriptive and literal, addressing "how."

Beyond linguistic variants, critical differences about causality (e.g., Aristotle's material, formal, efficient and final cause differentiation) and ways of knowing (e.g., intuition, reason, replication and revelation, each with specific insights and blind spots) underscore the difficulty in bridging the gap. Within the human cultural timeline the segment associated with the scientific empirical way of knowing is relatively short, spanning less than four centuries. The differentiation of science from theology reveals discrete purposes, assumptions, languages, evidence and goals to the end that it is wise to construe science as a bounded activity marked by objective and disciplined observation of natural events that are repeatable.

Psychology as a scientific discipline within the North American landscape is less than a century and a half old, and its presence in academia is colored by empiricism, functionalism, and environmentalism. Its truths are verifiable by observation across time, centered on the adaptability of behavior in a dynamic environment, with interplay between organism and environment. Collectively, these "isms" contribute to a strong emphasis in American psychology on learning, to the extent that persons are described as possessing an almost infinite capacity to learn both as individuals and in the aggregate. The rich and extensive capacity of the human nervous system reflects God's omniscience as *imago dei*. A dynamic God creates and sustains a dynamic universe; a dynamic universe reveals a dynamic God.

Perceiving the natural world as active and dynamic evidences the nature of God in the same way that artwork reveals the artist (i.e., Art reveals the Artist). Astronomy, biology, geology, and meteorology portray the natural world as one of movement and change with underlying, orderly, and dynamic rhythms (e.g., an expanding universe, new species, plate tectonics and weather systems). An alternate rendering of the creation narrative points to the continuing nature of the creative act, "In the beginning God began bringing into existence the heavens and the earth," in which the past progressive construction defines a definite beginning and continuing thereafter. One need only to witness the opening of a flower bud or the cognitive and language development of a toddler to affirm that creation continues in wondrous mystery and regularity. Here theology confronts the nature of God and embodies a fundamental understanding of the image of the divine as sovereign Creator described by Wesley.

> 1. He began his creation at what time, or rather, at what part of eternity, it seemed him good. Had it pleased him, it might have been millions of years sooner, or millions of ages later. 2. He determined, by his sovereign will, the duration of the universe; whether it should last seven thousand, or seven hundred thousand, or numberless millions of years. 3. By the same, he appointed the place of the universe, in the immensity of space.[2]

The loving investment in the maintenance of the creation is as important as the original creative effort. Human experience does not square well with a watch-maker God who constructed it, wounded it tight and left it to run alone. Similarly, it makes less sense to conceive of God as magician ("abracadabra," a flash of light and poof) than God as craftsman who lovingly designs and creates. That God could create the universe in seven 24-hour days, including the embedded fossil record, is not disputed, given God's omnipotence and sovereignty. Yet, is this how God, as person, operates? Omnipotence applies as much to developing and sustaining as it does to creating.

In grace God provides for, on a continuing and a sustaining basis, His creation; this focus embodies the theological discourse on providence as emblematic of grace through which God's purpose is accomplished in due time. "The question of providence concerns how God *thinks ahead* to care for all creatures, fitting them for contingencies, for the challenges of history, and for potential self-actualization to the glory of God."[3] God was close to creation on day 1, but equally close to life on a daily basis. Oden affirmed three core teachings about providence in His administration or oversight role:

- *God is preserving the creation in being (continuing presence).*
- *God is cooperating to enable creatures to act (first and second cause).*
- *God is guiding all creatures, inorganic and organic, animal and rational creation, toward a purposeful end that exceeds the understanding of those being provided for.*[4]

In the human sphere, without maintenance, energy dissipates throughout closed systems until heat is evenly distributed and no further work can be achieved. Entropy evidences randomness and disorder. Without the continual introduction of energy, systems deteriorate into random chaos (like a teen's room over time), yet careful observation of nature fascinates us with growing complexity and intricate detail. God maintains what He constructs in continuing creation and renewal through a continuing investment of energy.

In Francis Schaeffer's words, "How should we then live?" Academicians are notably gifted in offering definite opinions and expressing them firmly with conviction and often cruelly, if blog comments are normative. It seems as though dialog between proponents of extreme views is more provocative than conciliatory and productive. Closed-minded-ness produces alienation and termination of the potential for dialog and reconciliation.

Effective trans-disciplinary dialog must originate with careful definition of terms and explication of fundamental assumptions. Defini-tions exist at the denotative (literal, strict, and unencumbered) and con-notative (pregnant and rich) levels. Many of the technical terms rich and endearing to disciplinary specialists are stripped from connotations to denotation by either the common laity or disciplinary specialists from other fields. Without this grounding work academicians talk past each other and contribute to faulty learning and miscommunication. The abil-ity to bridge disciplinary boundaries and to span the gulf between spe-cialized disciplinary heuristics constitutes a special type of scholarship identified by Boyer as the *scholarship of integration*, translating the techni-cal language of one field faithfully into concepts and language of another without altering or omitting the deep meaning of the original discipline.[5]

Nor should assumptions be confused with data and law. In hu-mility we need to acknowledge the limitations of human ways of know-ing, affirming the epistemological boundaries of science and theology. Science and theology are both human thought and language systems.

Science and theology are human activities with differing purpos-es and methodologies, each operating within restricted and finite bound-aries. Science is an objective and disciplined need to know the perceived regularities and consistencies in the natural work, eventuating in the formulation of lawful descriptions, most often expressed in probabilistic terms. Broadly conceived, theology (literally human words about God, *theos* + *logos*) is a reasoned contemplation on ultimate purposes with at-tendant explanations. If theology is the human explication of God and His nature, God is not obliged to behave as humans have constructed Him. Similarly, we must articulate that scientific understanding is ill-equipped to speculate meaningfully on ultimate purposes, spiritual na-ture, and unique events.

The outcome of such a perspective is grace, humility, love, and reverence. St. Paul's letter to the Corinthian church captures this spiritual extraordinarily well.

> *For we know in part and we prophesy in part, but when perfec-*
> *tion comes, the imperfect disappears. . . . Now we see but a poor*
> *reflection as in a mirror; then we shall see face to face. Now I*
> *know in part; then I shall know fully, even as I am fully known.*
> *(I Corinthians 13:9-10, 12)*

ENDNOTES AND SUGGESTED READING

1. T. C. Oden, *The Living God, Systematic Theology*, Vol. 1. (Peabody, MA: Prince Press, 1987).

2. John Wesley, n.d., "Thoughts upon God's Sovereignty." In *The Works of John Wesley* (vol. X) (Kansas City, MO: Nazarene Publishing House, 1979) 361-363.

3. Oden, 271.

4. Ibid, 272.

5. E. L. Boyer, *Scholarship Reconsidered: Priorities of the Professoriate* (San Franciso, CA: Jossey-Bass, Inc., 1990).

38

EVOLUTIONARY THEORY AND MORAL DEVELOPMENT

Mark A. Maddix

Mark A. Maddix is Professor of Practical Theology and Discipleship and Dean of the School of Theology and Christian Ministries at Northwest Nazarene University.

Growing up in a Christian home, evolution was only referred with negative connotations. I was taught that evolution was an atheistic theory that undermined the authority of Scripture in general, and specifically Genesis 1 and 2. If a person believed in evolution he or she could not be a Christian. This view was supported during my first biology class at a nearby state college. The professor supported evolution and took great pride in degrading uneducated and ignorant Bible-believing Christians who denied evolution. The professor, teaching in the Bible Belt, enjoyed arguing with students who opposed his views. This experience confirmed the assumptions of my upbringing that evolution was from the "pit of hell."

A year later I sensed God calling me to be a pastor so I enrolled as a Bible major in a Christian liberal arts university, rooted in the Wesleyan tradition. During my first semester I took Introduction to the Old Testament. I was eager for the professor to support my view of the creation accounts and to deny a humanistic view of evolution. In my amazement, the professor said nothing about the creation-evolution debate. Rather began to explain that Genesis 1 & 2 was a hymn that was theological, and had nothing to do with proving or disproving creation from a scientific perspective. He said the author of Genesis, probably not Moses, (that created another anxiety), had no understanding of modern science and was writing to show God's relationship with God's creation. His explanation changed the course of my understanding of the creation-evolution debate, and helped me understand that Genesis 1 and 2 was theological not scientific.

I was now convinced that Genesis 1 & 2 had a different purpose and meaning, until I took a course in the natural sciences, taught by a young earth, seven day creationist. He argued that the creation accounts in Genesis could be scientifically traced, and the world was only 6,000 years old. He talked about dispensations of time, and used the Bible to support his views. Now I was really confused.

I continued to wrestle with what I believed until I took Introduction to Biology, a course that I had taken at the state university and had to take again because of a poor grade. In class the professor affirmed his belief in evolution by stating that Darwin's theory was the best way to explain how God created the universe. He affirmed what my Bible professor had articulated about Scripture. He also indicated that many scientists, who were Christian, see connections between science and the Bible. After class I asked the professor to explain how he could hold to evolution and creation. He responded by stating, "Believing in evolution does not reject Scripture, since Scripture was not written for such purposes."

My Christian liberal arts education provided me with a clearer understanding of a Wesleyan view of Scripture, particularly as it related to the creation accounts and a view of creation that could include evolution.

As a pastor, and now as a professor, this theological understanding of the creation accounts are foundational in discussing creation and science with parishioners, students, and constituencies. Many of them think that the more recent focus on evolution among evangelicals in general, and Nazarenes in particular, is something new. I often remind them that it was something that I learned in college over twenty-five years ago.

EVOLUTION AND MORAL DEVELOPMENT

Since I am not a scientist, I cannot speak about the details of evolutionary theory. I can only rely on the vast amount of research that supports evolution as a viable option in explaining how God may have created the universe. I can only speak, as a practical theologian, on the theological significance of the creation accounts and my expertise in the integration of theology and the social sciences. The evidence seems clear that evolution is a viable scientific argument for the creation of the universe, and it doesn't contradict a biblical view of creation.

Beginning with my doctoral studies in the interdisciplinary fields of Christian education, theology, and the social sciences, I explored how evolutionary psychology impacts the understanding of how people grow and develop. I began to see clear evidence of the impact of evolution on development theories as it relates to how we grow physically, cognitively, and morally. My studies included developmental theories of Jean Piaget (cognitive and moral development), Lev Vygotsky (socio-cultural), Lawrence Kohlberg (moral development), and James Fowler (faith development). These theories of were based on a structuralist approach that assumes that human persons develop through predictable stages of growth. They hold that human persons are more similar than dissimilar, and that a person's environment either inhibits or fosters growth. These theories have been foundational to our understanding of human development and growth. However, more recent studies in evolutionary psychology and neuroscience have expanded our understanding of how persons grow and develop. For example, we know from neuroscience that the brain has the capacity to grow and develop. The brain has the ability to change as a result of one's experience, which is referred to as neuroplasticity. As we will see later, this has implications for how persons grow and develop morally.

I want to explore in more detail how evolutionary theory impacts my understanding of moral development. In my search for understanding how persons grow and develop morality, I first asked whether humans are born with the capacity to know what is right or wrong (nature), or is morality shaped primary by our environments (nurture). I also had believed that humans are born with a nature that is bad instead of good. However, based on what we can learn from developmental psychology the human person's nature is good, and it is shaped by his or her environment. This does not negate that humans are fallen creatures in need of redemption, but it does mean that in general humans are good and when tested, typically respond with love and compassion. Developmental theories also argue that human consciousness, how we determine right and wrong, is developed during the first years of life through our interaction with our parents. In other words, human are created in the image and likeness of God, with the capacity to know what is good and evil, but a person's moral consciousness is shaped and developed by their parents and/or guardians. This is why some people have a higher level of consciousness (morality) while others do not. Since persons inherit a particular environment, it impacts their morality.

Also, we know from virtue ethics that when a person engages in regular practices, these practices no longer become habits but virtues. For example, if a person practices compassion on a regular basis the person develops the virtue of compassion. This has particular implications for how persons are formed and shaped morally. In the Christian context, persons are shaped and formed through their participation in such Christian practices as worship, Scripture reading, prayer, and service. Also, persons are shaped and formed by role models who display a moral life. In essence, much of morality is shaped by others and our environments.

A person's morality is shaped by culture, religious experience, upbringing, but it would be a mistake to say that morality is nothing more than one's environment. The question is whether humans are born with a sense of morality. Did God create humans with the capacity to be moral, and if so, how did this take place? Recent studies in evolutionary ethics show that morality is not merely learned through one's environment, but many of our moral instincts are inherited through our evolutionary past. We are created with a universal morality that is imbedded in our nature, which is biological. Thus, humans don't simply learn moral behavior, but humans are biologically designed to acquire morality. In other words, humans are biologically wired with the necessary components for morality. Humans are born with a universal morality that forces us to analyze human action in terms of its moral structure. This includes the innate part of human nature that includes many moral concepts such as knowing right from wrong, empathy, fairness, generosity, justice, and wrongs against others. This biological morality includes a person's ability to have a more sense about rights and obligations, proscription of murder, rape and other forms of violence, redress of wrongs, shame, and taboos. Therefore, all human persons, created in the image and likeness of God, have the inherit capacity for morality.

Evolutionary ethics does not contradict a Biblical view of human persons, but provides a scientific explanation for how God created humans with the capacity to be moral, and through our environments, we grow and develop morally.

39
MY STRUGGLE WITH EVOLUTION

Kevin Twain Lowery

Kevin Twain Lowery is Professor of Theology and Philosophy at Olivet Nazarene University.

"IN THE BEGINNING ..."

I will never forget my first grade Sunday school teacher, Miss Cook, a sweet but stern elderly lady at the small-town Methodist church where I was raised. The very first day of class with Miss Cook is still vivid to me. "In the beginning God created the heavens and the earth!" she emphasized with passion, pounding her fist on the table in cadence with the verse as we recited it with her. Miss Cook believed that the place to start was at the beginning, and that was indelibly impressed upon my young mind. I saw the creation story as a foundational part of Christian faith.

In the middle of my fourth grade year, my family started attending a Wesleyan church several miles away. The people there were much more self-assured than the Methodists I had known. The pastor and a lot of the church's leaders were rather outspoken on a lot of issues. It was a culture of legalism and fear. The fear was so gripping for me that during altar calls I would silently ask God to forgive me of any sin I had failed to confess, even though I could not think of any. I did this almost every service for the next five to six years.

That pastor (and church) claimed that only those who take every part of the Bible literally really believe it. Anything less is not genuine faith. Ironically, I have never known anyone to actually follow every edict in the Bible literally, including NT admonitions (e.g., women needing to keep quiet in church). Of course, the pastor dismissed evolution out of hand with jeers like, "I may have had ancestors who swung from their necks, but I never had any that swung from their tails!" The congregation always responded with boisterous laughter and amens. Evolutionists were disparaged with labels like "worldly," "humanists," "liberals," and "atheists." Scientists were considered the guiltiest of all. Like the atheists who opposed the Bible and prayer in public schools, scientists had set their sights on destroying everyone's faith in the Bible. Unfortunately, I bought into all of this hook, line, and sinker. As a result, grappling with evolution would require me to rethink a great number of my beliefs and presuppositions.

SURVIVAL OF THE FITTEST IDEA

I managed to make it through public high school with my belief system unscathed. In fact, it was pretty easy. I simply told myself that I was right and everyone else was wrong. After all, there were plenty of other people who didn't buy into evolution, even if they didn't care about or understand the Bible like I did. Moreover, I could always count on my local church to reassure me that we were on the right side of the issue (i.e., God's side). Whenever I would take a biology test or quiz, I told the teacher what he wanted to hear without taking any of it seriously. What made it even easier is that there were people like Henry Morris and Ken Ham who offered "answers" to the "Bible's critics." As long as they were on the job, I could rest easy knowing that the historicity of the biblical creation story could be defended intellectually.

Armed with the "answers" I needed, I was not afraid to debate those who tried to defend evolution. I was like a bulldog. I didn't back down for anybody or anything. We were talking about God's Word! One of my Catholic friends at school, Donna Pope (a great name for a Catholic), tried to convince me that Christians could accept evolution and still regard the creation story as inspired by God. She said that the two could be reconciled. I just couldn't accept that, and we argued about it many times throughout our senior year of high school.

College didn't pose much of a threat to my beliefs either. I attended a local state university, and since my two majors were physics and mathematics, I managed to all but avoid the subject of evolution while an undergraduate. I didn't have to take any chemistry courses, and the one required biology course was titled "Man and His Environment" (before gender neutral language became commonplace). Like high school, whenever evolution was discussed, I just let the professor's words go in one ear and out the other.

Nevertheless, one college course impacted me like no other. I was in the honors section of the required junior-level English composition class, and it was taught by a professor who was a lecturer and practitioner of Zen Buddhism. We read *God and the New Physics* by Paul Davies and *The Structure of Scientific Revolutions* by Thomas Kuhn, among other things, and between the texts, the professor's comments, and class discussions, a lot of my presuppositions were challenged. I didn't change any of my beliefs, but now I wasn't so cocksure of them. In spite of my numerous disagreements with the professor, he patiently listened to my perspective, and he simply showed me how to do quality work without forcing his beliefs on me or anyone else. I began to see that the stereotypes I held weren't very accurate after all. Not everyone who rejects biblical literalism is duplicitous or has some kind of anti-Christian agenda.

It was during that semester I decided to follow the truth wherever that might lead — the truth about God, the world, and myself. It was a turning point in my life. Even though I had not yet changed any of my beliefs, my attitude toward my beliefs shifted dramatically. I have always enjoyed learning, and I had convinced myself that I was objective, even though that was not the case. This class made me realize that. As a result, I became increasingly open to having my beliefs challenged. I learned to value the *pursuit* of truth, not just my beliefs *about* the truth. However, I still resisted accepting evolution, because it was so central to my thinking. The thought of working through the implications was daunting.

The most viable idea that I took away from college was the value of truth itself. If I really had the faith I claimed, I should not be afraid to explore and scrutinize my beliefs. I decided to have a genuine faith, one that is intellectually honest, even if that entails changing my beliefs or being different from everyone else. When my time comes to stand before God in judgment, I want to know I have done my best to know and live by the truth.

DIGGING UP OLD BONES

After working several years as an engineer, I left for seminary to pursue the call to ministry I felt. Even in a conservative environment, it didn't take long for my views on creation to be challenged once again. In my first semester I took Old Testament Intro, a course that examines the origins and context of the OT books. When I learned that the Pentateuch (i.e., the first five books of the Bible) was compiled from several sources and was not written by Moses, I became angry. I was not upset with the professor, for this information gave me my first glimpse into the hidden complexities of the Bible, and the Bible came alive to me in a new and interesting way. Rather, I was disgusted that I had spent my entire life in the church, going every time the doors were opened, and I had never heard anything remotely like this before. I was even more appalled to discover that this kind of information was at least one to two centuries old, and this was only the tip of the iceberg! I felt like my church and denomination had let me down.

During my time in seminary and the pastorate, I still held onto six-day creationism, but I grew increasingly tentative about it. On one hand, it was getting very difficult to regard the creation narratives (I learned that there are two in Gen. 1–2) as historical accounts. On the other hand, although many creationists had assured us that evidence would eventually be found to vindicate creationism and reveal evolution to be a hoax, that other shoe never dropped, in my opinion. When I began my doctoral studies, I took up the issue again in my spare time and in researching a paper I wrote for a class. As I read arguments from both sides of the issue, I became increasingly convinced that while the evidence to support evolution was rapidly mounting, the creationist explanations were convoluted and contrived. The creationists seemed to be desperately grasping for straws. Eventually I lost faith in their explanations and now had to face the difficult task of working through the various implications of evolution.

MAKING SENSE OF IT ALL

What does it mean that evolution is true? How does it affect our theology? Here are four key areas that it impacts.

First, and most obviously, evolution influences the way we view revelation. Biblical scholars tells us that the creation narratives in Genesis are adaptations of older creation myths that circulated in the ancient near east. We cannot view them as historical accounts, but the modifications the biblical authors made reflect their distinct beliefs about God, and these can certainly be regarded as revelatory. Besides, it is not obvious to what extent the ancient Jewish people viewed these narratives as historical or allegorical. Although Jesus mentions Abel in the gospels, we don't know whether he viewed Abel as a historic figure. Likewise, I am not convinced that viewing Adam as an archetype challenges the historicity of Christ as the second Adam.

Second, evolution shapes the way we view the origins of evil. Evolution shows that there was no pristine, Garden of Eden state corrupted by a literal fall. Rather, life evolved from its simplest form, and it is still evolving today. Each of us starts as a single cell, then we grow and develop into adulthood. We are born self-centered, only being aware of our own needs and desires. However, we also have certain proclivities that give us the potential to feel and express love. Sociobiology is a vast field devoted to understanding these moral predispositions. Our tendency toward selfishness is inherited, not through a curse but through biological and social factors. We are certainly creatures in need of divine forgiveness and transformation.

Third, moral accountability must be interpreted from an evolutionary perspective. Children gradually become morally accountable as their ability to reason develops and they better understand how their decisions affect others and themselves. Perhaps moral accountability starts with simple obedience, but it goes way beyond that, for even pets can be taught to obey. Rather, it entails the ability to discern good and evil, i.e., to weigh the potential benefits and harm and not just react according to stimulus and conditioned response. This illustrates another way a literal reading of the creation narratives is inadequate. How could God create two adults with developed reasoning without giving them false memories, thus influencing the result? Since we have evolved as a species, we must take responsibility for ourselves and aspire to be what God wants us to be with his help. The evolution of our higher reasoning enables us to move beyond impulse and instinct.

Finally, evolution affects the way we view divine providence. Granted, God's role in evolution can be depicted as an active craftsman, a general guiding presence, one who occasionally intervenes, or an observer. Nevertheless, the developmental nature of evolution suggests that God accomplishes his purposes incrementally, even over eons of time. This has implications for theodicy. Rather than wondering why specific bad things happen, we should simply accept the fact that God allows his creation to develop, the good alongside the evil. God's purposes will eventually be accomplished, and good will overcome evil through his grace.

LEARNING TO LOVE TRUTH

My primary purpose is not to offer a compelling intellectual argument for evolution, because I think we are inclined to believe what we want regardless of whether it is true. If we refuse to accept something emotionally, we won't be convinced by even the strongest evidence or arguments. We often go through the grieving process when facing a difficult truth. If we refuse to face the truth, we can become defensive and closed-minded, and this is personally stifling in many ways.

I want to emphasize the importance of being a lover of truth. John 8:32 is one of my favorite verses in the Bible, because truth is truly liberating and transformational when it is understood, embraced, and lived. Pursue truth, and let evidence speak for itself. It is not a coincidence or a conspiracy that over 99% of biologists accept evolution as scientific fact today. The evidence is overwhelming, and we should accept it for what it is. The truth may not always be the most palatable or pleasant at the moment, but in the grand scheme of things truth is far more important than the temporary pleasures we derive from self-deception. It is quite likely we will discover that the purposes of God are even broader and weightier than we had imagined.

40

THEOLOGICAL IMPLICATIONS OF THE EVOLUTION DEBATE

Joseph Bankard

Joseph Bankard is an Associate Professor of Philosophy at Northwest Nazarene University.

I have many fond memories of my time as an undergrad student at Point Loma Nazarene University. Some of the best memories center on late night conversations with my fellow classmates in Hendricks Hall. We would debate the historical accuracy of the Genesis narratives, the strength of the scientific evidence supporting evolution, and the ultimate origins of the universe. I was deeply troubled by the divergent creation stories found in Genesis 1 and 2. In chapter 1, the first humans are created *after* the sun, moon, stars, earth, animals, and vegetation; but in chapter 2, Adam is created *before* vegetation. Which order of creation is true? Furthermore, did the word "day" really refer to a literal 24 hour time period? How could there be a day before the sun was created? More troubling questions arose concerning Cain and Abel. After Cain kills Abel, he travels to the land of Nod, but where on earth did all the people in Nod come from? Questions like these led me away from a literal historical interpretation of the early Genesis narratives.

But what are the alternatives to a seven day creation? I was skeptical of evolution, even though most of the biology professors at Point Loma endorsed a form of theistic evolution, and so I took a very generic position. I argued, as many of my current students argue, that it didn't matter HOW God created the heavens and the earth as long as one affirms THAT God created the heavens and the earth. It didn't much matter if God used a big bang and evolution to bring humans into existence or if God created the entire thing is seven miraculous days.

Over the years, my view on these issues has changed dramatically. I now believe that the manner in which God created the universe we inhabit matters a great deal. If macroevolution is in fact true and humans are the result of billions of years of natural selection, then several important theological questions emerge. First, what happens to the doctrine of the fall of humanity in light of evolution? If evolution is true, then the universe is very old, humans evolved from primates, and the historical accuracy of the Genesis narratives is in serious doubt. Because of this, almost all who support a version of theistic evolution argue for a metaphorical or allegorical interpretation of Genesis 1-3. Logically, this also means that the fall is not a historical event. But now the questions really start to mount. If the fall of humanity is not a historical event, then how do we make sense of original sin? John Wesley argued original sin was the only empirically verifiable doctrine due to the massive amount of injustice, pain, and violence created by human actions. Yet, if human nature is not sinful due to the fall, then where does humanity's propensity to sin come from?

In an Augustinian worldview, the fallen state of the world has a relatively simple explanation. God created the first two humans in a state of perfection and placed them in paradise. It is only due to the rebellious actions of Adam and Eve that they are cast out of the garden. As a result, humanity inherits a sinful nature. In this framework, humanity is responsible for their situation. God doesn't create humanity with a sinful nature. Rather, humanity willfully disobeys God and original sin is the punishment. However, if there is no literal fall, then how do we explain humanity's propensity to sin? Did God intentionally create humanity with a fallen nature? Such a view raises serious questions about God's character and God's goodness.

A second set of theological questions that arise in light of evolution is related to the role of the cross. Many Christians believe that Jesus is crucified in order to restore humanity's relationship with God. Sin created a divide between God and creation. Jesus' death was a necessary sacrifice to bridge this gap. However, if denying the historical fall calls into question the doctrine of original sin, then it also calls into question the role of the cross of Christ. If Jesus doesn't die in order to overcome humanity's original sin, then why did Jesus die? What is Jesus–the second Adam–attempting to restore with the cross, if not the sin of the first Adam?

Finally, evolution raises serious questions related to the problem of evil. Without a historical fall, sin, death, disease, and natural disasters have no identifiable origin. Why do humans die? Why are so many decimated by disease? Why do we live in a world with earthquakes, tsunamis, and hurricanes? Did God intentionally create the world with a fallen nature? If the state of the world doesn't depict a fall from paradise, but rather, reveals the intentional creation of God, then questions arise concerning God's character, God's goodness, and the origin of evil. Looking at the history of evolution doesn't make it any easier. For billions of years, organisms have been in a perpetual battle for survival, one that Darwin calls "red in tooth and claw." The vast majority of these organisms are now extinct. Why would a loving God choose to create through an evolutionary process that requires so much pain and death?

Difficult questions like these show that the naïve view I held during my college years is no longer tenable. The debate surrounding creation and evolution has profound ramifications for Christian theology, ramifications that should not fly under the radar. But how should Christians respond in light of these new difficulties? Some argue that evolution should be rejected because of the theological implications listed above. To endorse evolution is to lose vital elements of the Christian faith. The problem with this view is the scientific support for evolution is overwhelming, and it grows with each passing day. Not to mention that well over 90% of experts in biology endorse some form of evolution. Because of this, I suggest that Christians must begin to do theology in light of evolution. We can no longer sit back and hope that evolution will eventually go away. Instead, Christians need to be passionately engaged in the dialogue between science and religion, and at the forefront of synthesizing evolutionary theory with Christian theology. This is not an easy task. Even so, it is necessary if the Church wants to maintain theological credibility in a scientific age.

41
HUMANITY IN THE IMAGE OF GOD

Michael Lodahl

Michael Lodahl is Professor of Theology & World Religions at Point Loma Nazarene University.

I don't believe in evolution, I always want to be free;
Ain't gonna let no anthropologist make a monkey out of me.

The late Larry Norman is one of my favorite Christian musicians. But I always wince when I hear those lyrics.

It's the sort of rhetoric we hear often. Not long ago one of my students said to me, "We're made in God's image, not in the image of monkeys." Just last Sunday, a popular local preacher proclaimed to his sizable congregation that "science will tell us that my ancestor is an ape," but "I can tell you my ancestor isn't an ape; the ape's ancestor is an ape and a dog's ancestor is a dog." "To accept evolution," he continued, "is to deny God's creation of man in his own image."

Are we really confronted with such an either-or scenario? No.

I remember when I was in high school a friend asked me, "What will you do if they find 'the missing link'?" (This was a long time ago!) I recall that the question bothered me greatly. *What **would** I do?* I remember wondering to myself. I assumed then that my Christian faith would be left in shambles, ground into the dust of archaeologists or absorbed by strands of DNA.

In the intervening years, I've become far less troubled by such issues. I want to try to explain why.

I still believe that God, revealed in the history of Israel – and revealed supremely in the person and works of Jesus – is the Creator of all things. I still believe that God has created human beings in the divine image. I also assume that God's mode or method of creating is through the painstakingly gradual processes that we call 'evolution.'

Much of the Christian resistance to this last proposition seems to be rooted in the anxiety Larry Norman voiced when he sang his refusal to let evolutionary theory "make a monkey out of me." There is a fear that believing in evolution necessitates an attack on human dignity and uniqueness. It even begins to sound a little like human pride speaking: "Don't reduce me to some animal!"

I doubt that the Bible encourages that sort of human pride. It is true that Genesis 1 instructs us that God created humans in the divine image, male and female. It is clear, too, that humanity (the Hebrew word for 'human' or 'humanity' is *adam*, from *adamah*, 'ground') is entrusted with the task of 'ruling over' all of the non-human creatures.

While I do not assume that the opening chapters of Genesis compose a scientific textbook presenting a play-by-play historical description of the beginning of the world, I do believe they point us toward powerful and important truths. I assume these truths are fundamentally theological, anthropological, and cosmic: Genesis narrates to us, through poetic language and metaphorical imagery, a deep sense of our relations to our Creator, to one another as fellow humans, and to the marvelous more-than-human creation of which we are inextricably a part.

When we read Genesis 1 in this way, we may find it significant that while, indeed, *adam* as male and female is created in God's image in order to exercise the function of 'ruling' over God's beloved creation (judged repeatedly by God to be 'good'), the human creatures do not have a day of their own. Like the "cattle and creeping things and wild animals of the earth of every kind" (1:24), *adam* is created on the sixth day. This suggests, I think, far more kinship between humans and other creatures than many contemporary opponents of evolution would welcome.

Recently I have been struck, also, by the fact that in Genesis 1 human beings are not the first creatures to be directly addressed by God. In 1:22, God blesses the creatures of sea and sky and invites them to "be fruitful and multiply," to thrive in making earth their home. Indeed, it seems clear that humanity's God-given task – to "image" or reflect the goodness of the Creator – is directly expressed in ensuring that all of these other creatures are enabled to fulfill God's purpose for them. That purpose is to live, to eat (1:30), to reproduce.

This would mean that Genesis 1 does not encourage us to think of our being created in God's image in terms of hierarchical superiority or absolute difference from all of the rest of God's creatures. Instead, we are entrusted with a *task* that roots us deeply in this world with our fellow creatures. That task, to be sure, requires intelligence, creativity, and imagination. But there is no reason to assume that these capabilities could not have developed slowly and gradually through the processes we now identify as 'evolution.'

Genesis 2 makes a similar point in even more dramatic, almost parabolic imagery: God forms or shapes the *adam* from the dust of the ground (*adamah*) – and also forms "every animal of the field and every bird of the air" (2:19) from the very same ground. It would be difficult to impress upon us more deeply our earthy kinship with all of the rest of God's creatures! Granted, God "breathed into [the human's] nostrils the breath of life" whereby the human "became alive" (2:7). But we should note that Genesis 1 attributes that same "breath of life" to all the beasts, birds and creepy-crawlies of earth (1:30). Indeed, Psalm 104 celebrates the life-giving "breath" or "spirit" (*ruach*) of God that enlivens all creatures, not just humans (vv. 24-30).

Again, the point is not that these biblical texts are presenting scientific information about the world (including us humans). They need not, and should not, be placed in a competitive relationship with the natural sciences. What they do present, I believe, are deep truths about our common life with all of the rest of God's creatures – and our God-entrusted vocation to work for their flourishing. The natural sciences can help us to understand ourselves, and this task, even more deeply and truthfully.

42

MUCH NEEDED CONVERSATION

Mark R. Quanstrom

Mark R Quanstrom is Professor of Theology and Philosophy at Olivet Nazarene University. He is also the University Campus pastor at College Church of the Nazarene in Bourbonnais.

I am appreciative to those who recognize that there ought to be a place where serious conversation can take place regarding the relationship between evolutionary theory and Christianity's faith affirmations.

I'm appreciative because I am not of the opinion that evolutionary theory poses no challenge to Christianity. I don't think that if we just appropriated the right Biblical hermeneutic, or understood the respective epistemological domains of science and religion, or insisted on science recognizing its "faith" presuppositions, then all would be well.

I'm appreciative because neither am I of the opinion that the challenges that evolutionary theory pose to creedal Christianity can be ignored or dismissed. (And just for the record, I am using the word "theory" here in its scientific sense, not in the "detective novel" sense.) I am not in agreement with the young-earth creationists who dismiss or explain away the scientific evidence for evolutionary theory, even if I am sympathetic to their recognition of the problem evolution poses. Evolutionary theory must be taken seriously, as it is providing the best theoretical framework for understanding biological life on this planet.

So this is much needed conversation, and for that reason, I would like to raise a few of the issues that I believe confound an easy reconcil-iation between evolutionary theory and Christianity. I don't think that the three questions I am raising exhaust the issues, but in my mind, they seem to be three that are worthy of reflective consideration by Christian theologians and Christian biologists alike.

1. IS EVOLUTIONARY THEORY NECESSARILY TELEOLOGICAL FOR THE CHRISTIAN?

The first question that I believe is relative to some sort of rap-prochement between creedal Christianity and evolutionary theory con-cerns how evolution is to be understood itself. There is considerable con-versation among evolutionists about whether or not evolutionary theory is teleological in nature; that is, whether the theory necessitates purpose or direction, or whether it is simply descriptive of a blindly mechanistic universe. John Dupre, Professor of Philosophy of Science at Exeter Uni-versity, in his review of John O. Reiss' *Not By Design: Retiring Darwin's Watchmaker*, stating the facts of the matter, writes:

> Followers of the debate between evolutionists and various waves of creationists, most recently the advocates of "intelligent design," will have been struck by one curious convergence be-tween the views of the opposing parties. Both sides agree that life, whether or not literally designed by an intelligent agent, seems just as if it had been designed.[1]

This philosophic presupposition that evolutionary theory is guided by some teleological principle ("survival of the fittest" or "natural selection" for example) is being rejected by many evolutionists precisely because a teleological principle cannot be empirically verified.

So John O. Reiss, Chair of the Biology Department at Humboldt State University, believes it absolutely necessary that evolutionary theory be understood non-teleologically. In the first chapter of his book, he ex-plains his project.

> In this book, I try to show that the concept of natural selec-tion is often invoked to explain evolutionary transformations for which we have no evidence that the mechanism of natural

selection, as currently understood, was wholly or even partially responsible for the transformation. I argue that we have never been able to overcome the major weakness of this metaphor... This weakness is the implication that there is, in nature, an agent with actions analogous to those of the breeder in artificial selection, a teleological agent that intentionally, and with foresight, 'selects' variations directed toward the improvement of the organism. [2]

Reiss insists that evolutionary theory, for it to be coherent, must reject any implication or indication of purpose.

David Hanke, Senior Lecturer of Biology at the University of Cambridge, goes further and insists that the whole evolutionary theory is compromised precisely because evolutionists infuse it with purpose. In a chapter titled "Teleology: the explanation that bedevils biology," he writes:

Biology is sick. Fundamentally unscientific modes of thought are increasingly accepted, and dominate the way the subject is explained to the next generation... One major reason is the manner in which Natural Selection slipped seamlessly into the place of the Creator: the Natural Selector as the acceptable new face of the Great Designer... Predictably enough, anthropomorphizing Nature as your selector leads inevitably to the false supposition that there exists the quality of selectability, called 'Fitness' on the basis of which Nature selects... 'Fitness' does not exist – it is another phantom construct of the human mind...

There is no selection, only differential survival... ...both 'natural selection' and 'survival of the fittest' amount to no more than survival of the survivors, reflecting the uncreative emptiness of the continuous sieving of living things... [3]

According to Hanke, there is no "natural selection" or "survival of the fittest," as if "selection" was the means and "survival" was the end. No, it was simply "survivor of the survivors."

It seems to me problematic if the future paradigm for evolutionary biologists necessarily precludes a *telos* or teleological principle. Those who adhere to theistic evolution will necessarily be engaged in conversations about the definition of evolution itself and how the presupposition of purpose affects the scientific methodology. So the first question that I have is this one: "Is evolutionary theory necessarily teleological for the Christian?"

2. IS THERE A PLACE FOR NATURAL THEOLOGY OR GENERAL REVELATION IN LIGHT OF EVOLUTIONARY THEORY?

The second question I have concerns the place of natural theology or general revelation in an understanding of the Christian faith. I should confess at the outset that I am not Barthian in this matter. While I recognize the absolute and definitive uniqueness of the special revelation of God in Christ, and while I understand the Reformed rejection of natural theology per se, I would like to accept as true Paul's word in Romans 1:20a, which says: "For since the creation of the world God's invisible qualities – his eternal power and divine nature – have been clearly seen..." (NIV)

And I should note that our theological tradition acknowledges the place of general revelation to a knowledge of God. H. Orton Wiley wrote:

> *The Scriptures recognize the fact that nature reveals God, not only by frequent references to the work of nature but also by direct assertion. The heavens declare the glory of God; and the firmament sheweth his handiwork. Day unto day uttereth speech, and night unto night... The Apostle Paul... makes it clear that nature reveals God sufficiently to lead men to seek after Him and worship Him...* [4]

However, in light of what evolution has taught us about "creation," I'm thinking I might need to be afraid to ask what nature teaches us about the Creator. How is Hume's critique of the teleological argument for God's existence to be answered by Christian evolutionists who embrace natural theology or general revelation?

Look around this universe. What an immense profusion of be-ings, animated and organized, sensible and active! You admire this prodigious variety and fecundity. But inspect a little more narrowly these living existences, the only beings worth regard-ing. How hostile and destructive to each other! How insuffi-cient all of them for their own happiness! How contemptible or odious to the spectator! The whole presents nothing but the idea of a blind man, impregnated by a great vivifying principle, and pouring forth from her lap, without discernment or paren-tal care, her maimed and abortive children." [5]

If general revelation, through creation, is a true revelation of the divine nature of God, then are we not with Tennyson, who wrote that nature was "*red in tooth and claw*" and who then was compelled to ask:

Are God and nature then at strife,
That Nature lends such evil dreams?
So careful of the type she seems,
So careless of the single life.

Indeed, Jerry Coyne, Professor in the Department of Ecology and Evolution at the University of Chicago, calls into question the natural the-ology/general revelation of the Christian community in his blog when he challenged BioLogos' use of evolutionary science to draw conclusions about God's character. BioLogos, which is a "community of evangelical Christians committed to exploring and celebrating the compatibility of evolutionary creation and biblical faith," argued on their web page that God's character can indeed be discerned from evolutionary science. Spe-cifically, they posited that God is "Extravagant" (in light of the diversity of life), "Patient" (in light of the length of time evolutionary processes take) and a "Provider" (in light of the complex ecosystems that are necessary for individual species to survive).[6] Coyne responded:

As an evolutionary biologist, I would see this as deliberate hu-mor if I didn't know better. For I could think of several not-so-nice characteristics of God also manifested by "studying evo-lutionary science." But I'll leave this amusing exercise to the readers...

And then Coyne asks: "What characteristics of God do *you* see from studying nature and evolution?" [7]

And so the second question I have concerns the place of general revelation/natural theology in light of evolutionary theory? Can we continue to look to nature to discern the Creator?

3. WHAT PRIORITY IS TO BE GIVEN EVOLUTIONARY SCIENCE IN DETERMINING CHRISTIAN DOGMA?

The third question I have concerns the specific challenges evolutionary theory poses to the affirmations of the Christian faith. I'm not speaking of those affirmations that are dependent on a fundamentalist hermeneutic, but rather those creedal affirmations that are grounded in the Bible-entire and not in any one particular passage or dependent on any one particular hermeneutic.

For example, granting that the first three chapters of Genesis are primarily theological in nature, how is the doctrine of original sin or inherited depravity to be understood? If Adam and Eve are archetypes, then how is the "fall" to be explained? Is a primeval paradise from which humanity fell and to which it longs to return essential to the Christian Faith as it has been understood in the West?

Related to the above questions is the question of death. Christian faith teaches that death was an intrusion on the created order. Death was the consequence of the fall, is judgment on sin and is an enemy to which the resurrection of Jesus Christ was the victorious answer. Evolutionary science demands that death be understood as an essential part of the biological world. If death is essential to God's creation and therefore a necessary good, then why is there a need for resurrection from the dead? Why has the Christian faith considered death to be an enemy?

Evolutionary science poses challenges to the Christian understanding of Jesus Christ as well. In short, was He the God-man, the prototype of a restored humanity, a second Adam? Did all the fullness of God dwell in human form? Or was he a homosapien on the evolutionary continuum? If so, was He perhaps an exception to evolution and therefore a "*tertium quid*," which means not fully human after all? If He wasn't human as we are human, then we must rethink atonement as well as Christology.

The real issue for Christians which I believe confounds an easy reconciliation between evolutionary theory and Christianity is nothing other than the incarnation. The first confession for Christians is the confession that "Jesus is Lord," that "the Word became flesh." I believe this foundational confession precludes Gnostic answers to the challenges that evolutionary theory poses, for example, that death must be understood in a spiritual sense; that resurrection is symbolic; that the new creation is immaterial. If we take incarnation (and therefore Christianity) seriously, we must take Christ as fully human seriously, and we must take creation as *good* creation seriously.

So I am not of the opinion that evolutionary theory poses no challenge to Christianity, but neither am I of the opinion that evolutionary theory can be ignored or dismissed. The questions therefore that must be answered, among others I'm sure, are:

1. Is evolutionary theory necessarily teleological for the Christian?

2. Is there a place for natural theology or general revelation in light of evolutionary theory?

3. What priority is to be given evolutionary science in determining Christian dogma?

ENDNOTES AND SUGGESTED READING

1. John Dupre. "The Conditions for Existence," *American Scientist*, Volume 98, Number 2 (March-April 2010): 170

2. John Reiss. *Not by Design: Retiring Darwin's Watchmaker* (Berkeley: University of California Press, 2009) 4.

3. John Cornwall, ed. *Explanations: Styles of Explanation in Science* (Oxford: Oxford University Press, 2004) 143-155.

4. H. Orton Wiley. *Christian Theology,* Vol 1. (Kansas City: Beacon Hill Press, 1940) 51-52.

5. Dorothy Coleman, ed. *Hume: Dialogues Concerning Natural Religion and Other Writings* (New York: Cambridge University Press, 2007) 86.

6. http://biologos.org/

7. http://whyevolutionistrue.wordpress.com/2012/10/01/biologos-goes-all-natural-theology/

43

EVOLUTION AND FAITH:

MY JOURNEY THUS FAR

Daniel Hamlin

Daniel Hamlin is currently employed as a Network Administrator at a midwest university.

Christianity is a lie and I've been duped.

This conclusion seemed inescapable. I had just finished reading about the genetic evidence that humans and primates were related and shared a common ancestor. After months of studying and reading about evolution and common descent, the weight of the evidence was overwhelming. Multiple lines of evidence in disparate fields of science, such as Geology, Biology, and Genetics, all supported the basic idea that life on earth had developed over a long period of time and all organisms were modifications of a previously existing common ancestor. To deny the reality of evolution would be like denying the reality of gravity. However, echoing in the back recesses of my mind were the voices of dominant leaders in the Christian community. For years they had been proclaiming the lack of evidence for evolution and its incompatibility with Christianity. Now, faced with the evidence supporting evolution, I had no choice but to conclude that since these leaders had mislead me about evolution they had also lied to me about Christianity. My faith was in crisis.

The crisis began in March 2006. The previous December a judge had ruled in the Kitzmiller vs. Dover Area School District case. The ruling sparked discussion in a local newspaper's online comment section. Desiring to defend creationism, as I had done in seventh grade biology many years before, I joined in the discussion and cited popular creationist literature as evidence against evolution. After several back-and-forth exchanges with individuals, I quickly realized that not only was the evidence I was using erroneous but I was also ignorant of evolution, the evidence supporting it, and the basic principles of science. To overcome these weaknesses I decided to study evolution and common descent. After months of reading and studying numerous books, online articles and scientific journals, I realized that the Theory of Evolution accurately described the development of life on earth. Now, with the ingrained dichotomy between faith and science, I was forced to choose one over the other. Since the evidence was overwhelming I chose science and for a time questioned the existence of God.

Thus began some of the darkest months of my life. I felt as though I had been deceived by Christian leaders regarding evolution, and by extension, Christianity. I could not deny the science behind evolution, but neither could I deny the existence of God and the miracles I witnessed him perform throughout my life. The cognitive dissonance produced by the combination of evolution and Christianity was challenging to my faith. Thankfully, God had given me an "Ebenezer" several years prior to this crisis, and it was this monument to his faithfulness that helped me pick up the pieces of my faith and rebuild.

As I rebuilt my faith I had many questions that needed answered, one of the most important and fundamental concerned the Bible. What is the Bible? What is its purpose and in what areas is it authoritative? What impact did the writers' worldviews have on what was written? I had to carefully balance the extremes of bibliolatry and the secular view that the Bible is simply a collection of ancient literature. As I studied the culture of the Ancient Near East it became apparent that the writers of Genesis were writing from within their own worldview. The words and concepts used to describe various aspects of creation were similar to those of the surrounding cultures and revealed that the authors shared the same primitive understanding of how the universe functioned. At first this new knowledge was troubling. After all, if the Bible described the sky as a solid firmament how could I trust it to accurately describe anything else?

I resolved these issues by looking at the life of Christ. As Christians we believe by faith that Christ was both human and divine, and although this paradox can be difficult to comprehend, it is not a stumbling block to our faith nor does it hinder us from having a relationship with him. Similarly, the Bible is both human and divine. The original authors recorded God's self-revelation as he interacted with humanity and the people of Israel. As these interactions were recorded, they were written within the worldview of the author and in terms that the original audience could understand. Because of this, parts of Scripture contain evidence of an ancient understanding of the world. However, God accommodated this understanding so that his story could be told, his message understood, and his love displayed. This accommodation continued during Jesus' ministry with his use of parables that were familiar to his first-century audience. Though our understanding of the physical world is significantly different than what is recorded in Scripture, we can be confident that the message we have today is the message God intended for us to have and by faith believe that Scripture "inerrantly reveals the will of God concerning us in all things necessary for our salvation."

Even though I have resolved my concerns about the Bible, there are still unanswerable questions, difficult doctrinal issues, and at times doubts. However, my faith does not rest in being able to answer every question and resolve every tension; I already know The Answer. I can say with the father in Mark 9:24, "I believe; help my unbelief." Recently, a cousin who holds an old-earth creationist viewpoint learned of my position as an evolutionary creationist and wanted to discuss the issue. Knowing that discussing creation can be divisive, I was somewhat apprehensive. However, as we sat down to talk, he prefaced our conversation by saying, "It doesn't matter what we believe about creation or the Bible; what matters is what we believe about Christ." With that understanding setting the tone of our conversation we were able to discuss a controversial subject in a God-honoring way. My hope and prayer is that the Christian community can focus on the Christ who unites us, instead of spending time and energy on non-essential issues that divide us.

44

CHRISTOLOGY AND EVOLUTION

Rusty Brian

Rusty Brian is Pastor at Payette Church of the Nazarene in Idaho.

> *"What has not been assumed has not been healed;*
> *it is what is united to his divinity that is saved. . ."*
> —Gregory of Nazianzus, Epistle 101

This statement from St. Gregory of Nazianzus has served as an important answer to the question of why did God become human (*Cur Deus Homo?*) for close to two millennia. Why the incarnation, the cross, and the resurrection? –that creation might be saved. According to Gregory, it is that which is united with divinity, after all, that is made capable of being saved.

There is something very powerful about the notion that the incarnation (life, death, resurrection, and ascension) of Christ Jesus reveals the fundamental harmony between divinity and humanity. Jesus was human, flesh and blood. As such he was tempted; he felt pain, sorrow, and frustration. He went through puberty, quarreled with his parents, and felt the stinging loss of betrayal by some of his closest friends. Jesus was truly human, like us in every way – only perfectly so. In being divine, he redeemed all that is human. The harmony of divinity and humanity that is Jesus reveals what is true about both God and humanity; specifically, humanity is made for God, and it is God's very nature to be in loving relationship with creation.

I wonder what this might mean for evolution? I am not a scientist, and I claim little knowledge of evolutionary biology. It seems to me, though, that looking to the person of Jesus gives us [at least] the ability to conceive of creation as being something that is both profoundly theological – i.e., God did it, period – and yet in line with much of evolutionary science as well. Many will say, though, that you must either believe in a literal 6-day creation or else in the Big Bang and the resulting billions of years of evolution that have led to this very day. Must it really be either/or? Is it possible that our understanding of both is limited at best? Is there more to this argument? For example, in the *City of God*, St. Augustine keenly asks what it means to have a day before there is a sun. How is such a thing possible? It is, because Genesis describes there being a day and a night prior to the advent of the heavenly orbs known as the sun and moon. Yet by definition, the sun and the moon, along with their gravitational rotations, are required to have a day. Does this mean there were no days prior to the creation of these heavenly bodies? No. Does this mean, though, that Scripture is not "true?" Certainly not. It might be the case that what science often describes as the Big Bang and the ensuing evolutionary process it enacts might simply be a scientific description of the majestic creative work of our God.

As I ponder the creative processes that resulted in the vast solar system, I can't help but think of another creative process. It is one that is common for all human beings, one that Jesus himself experienced, and therefore saved or redeemed: a child's growth and development in its mother's womb. Have you ever stopped to consider the majestic beauty and mystery that is the inception, growth, and ultimately, the birth of a child? That a few chromosomes would overcome immense odds to mix together and germinate new life is truly incredible. The ensuing nine months of growth and development, prior to a child's birth, is even more amazing. Where there was previously nothing, God weaves together something – a tiny baby. Limbs and lungs, skeleton and nervous system, a brain and a heart, fingers, toes, eyes, nose, and a little mouth all emerge where nothing used to be. Moreover, these things all emerge in an ordered, purposeful way. The inception, development, and birth of a human child is a miracle. I believe it is not a coincidence that Jesus went through this very process inside of his mother Mary.

Unlike any other religion, Christianity claims that Jesus, the very Son of God - God from God, light from light, true God from true God, who was begotten and not made - became incarnate through the miraculously mundane process that every single human being goes through. Jesus did not appear as an avatar – as a ready-made and full-grown adult demi-god or Titan. No, Jesus grew from nothing inside Mary into a tiny baby boy. He was birthed through the beautiful and painful process that most all other human babies go through. He was born weak – completely helpless as a matter of fact. Jesus was dependent in every way upon Mary, Joseph, and others. As one who is fully human, this dependence would continue from the day of his birth to his death – for we are all, each of us, dependent upon one another. Our humanity is wrapped up in each other.

I think it is telling, therefore, that Jesus grew in Mary's womb, that he was fearfully and wonderfully made, as Scripture says of all human beings, that he was born a helpless baby, and that he grew up through all the clumsiness and awkwardness of childhood and adolescence before becoming the man that he is remembered as. If that which he was united to has been saved, then the miraculous process of forming an unborn child has been saved. In the same way that Jesus was knitted together in Mary's womb, might it be possible for God to have knitted the universe together in the womb of God's mind as well?

Rather than sending the Son as an avatar, God the Father opted for the organic process of growth that defines human life. If the Father chose to affirm and save humanity – indeed all of creation– in such a way, might it not also be possible that God chose to form all of creation in a similarly organic way?

As Christians, when we consider Creation, let us think precisely that – all things are created. This is not up for debate if we are to affirm the Christian faith. Perhaps, though, the how of Creation, might just take a cue from the how of the incarnation.

45

CREATION, INCARNATION, AND EVOLUTION

Mark H. Mann

Mark H. Mann is Associate Professor of Theology and Director of the Wesleyan Center at Point Loma Nazarene University.

"In the beginning was the Word, and the Word was with God, and the Word was God.... All things came into being through him, and without him not one thing came into being. What has come into being in him was life.... And the Word became flesh and lived among us, and we have seen his glory..."

These famous words from the prologue to John's gospel have become an ever-increasing source for theological reflection for me regarding the ways in which God relates to the universe as its creator. Indeed, they powerfully spell out for us what we theologians call the 'doctrine of the incarnation,' which we celebrate each Christmas. Jesus Christ, the Word and Son of God, became flesh. However, I think that we do not often understand the full implication of this biblical affirmation. In the past, I often thought of Jesus' flesh as nothing more than a vehicle for the life of Christ in the world, like clothes that he put on so that he might, in resembling us, communicate to and be understood by us. Likewise, I thought of Jesus' flesh as simply something that Christ had to 'take on' so that he could die on the cross and fulfill his purpose for being born. Indeed, I am not the only one who has thought this way. Last Christmas, I heard a Baptist pastor misquote John 1:14 in exactly that way: "The Word," he proclaimed to the congregation, "'took on' flesh." The indication here is that Christ's flesh and humanity were somehow secondary to who Christ REALLY was—the spiritual, fully divine Son of God.

Historians call the belief that Christ was essentially a divine being merely dwelling in a human body Appolinarianism, after the theologian (Appolinarius) who founded the teaching. Appolinarius was declared a heretic by the Council of Chalcedon in 381, because such a view fails to take into account the full implication of John's prologue—namely that "the Word *became* flesh and lived among us." Rather, the early Church affirmed that in the one person of Jesus Christ there co-existed *two* natures—one fully divine and *one fully human*. To view the nature of Christ as solely divine, or rather to dismiss Christ's humanity as a mere vehicle for spiritual salvation, is to miss the rich theological value of John 1. The historical Church saw the danger of missing out on what Christ's humanity has to offer us, but as my previous misconceptions and the Baptist pastor's sermon indicate, some in the modern Church still suffer from a lack of understanding the value of Christ's humanity.

So, what if we were to take the gospel writer and the early Church's teachings regarding the incarnation of Christ seriously, especially in light of what John has to say about the role of Christ ("the Word") in the creation of the universe?

First, we are left with a very different view of God's relation to creation than is prevalent among many, if not most, Christians today. The popular view is that creation is just a bunch of material stuff that, while initially created 'good' by God, is irreparably fallen and awaiting its final destruction by God with the second coming of Christ. But what John 1 points to is a universe alive with the presence of the Word of God, Jesus Christ himself. I am not suggesting that sin is not a real problem in our world today, but instead that sin has not eradicated God's presence, and particularly God's presence in Christ. Indeed, as Colossians 1:16-17 boldly declares, not only in the beginning was it true that "all things have been created through him and for him" but in the present age "in him all things hold together." It is not surprising, then, that the psalmist can claim that the heavens themselves "declare the glory of God" (Psalm 19:1), or that the apostle Paul can say that "since the creation of the world his invisible attributes are clearly seen, being understood by the things that are made, even his eternal power and Godhead" (Rom. 1:20). God's presence in Christ pervades all creation and gives the universe its structure and order that scientists seek to uncover, even if unbelievers are not able to see the handiwork of God in what they study.

Second, it is perhaps not so surprising, then, that God, in Christ, might *become* flesh—that is, become incarnate as physical, material 'stuff.' From the very beginning Christ has been intimately involved in that stuff, as the one through whom it was created and in whom it all holds together. In this sense, the birth of Jesus 2000 years ago was merely the becoming particular of what was already universally true—that is, the Word of God universally present in all of creation became fully evident in one little bit of creation—the person of Jesus of Nazareth, born of the virgin Mary—at a particular place and time. This is NOT to equate Jesus with the rest of creation or to fall into the trap of pantheism wherein there is ultimately no distinction or difference between God and creation. Instead, it is to say that the same God who reveals himself in and through creation also reveals himself in the person of Jesus Christ.

Early Christian theologians, such as Justin Martyr, Clement of Alexandria, and Augustine of Hippo, clarified this point by distinguishing between the Word or (in Greek, the language of the New Testament) 'Logos' of God and what they called the 'logoi spermatikoi'—the 'seeds' of the Word. In this, they were drawing upon both Scripture and the philosophy of their time, which understood the Logos to be the ordering principle through which the Demiurge (the Greco-Roman philosophical term for 'God') gave order and being to the physical world. But they had good reason for baptizing these ideas and making use of them for Christian purposes in explaining the incarnation and God's relationship to creation. Not only did John's gospel identify Christ with the Logos, but so did many passages in Genesis. Take, for instance, Genesis 1 in which God 'speaks' the world into being, giving it being, order, goodness, and beauty. The same goes for humans: we are spoken into being by God's words in God's very image (Gen. 1:26). What John, Justin, Clement, and Augustine all sought to convey in identifying God's creative work in and through the Word of God is exactly what Genesis points to: all of creation reveals *in part* the wisdom, truth, and goodness of God, which Christians understand became *fully* manifest in the person of Jesus Christ.

All of this, I think, points to some fruitful ways that Christians may fully embrace contemporary science and even begin to think about the evolutionary process as a manifestation of God's creative work in the world. First, science, properly understood, is the disciplined study of the physical world through observation and testing. If, as scripture declares, the world is held together by and expressive of the Word of God, science provides an important way for us to understand God's handiwork. In other words, Christians should not fear science or its findings, even when it would *seem* that scientific findings *might* be in conflict with Scripture. Indeed, there is only *one* Word of God—Jesus Christ—who has been made known to us in complimentary, albeit different, ways in both creation and Scripture (what some, like Galileo, have called the 'Two Books' of God). So, if they would seem to be in conflict, it is because we are 'reading' one of them incorrectly. It's entirely possible at times that science (our reading of creation) might need to be corrected, but it might also be that our reading of Scripture might need to be corrected. The latter was the case in Galileo's time, when Christians incorrectly believed that Scripture necessarily affirmed that the earth was the center of the universe. I believe that this is the case with evolution—that the time has come for Christians to come to see that their opposition to evolutionary theory is based upon an incorrect reading of Scripture.

More to the point, I wonder if reclaiming a traditional, scriptural understanding of the creative work of God in the Logos might just help us to come to terms with evolutionary theory. Consider, for a moment, what we might mean when speaking of Jesus Christ as the Word of God. What exactly is a 'word'? In its most basic sense, a word is a small package of information, a collection of letters or sound waves that communicates something meaningful. God's Word, Jesus Christ, reveals God's wisdom and truth within the materiality of the created order. Indeed, the Word is—as John and Colossians both announce—the principle, the information, the conveyed meaning that gives material creation its very order and life. In this sense, it is not unlike DNA, small but incredibly complex rich packages of information that give order and life to everything from bacteria to trees to tigers to human beings (including Jesus himself, since we affirm that he was fully human!). What I wonder, then, is whether we might think of DNA as a sort of expression of the Logos or perhaps, better, 'seeds of the Logos' that are the way in which God, in Christ, has fashioned life to be what it has become. If there is some truth to this, what DNA provides for us is a way to envision—as John 1 clearly indicates—all things were brought into being by and through the Divine Logos. This would suggest that the entire process of evolutionary development—in which DNA plays a pivotal role—has been the means through which God, in Christ, has created all life as we know it. It would also suggest that the ultimate purpose of creation is, through evolution, the eventual self-revelation of God in the person of the God-man, the Divine Logos made flesh, our savior Jesus Christ.

Please understand that these reflections are essentially speculative. I do not mean to claim that this is the way that we Christians *must* understand the doctrine of the incarnation. Nevertheless, what I think is clear is that evolutionary theory not only can be demonstrated to be commensurate with Scripture, but can also give us deeper insight to what Scripture has to say about how God is at work within creation.

46

GODLESS EVOLUTION?

Rob L. Staples

Rob L. Staples is Professor of Theology Emeritus from Nazarene Theological Seminary.

The Christian Faith has always had to adapt to the proven findings of science. For example, the biblical writers all reflected the "cosmological" view current in their day. They thought the world was flat. Above it was the blue dome of the sky, and above that lived God, the angels, and departed saints. Below the earth was hell, where lived Satan, the demons, and the wicked dead. It was a "three-story universe." This can be seen in Phil. 2:10 which speaks of "every knee" bowing—"in heaven, on earth, and under the earth."

We now know that the idea of a three-story universe is untenable. But this does not obviate the message of Phil. 2:10. Now, we can see it as simply declaring that everyone in the universe will eventually have to acknowledge the lordship of Christ. Such acknowledgment may be by choice or by compulsion. And the difference between choice and compulsion is the difference the Christian faith makes between salvation and damnation.

The ancients believed the sun revolved around the earth. Copernicus (1493-1543) overturned that theory and held that the earth revolved around the sun. Galileo (1564-1642) was condemned by the Catholic Church for agreeing with Copernicus, and, ironically, just recently was rehabilitated by the Church. It took over three centuries, but eventually the Faith had to adapt.

Then came Charles Darwin (1809-1882) with his theory of evolution, which many Christians saw as a threat to the Faith. But adaptation had to come and many Christians (not including those with a fundamentalist viewpoint) now see evolution simply as God's method of creation. This is sometimes called "theistic evolution" to distinguish it from a purely "naturalistic" view. God has plenty of time—never seems in a hurry! The New Testament declares that "with the Lord one day is like a thousand years, and a thousand years are like one day" (2 Peter 3:8). The book of Genesis says "the Lord God formed man from the dust of the ground" (Gen. 2:7), but it does not say how long God took to do it. Maybe millions of years?

Furthermore, the Genesis creation account is a theological statement, not a scientific one. It affirms the theological truth that God is the ground of all creation. According to H. Orton Wiley, sometimes called the dean of Nazarene theologians, the Genesis account of creation is not a scientific statement but "an inspired Psalm" sometimes known as the "Hymn of Creation" or the "Poem of the Dawn." Although Wiley views it as historical, he says it is "poetically expressed."[1]

Poetry is not necessarily to be taken in exact literalness. Rather it is descriptive of a reality that is still taken seriously but can be better said in poetic form than in plain straightforward prose. My daughter, who is an English teacher, likes to say that "poetry is the literature that says the most in the least amount of words." When we see the Genesis account as poetry, it expresses much more profound truth than literalists will ever see. We see that God is creative, and we are made in his image—we are creative too. When the garden is metaphorical, suddenly it is my story and your story—evil will be seductive, and I will do wrong trying, then, to persuade someone else to join me in my sin. The Genesis account of creation has much in common with other origin stories around the world. When we see these stories as expressing "truths" even though they may not be literally "factual," we come to a more profound understanding of God's nature as well as our own.

There is a view held by some conservative Christians called "Creation Science" which denies evolution. It also advocates a "young earth," denying that the created order is very old. But Creation Science is not "science" by any accepted definition of the term. Evolution seems to be a well-established fact. And Christian faith must adapt to it, as it has done to most other authentic findings of science.

The eighteenth-century Deists, contemporaries of John Wesley, often said that to study the physical universe, to detect the natural laws that govern the movement of the planets, and to seek to understand the workings of the created order, was "to think God's thoughts after him."

Before I became a professor of theology at Nazarene Theological Seminary, I taught religion courses at a liberal arts Nazarene college (now a university) for thirteen years. One of the things I enjoyed during that time (and one thing I missed at the seminary) was the privilege of attending some of the science meetings and entering into dialogue with the science professors. Most of them accepted some form of evolution, although they had, of necessity in those days, to be cautious in how they spoke of it. But I saw that they were sincere dedicated Christians. This helped me come to see that there could be no real conflict between good science and good religion. Conflict comes when at least one of those disciplines is bad or inadequate.

For me it all comes back to what I said above, a conclusion to which I came many years ago: Evolution can be seen as God's method of creation, and in keeping with Christianity's history of adapting to the authentic proven findings of science, that is doubtless the way it *should* be seen.

The Church of the Nazarene's Manual statement on creation states, "The Church of the Nazarene believes in the biblical account of creation ('In the beginning God created the heavens and the earth . . .'— Genesis 1:1). We oppose any godless interpretation of the origin of the universe and of humankind (Hebrews 11:3). (1, 5.1, 7)" (2009). The key word there is "godless." Of course we are to oppose any view that leaves God out of the equation, but to hold evolution to be God's method of creation is not a "godless" position.

ENDNOTES

1. H. Orton Wiley. *Christian Theology,* Vol 1. (Kansas City: Beacon Hill Press, 1940) 449.

SECTION 4

A

PASTORAL

PERSPECTIVE

47

EVOLUTION:

A MISSIONAL CONSIDERATION

Roland Hearn

Roland Hearn serves as Registrar and Dean of Students at Nazarene Theological College –Brisbane, Australia.

Every Sunday in our new church plant in north Dallas, TX seemed to be an exciting one. Each time we gathered someone would be confessing a new found faith or the breaking of an old struggle in their life. It was one of those periods in ministry that you just hold on while you watch God doing things in people's lives that reflect your highest hopes. On this particular Sunday one of the individuals that had recently come to faith asked me to step into a back room. He told me how many years before he had given up on any desire to be a part of the church. He retold some painful experiences in his encounters with people that identified themselves as Christian. He then shared the joy of his new discovery of faith through this church that had so adequately embraced him with all his struggles. He looked at me with a slightly averted gaze and spoke with an uncertain tone. He told me that he loved everything about his new church, but that he had a confession to make. I prepared myself for a journey into a deep and profound struggle as he drew breath and stead-ied himself to share his deep burden. At that point he fixed his eyes on me and uttered the words that he was sure would bring his new found acceptance to an end: "I believe in dinosaurs," he declared. It was this that caused him so much uncertainty. I smiled, encouraged him, and told him that things were going to be ok. I assured him that faith was not at odds with discoveries of the natural world, whether they are related to ancient or modern times. He relaxed as an enormous weight was lifted from his shoulders.

He had been convinced of the uncrossable gulf that exists between faith and science. In his mind to accept faith meant to reject scientific discovery, particularly if it had to do with the beginnings of life. What he was wrestling with was a reflection of the struggle in which many find themselves. He was fortunate to discover a community of faith that met his need for love first, but he was certain there would be a day of reckoning. In that brief conversation I became aware of one of the great challenges that is before us missionally. There is a perceived gulf between those outside faith and the church that needs to be addressed. It is a gulf of perception not of reality. In truth there are many such misperceptions, but this is one that increasingly needs our deliberate attention because it is so eminently possible to bridge it. At the time I had this conversation I was not as far along in my own understandings of this issue as I now am. However, my journey aided me in providing a helpful grace-enabled response. Allow me the privilege of sharing some of that journey. I do so as one committed to the mission of the church.

I grew up in the Church of the Nazarene. I was in Sunday school before I can remember. I loved the stories. I loved the precision, control and competence they reflected of God's interaction with humanity. There is a great deal of comfort in the idea that God is intimately involved in the moments of existence. He is carving a path through history and personal circumstances that will ultimately allow me, and all who have faith, to arrive safely at the goal of life's journey. I was not, however, more than seven or eight when I began to wonder why the dinosaurs played no major role in the story of creation. They seemed to be everywhere in popular imagination. When I shared my concern with my mother, her response set me free – for the rest of my life. It is hard to remember the exact words but the lasting impression was that she told me there was no need to worry about a conflict between science and faith. In the story of creation there is plenty of room for all that science discovers regarding origins to fit within the first two chapters of Genesis.

From that moment, I went on believing that God had been intimately, precisely and competently involved in a process of creation that had stretched over eons. Somewhere in there, God's creative power included all the unexplained bits, and Genesis merely reported the highlights. It reduced it down to a story of seven days for the impact of revealing what needed to be said about God. I still, however, rejected any idea that evolution beyond intra-species evolution was involved.

I guess I was 12 when I first encountered the notion that the only acceptable Christian view was a literal seven days of creation taking place less than ten thousand years ago. That seemed an odd stance. The force and harshness with which it was stated convinced me this position was inadequate.

Fast track some 20-25 years and I met my first Christian Nazarene Academic who actually maintained an acceptance of evolutionary theory as the best explanation for the origin of life. At first I was horrified. However, I loved the individual and valued deeply the views espoused on many issues. I began to carve out room within my imagination that allowed me to play with the idea and see if it confronted my faith. It was not my first, or even a major obsession, but it did return repeatedly to my conscious thought.

Finally, I felt that very little was gained, in the face of insurmountable evidence, for holding to a view that God created a virtually finished product. I had begun to realize that God acted less in the moments and circumstances of life than He did in the lives themselves. He was, and is, empowering individuals to walk through circumstances and become more Christlike. I had embraced an understanding of love that means it cannot coerce or control, but only enrich and lead. I had observed that God intervenes in historical and personal contexts far less often than people liked to imagine. It is not so much that God is working in the moment in precision, control and competence but that He is working in individuals with love, grace and revelation. Those two constructs are not mutually exclusive, but there are often times they don't sit well together. That does not mean He doesn't work in circumstances; the Bible reflects that He does. However, God's usual response is to change people not circumstances.

I began to see that evolutionary theory actually did more to re-inforce a God who is interactive with his creation than one that had the creator plop finished products into existence. In the end, the idea that I can look into space and see starlight from millions of years away potently suggested to me that God was in this for the long haul. The response from literal creationists that God placed that light already along its journey just seemed wildly inadequate. My faith works better when I embrace evolu-tion. It was about that time that I came across the influential writings of one of the foremost Christian thinkers in the area, John Polkinghorne. Polkinghorne addresses the debate between theology and science when he suggests: "Of course the first thing to say about that discourse [theo-logical expressions on creation] is that theology is concerned with onto-logical origin and not with temporal being."[1]

Allow me the privilege of offering two ideas that reinforce this for me and then one problem I am still working on for my own satisfac-tion. A significant struggle I have had in adopting an evolutionary view is the seeming disconnect between evolution and the idea of God's involve-ment. Evolution does require random, unplanned, unmanaged steps in order to be legitimate. Theistic evolution, the idea that God is overseeing the process of evolution as his creative vehicle, struggles to adequately reflect on the conflict, apparent in the notion that God can both manage and not manage at the same time. In an article in the journal *First Things* in 2007, Avery Dulles articulates a construct known as teleological evo-lution in which he suggests the "dynamic presence of God" is infused in His creation. He suggests that within creation there is a thrusting for-ward through each stage of development according to the purpose for which it was designed. Thus God's presence is in creation, empowering the evolutionary process, and all of creation is moving toward its ultimate "teleos."[2] I love that idea. It seems completely consistent with the thrust of the Genesis narrative. No position that suggests there is no creator can be adequate. Nor can we accept an idea that has God removed from His creation. These are legitimate concerns when one is considering how evo-lution and faith interplay. Yet, the idea that the presence or identity of God is intimately and continually connected to His creation leaves one with a continuing sense of wonder.

A second idea that is illuminating for me comes from the observation that culture began to identifiably emerge around 50,000 years ago. In order for culture to exist, language is a prerequisite. The human brain achieved its current size, and therefore presumably capacities, around 200,000 years ago. However, the first signs of identifiable language do not come about until around 50,000-70,000 years ago. Klein and Edgar in their book *The Dawn of Culture*, note that around 50,000 years ago, a transition, within humanity, of considerable significance took place. "In its wake, humanity was transformed from a relatively rare and insignificant large mammal to something like a geologic force."[3] They go on to note that this change was an organizational change within the brain, and a mutation of perhaps one single gene was responsible. Is it possible that, in one of the few moments where God stepped into His creation, and I certainly allow Him that capacity (big of me I know), God moved humanity to the center of his creation and focus? He did it by engineering a genetic mutation that allowed speech, and then culture, and then revelation. Conjecture, for sure, but I find it fascinating. Here we can potentially see the story of Adam and Eve having a foundation.

I have noted across the years, and here I reflect on a problem needing to be addressed within evolutionary theory. The single most identifiable reflection of broken relationship with God is the human's species-wide struggle with shame. We sin because we want to respond in our own efforts to our feelings of shame, at least that is one way of looking at the human struggle. We do have a leaning toward sin, and it is universal. The simple story of Adam and Eve explains why that is species-wide and hints toward Christ as the adequate response. Evolutionary theory has yet to adequately reflect on the reasons behind broken relationship with God as a human condition in the way that a simple story about a garden and an original couple do. That doesn't to me suggest there isn't one, but more work needs to be done.

Faith in a God of grace and love is not in any way at odds with a God that is identifiable as acting consistently with the laws of the universe, which humanity is getting better and better at revealing and understanding. Our mission as the church is enhanced when we can present, to an educated world, a faith that does not require an intellectual disengagement from the world of science. Sin, and the separation from God it brings, is gulf enough between the world and the community of faith, there is no need to allow another, far less legitimate gulf to exist. In truth it does not even require those that hold to a view of creation couched in six 24 hour periods some six thousand years ago to adopt an alternative view. It simply requires the willingness to accept that such a view is not inconsistent with faith and present it as an option in a way that might remove it as a barrier for those coming to faith.

ENDNOTES AND SUGGESTED READING

1 John Polkinghorne, *Science & Christian Belief* (London: The Society for Promoting Christian Knowledge, 1994).

2 A.C. Dulles "God and evolution," *First Things*, http://www.firstthings.com/issue/2007/10/october, 19-24.

3 R. G. Klein & B. Edgar *The Dawn of Human Culture* (New York: John Wiley and Sons, 2002) 24.

48

A REFLECTION ON
THE CHURCH AND EVOLUTION

Stephen L. Borger

Stephen L. Borger is District Superintendent for the Intermountain District Church of the Nazarene.

This is a very personal story; it is my story. One of the reasons I agreed to join in this conversation was that I do believe we all grow and learn as we hear other's stories. Although no other person has a story just like mine there are some very common threads that can connect us in conversations like this. It is my hope that what is common to us will overcome the differences that so often divide.

I truly do not remember whether I was ever taught or personally believed what would be referred to as a "young earth six day creationist" belief. I do know that I grew up in a very conservative and legalistic Iowa Nazarene parsonage. There were some things that were a very big deal but I don't think creation versus evolution was a major issue in my home or in the church. I attended public schools and took high school biology class as well as other science classes. I do not recall any great moments of confusion or conflict. I do not recall any conversations with my parents where they warned me about the dangers of those "unbelieving public school teachers." The only situation that comes to mind at all is when I was a junior in high school my dad told me my Sunday School teacher (who happened to be a public high school teacher) had complained that the pastor's son (me) was disrupting the Sunday School class with too many questions. I really don't recall but I think perhaps I was asking some fairly difficult questions in regards to science, theology, philosophy and the Bible. I did honor my dad's request that I stop asking questions but I've not outgrown the desire to ask "why." I also think it was that kind of experience that formed in me a desire to answer any and every question as fully as I was able.

The next encounter I recall with the subject of creation/evolution came as a student at Olivet Nazarene College. I was a business major and needed to choose a five hour science class. I did not want to take biology or chemistry so I chose geology. I loved that class. Dr. Max Reams made the subject come alive. As I think back on that experience what I recall is not only a professor who made the subject matter so interesting but I observed his life and journey as well. Dr. Reams projected a life of vital faith and he was also an outstanding churchman. It was absolutely fascinating to me to study the formation of our home called earth. I would never again stand at the rim of the Grand Canyon or drive through the deserts of the West without marveling at the layers and formations and the story they tell. I truly do not recall the issue of evolution versus creation ever coming up. I think it was just assumed that "God created" and science is discovering some incredible things about this creation.

The next event that I can recall on this topic was as a student at Nazarene Theological Seminary in the mid 70s. I was in a Missions class taught by a long time missionary. He enjoyed telling how the Koreans would laugh about their lack of thick facial and body hair and the American's thick beards and hairy chests and remind the missionary that "they were further along on the evolutionary ladder." We laughed and I do not recall anyone challenging the professor on his personal belief about evolution. It did not seem to be a big deal, but I believe we could have discussed the topic with honest inquiry if it had seemed to be a pressing issue.

As a parent I don't recall that this topic was that difficult or controversial. I do recall when our children were grade school age we took a family trip to Disney World. The day we went to Epcot Center I spent a lot of the day adding commentary in the tour exhibits that brazenly describe exactly how everything had happened 200,000 to a million years ago. I would remind my kids that much of what was being said was a theory, a statement of faith. There was scientific evidence for some of what was being declared but much of it was a matter of "belief." As a parent it was important but it did not seem to be a big deal, and perhaps I had a confidence my children were already developing a sense of balance between faith and science. During that time I was pastor of a church in Colorado Springs. As I think back it is rather astounding to me that in a city with 50 plus "para-church" organizations the subject of creation/evolution was never a matter of conflict or concern in our church.

When I moved to Nampa, Idaho in 1995 to pastor Nampa First Nazarene this topic was a big deal. I found out there were sides being drawn up even within our church. In August 1995 I preached a message at Nampa First with the title "Creation versus Evolution." I started with the statement: "The lines have been drawn! On one side stand those who have given their life to pursue the study of science. On the other side stands the church....You probably already know which side you are on. Or do you?" I went on to tell them I was not talking about the creation versus evolution debate but the debate between the church and Copernicus in the 16th century. Then I asked, "Now which side are you on?" In the message I tried to speak a balanced approach to the topic. I ended by asking them not to draw up sides on such an issue within the church family and that scripture and science both had much to teach us. At the conclusion of the message I finally answered the question many had come that Sunday specifically to hear. I concluded, "Here is where I stand, Genesis 1:1 'In the beginning God created the heavens and the earth.' I am ready to engage in the questions brought by both science and faith but I will not head down a path that assumes a Godless evolution. That position does not respect the authority of the Bible nor does it honor the historic creeds of the church."

As District Superintendent I recently spent time talking with a church board on this very issue. I listened to the concerns and the positional arguments. There were a couple of board members who had been influenced by some who declare, "If you do not believe and interpret the first eleven chapters of Genesis the way we interpret it you can't be a Christian." I am still amazed and saddened that anyone would make such a statement. After listening to how important a "creationism" belief had been for one member I suggested that we should be encouraged by what was happening. I said, "Here we are a DS and members of a church board, and you (speaking specifically to the one who had been most vocal) and the DS have a different way of understanding the first few chapters of Genesis but we are a part of a church that says 'that is okay.' I respect your view and belief and I'm glad you are part of the church. I assume you respect me and my view.....you do respect my view don't you?" I think he did.

There was another occasion when a church member called me to ask "what the DS believed about this issue." I did listen for a time to the arguments of why the Church of the Nazarene and the educational institutions had lost their moorings all the while trying to help provide a balanced view. After criticizing the viewpoints of many within the church the caller finally asked the pressing question; "So, what do you believe?" My response was that I did read the first eleven chapters of Genesis literally. There was a huge "well, okay" from the caller. After he had begun again to attack my church and university I told him that perhaps there was a misunderstanding. I told him that indeed I read the first eleven chapters of Genesis literally, but I did not interpret every word in the way that he insisted on interpreting them and from the particular English translation that he insisted upon. The response was, "Well, that's what I thought," and he hung up the phone.

It seems to me that this issue is only a "big deal" if we can't talk to each other with civility or if we draw up sides to divide the church. Within the church one should not be condemned for seeking knowledge and understanding nor should anyone be ridiculed for faith and belief. Within the living-in-community-people called the church it is not helpful for anyone who has given their life to the pursuit of science to ridicule another's position or belief by suggesting they are "silly," "unsophisticated" or "uneducated." It is also not helpful for one who has come to a firm "belief" position to accuse someone else of not believing in God or of not respecting the authority of Scripture just because that person understands how God has been at work in ways that differ from the other person's point of view.

In twenty-five years as a local church pastor and eleven years as district superintendent I have encountered many different opinions on many different subjects. My desire has always been to encourage the church family to carefully listen to one another, ask clarifying questions if uncertain and respond with respect for one another. As the Apostle Paul reminded the early church many times, "let's be kind to each other." As one who has felt the responsibility to shepherd people with diverse life experiences and opinions I have appreciated the wisdom of the early leaders in the Church of the Nazarene. The Articles of Faith express clearly what we hold as our foundational doctrines and yet there is room to allow for differing opinions without exclusion or division. I trust we will always be able to keep that careful balance between intellectual honesty and doctrinal conviction.

I am thankful for those who have influenced me through the years to seek intellectual honesty while holding to my theological beliefs. As a student at NTS I had the privilege of hearing the preaching of Paul S. Rees in a week-long series. I still remember a statement he made in that kind and yet powerful way that shocked me a bit at the time but I've never forgotten. He was speaking about a particular doctrinal belief and confessed his own theological blind spots. And then he leaned out over the pulpit and said with such grace, "We all have them you know." I am always saddened by those who would divide the church over something that just might be a "blind spot" in their own thinking. I want to be a part of a church that holds firmly to the historic Christian faith and yet allows and encourages the pursuit of knowledge and understanding. To paraphrase Charles Wesley, may "knowledge and vital piety" always be united in our church.

49

ERNESTO AND EVOLUTION

Steve Rodeheaver

Steve Rodeheaver is Pastor of Southeast Church of the Nazarene in San Diego, California.

Ernesto came home from tenth grade Biology fuming at being taught that he had come from an ape, that he was nothing more than a randomly developed beast! The textbook and the teacher both told Ernesto that he had come from an animal and that he was an animal. This was about the last thing Ernesto needed to hear. It reinforced the lie that he was an unwanted, rabid dog.

Ernesto was the oldest son in a blended family. When his parents split, his dad and his dad's family wanted nothing to do with him. His mom remarried and had another son and two daughters. One day Ernesto made the gruesome discovery that his step-dad had committed suicide. Ernesto was the one who found him, the one who had to call for help, the one who had to tell the rest of the family the gory details. Ernesto's mom went into a relapse, returning to street drugs in her grief. Soon the family was not only fatherless but homeless. Ernesto's mom made her way on the streets in the gang and drug culture. His younger siblings went to stay with their deceased father's sister. But no one wanted Ernesto. He was too wild – too much trouble and bad news. Ernesto was an animal.

Ernesto's family wasn't alone in seeing him as a wild animal. Societal expectations for Ernesto labeled him as one who would never graduate from high school, never be educated nor disciplined enough to hold a job; he would father multiple children with multiple women, and he would eventually be taken off the street and locked up, assuming he didn't do something to get himself run-over first. Ernesto and his friends had bought this expectation, greeting each other, "What's up, Dawg?" and referring to females as "bitches." This animalistic perception of their existence was in all of their music and art. The street logic went this way: since you're an animal, be a beast!

So why was Ernesto so upset that his teacher and his textbook were simply reinforcing a vision of his "humanity" that he was already embracing? Ernesto had started coming to church about the time his family exploded. He was among a people who knew he was created in the image of God and treated him as such. When it was learned that Ernesto had no place to go, a family in the church took him in. Ernesto was beginning to realize, perhaps for the first time, that he wasn't a wild animal and that his existence wasn't an accident. He was discovering that God created him, on purpose, and in God's own image. This love and this news started Ernesto questioning what he believed about himself and about how he was living. He was beginning to take on a new vision of himself, one in which he was created higher than the beasts. And then came along tenth grade biology with its "descended from apes" message. Every fiber of truth in Ernesto's newfound identity shouted "No! He was not an animal! He was not an accident! He was not going to be reduced and squeezed into living an animal life!"

Ernesto's teacher and textbook gave him one option: Godless evolution. (I capitalize "Godless" because this textbook understanding of creation lacks the person/being of God. Godless evolution is not godless; it has idolatrous gods in the place of God.) In Ernesto, I saw that Godless evolution is just plain deadly. However, it is not deadly because it is evolution; it is deadly because it is Godless.

Who says that Godless evolution is the only option, let alone the right option? Evolution does not require a Godless view of creation, any more than antibiotics demands a Godless view of healing. If God created and attends (perhaps better, superintends) to the processes by which antibiotics bring about health, then God could have just as easily created and attended to and superintended the processes by which evolution brings about forms of life, including human life created in the image of God. (I use this "creating, attending, superintending" language to guard against a deistic perspective, in which God creates and steps aside, leaving creation to develop and run on its own, only to jump into the world every so often to do something new. Neither penicillin nor evolution works apart from the engaged presence of God.)

How might God work in and through evolution to bring about the creation of humanity in God's image? How might God create from an ape a human in God's own image? I don't know that God did or did not create us from apes, or whether we share a common ancestor with apes, but it's interesting how that is kind of a disturbing question. We don't want to come from apes or amoebas. Yet we aren't too troubled about being made from dirt, presumably the same planet earth dirt that God used in creating all the animals, even apes. And lest we take too much pride in being made "living beings" by God breathing God's breath into our nostrils, it should be noted that the other creatures are referred to likewise as "living beings," presumably also receiving the breath of God else they remain clay. So Genesis 2 portrays humanity as distinct from, yet very akin to, the rest of creation in general and the animals in particular. This, of course, follows the Genesis 1 witness that we are created in the image of God.

So again, if perhaps God did in God's wisdom create us from ancestral apes, how might God move from the animal apes to humans created in the image of God? Honestly, I don't know. But it helps me to think of it in this manner: what is the process, the journey, by which God's image is restored in me? How do I go from being a sinner condemned to death to being born again, a child of God, a new creation? God takes a life in which his image is distorted and corrupted, and through Christ and the work of the Spirit, creates a new, redeemed life in which His image is restored and becoming more so. Before my conversion I was a creature of God but not a child of God. Yet the Holy Spirit was active upon my life, hovering over my life, sustaining, convicting, convincing, and drawing me unto Christ. I was brought to a conversion crisis, a baptismal moment, in which I became a child of God and now I live a new life. I tend to think of this new life as a life of grace and holiness versus the old life of sin and destruction. When I think from Ernesto's perspective, the old life is an animalistic, beastly life and the new life is a human life, an image of God life. Here's my point. If God the Father, through the work of God the Son and God the Holy Spirit, can bring about a holy life from a sinful life, a human life from a beastly life, an image of God life from a profane life, then might also God the Father through God the Son and God the Holy Spirit bring about a new species in God's image from that which was alive but not in God's image? Might there be a conversion moment, so to speak, when God creates, from the apes, humanity in God's own image?

Clearly, I don't know how God created us in God's own image, nor how God created the rest of creation, other than speaking it into being (and occasionally using His hands in Genesis 2). And just as clear, I am not a student of evolution to where I could teach it or adequately explain it. Yet I think I am clear on this: there is nothing in Scripture, including Genesis 1 and 2, that would preclude the possibility of God creating and working in and through the processes of evolution. What is precluded is Godless evolution, the brand of evolution that Ernesto was being taught, the brand that left him, intentionally or unintentionally, as a rabid dog.

Ernesto is why I write. Yes, I am concerned about those who turn away from God and reject Christianity because they are convinced of the scientific truth of evolution and the only evolution brand they know is Godless evolution. But I am even more concerned for the countless Ernesto's of the world; kids (and adults) who aren't all that concerned with grasping the scientific explanation of how we came to be, but nonetheless become caught by the "this is who we are" answers of Godless evolution. Godless evolution has permeated our cultural air. Breathing it leaves us less than human, mere animals trying to be top dog as we hopelessly fight to postpone death and extinction.

From my Ernesto vantage point, the fight is not so much against evolution as it is against Godlessness. If we quit fighting so much against and about evolution, but start contending for the God who certainly has the tool of evolution at God's own disposal, then a victory can be scored against Godlessness. And Ernesto, and the rest of us, can be possessed by God's "this is who we are" answer for us. We are created by God in the image of God to bear God's image to the rest of creation.

50

DON'T GET SIDETRACKED

Kyle Borger

Kyle Borger is Associate Pastor at Cody Church of the Nazarene.

A few days ago, my son and I had one of those spur of the moment talks that really excites a father. My son had questions about the Bible and was interested in actually listening to what I had to say about it. My son is now a teenager, so the fact that he was willing to listen was cause for a celebration!

I no longer remember his exact question, but it did lead us into a discussion regarding the Bible and a few things that he didn't understand. One area of discussion centered on Genesis 4. If Adam and Eve are the only people that God created, then who is out there that could kill Cain? Who does Cain marry? Can there be a land of Nod if there are no people living there?

The discussion caused us to wonder if the Bible simply doesn't list all of the children that Adam and Eve produced. Perhaps a longer period of time had eclipsed. However, our speculation seemed empty and dangerous. The only appropriate solution was to go back to the passage and ask what God wanted us to understand through Scripture.

In reviewing the passage, it was clear that God was not interested in giving the specific details that made the story possible. Instead, God wanted us to see and understand the dynamics at work within the family. In this small portion of Scripture, we witness birth, jealously, and anger;

we witness fear and feelings of inadequacy; we experience consequences and redemption.

As my son and I discussed the passage, it became clear that I had a choice to make. I could teach my son what I had been taught, which would be safe in many churches, or I could challenge my son to explore *who* God is and *how* God interacts with us. I felt it was important for my son to believe in God based on who God is in his life and who God has been in the lives of those before him, rather than believing in God based on whether the Bible accurately speaks scientifically. Is it important that God created in 6 days or 600 billion years? Perhaps it is more important to understand that God created and why God created. Is it important that Adam and Eve were the first and only humans created by God or is it more important to understand the relationship God had with his creation at that time?

There are a lot of things about this world that I don't understand. There are a lot of things about God that I don't understand. I am not sold on everything that is embraced within biological evolution, but I no longer see evolution as a threat to God. If evolution is correct, it will never lessen the fact that God exists, that God loves me, and that God desires to live in relationship with me.

I know there are some whose belief in God will be shaken if some part of the Bible is found to not be 100% accurate. I used to be one of those people. I gave speeches and I wrote reports in school fighting what I was being taught. I suggested that the world was too complex to have randomly fallen into place. I still believe that. The Big Bang Theory suggests that there was nothing and then there was something, and this something continues to expand creating everything we know. There is evidence that suggests some things become other things and that some events impact other events. However, it certainly takes a lot of faith to suggest that something came out of an unknown nothing. Where some scientists attempt to suggest that this means there is no God, I see proof or evidence that there could be nothing less than God. I can't explain how something came from nothing. I can't explain what there was before there was something. I don't know where God came from. I can't fathom how God exists or how

God can love and communicate with all of His creation, and yet He does. God exists whether man says He does or not.

I imagine God knows He needs to keep it simple because I wouldn't understand. I think God revealed the creation story and the rest of the Bible the way He did so that I wouldn't get sidetracked with the details and would instead focus on the main message. We are created in God's image. God is love. We are to love God and love others and not focus too much on ourselves. We are who we were created to be when we love others as Jesus loved us. As a church, we may ponder, wonder, and dream about how God created. We may have healthy debate and wonder some more. In the end, we must, as brothers and sisters in Christ, love as Jesus loved us.

51

BEGINNING TO LISTEN:
CREATING LOVING CONGREGATIONS

Bethany Hull Somers

Bethany Hull Somers serves as Chaplain at Skagit Valley Hospital.

In the beginning I was a Nazarene. And although according to statistics, people my age are unlikely to continue to be a part of the church, I am still a Nazarene. I believe that it has something to do with the way the community of faith that formed me dealt with my doubts and questions.

Not only am I a Nazarene, but I am a purebred Nazarene – third generation on both my mother's and my father's side. I have attended church since before I was born. I have been a Nazarene since before it was ok to wear pants to Sunday morning church (women that is, for the record, men could always wear pants to Sunday morning church).

As a child, I was entrenched in church culture. I attended a private Christian school and went to services at least three times a week. I remember feeling very nervous as a kindergartener about being on a youth soccer team with non-Christians (the mythical beings that I had heard so much about and yet never met).

One Sunday, after my preschool Sunday school teacher told me that anyone who was not a professing Christian was going to hell, my mother found me squatting in front of my cat, Fluffy. My Sunday dress brushed on the dirty ground of the garage, while my tiny children's Bible that I couldn't read yet was propped open to who knows what book in front of my cat's face. When my mother asked what I was doing, I told her that I really wanted Fluffy in heaven with me, and according to my understanding of my Sunday school teacher, this was the only way. My mom resisted the urge to laugh and assured me that Fluffy would be there, but I was suspicious of her cavalier attitude and held the Good Book in front of Fluffy for a few more minutes for good measure.

In addition to the hours spent in the pews, fearing my soccer coach (who did not attend church but miraculously was a really nice man) and evangelizing to my overweight tabby cat, I also remember what it felt like to have my "Christian bubble" burst. In junior high, I went to public school and realized that some of the things I was taught from the time I was a child were not universally held beliefs and, in fact, were believed by some to be untrue. It was confusing to be told by teachers and students that the story of Creation was a theory at best and at worst a fanciful myth to add to the countless other creation stories from cultures and religions across the globe.

Even stranger to my naïve understanding was that my science teachers were well-rounded, well-educated, kind people who were not the evil worldly anti-God folks that I assumed non-believers would be. This made the oblique answers I got from Sunday school teachers about the science teachers and textbooks being flagrantly "wrong" not set well. Equally unthinkable in my mind and heart was to let go the conviction that the creation of the heaven and earth started with God ordering the chaos. This dichotomy – created by the church– was and is frustrating to me and many.

But this dichotomy does not have to exist. The theory of evolution does not preclude God, and the Creation story found in Genesis does not preclude evolution. Both hold space for the other to a person with confident faith in a God who can do whatever God wants, however God wants. If this makes you uncomfortable, pray. The urge to first debate or draw lines in the sand will not bring anything akin to the fruits of the Spirit. And it will not help us in our evangelism to our children and neighbor. We, as Christians, must learn to first pray and love, and then discuss and debate. For us, Evolution and Creation is only the beginning

– literally and figuratively.

The debate over Creation – whether the world was produced in six 24 hour days or through a slow process over the millennia – is only part of the puzzle. It is an important conversation but only one patch in a quilt that encompasses many theological questions and differences. How we respond to this question sets the tone for many other conversations, which will lead to either larger possibilities for evangelism and understanding or closed doors on possible faith connections.

One of my professors at Divinity School, Dr. Stanley Hauerwas, would often say that one of the biggest jobs of the church is to evangelize to our children. He posits that there are no grandchildren in the family of God – only children. Therefore, we must live and worship in such a way that our children are drawn to the faith, for being a third or fourth generation Christian does not guarantee faith.

Indeed, I am 35, and many of my contemporaries and those younger than we are have fled the traditional church. According to a study by the Barna group, among the top six reasons young people leave church are the church's antagonistic approach to science and the perception that the church is unfriendly to doubters.

When I have looked at these studies and the experiences of many of my peers, I am forced to look at how my experience was different. Although I had the same questions and concerns as many other evangelical young people about the inerrancy of Scripture and the dissonance between what we were taught in Sunday school and what we are taught in the secular classroom, I stayed. Not only did I stay, but I pursued ordination in this church and have served it as faithfully as I know how for the last thirteen years.

I believe that the local church, for me, made all the difference.

As a young person, I had an amazing pastoral staff who were unafraid of questions and helped me and my peers in the church explore not only the ideas of evolution but also other theological and social questions.

I was part of a Nazarene church that supported its young people without question – loving us and welcoming us regardless of what strange color our hair was, where our newest piercing was or who got caught drinking wine coolers and smoking cigarettes at the last youth retreat - let alone whether we had written an A+ essay on Darwinism in honors Biology. Their love and openness allowed me to find a place in the confusion and know that God is bigger than debates and differences.

I cannot emphasize enough how much the unconditional love of the community of faith formed my theology. Rigidness excludes, love includes. Fear is closed; Love has It's hands nailed open. Because the law of love ruled over my faith formation, I was given space in my mind, heart and faith to prayerfully ask hard questions and contend with difficult – sometimes uncertain –answers.

As a pastor and chaplain, I hear people's doubts and fears all the time. Doubts, confusion and pain are perhaps what makes us most alike, and yet, in the context of the church community we try and hide these things. Doubt is the beginning of deep faith because it establishes a faith that is not based on whether or not we receive what we want or whether we can explain perfectly every mystery. Doubt and questions allow us to approach God and faith in a way that will survive our darkest days and allow us to move from the valley of the shadow of death to streams of living water without our faith being shaken or obliterated.

The future of the church is at an impasse. If we are going to move forward and create a habitable space for our young to return, we must allow God's powerful Love and our own vulnerability to shape our future.

Regardless of our personal convictions about Creation, our demeanor and spirit matter more. For me, all that matters is that God did it and it is GOOD. If it is important for you to take a strong stand on one side or the other, great. But do so in the purifying love of Christ.

Let us, as a church, be willing to house folks with differing ideas on Scripture (and politics, science, lifestyle, etc) who can worship together, serve together, weep together, and rejoice together. And – above all –

let us be willing to bring the Kingdom of God generation after generation.

May the God who formed order from the chaos calm the chaos of our hearts and churches so that we may exhibit God's power and Love. *Glory to the Father, and to the Son, and to the Holy Spirit: as it was in the beginning, is now, and will be for ever. World without end, Amen.*

52

OUT OF THE DRAGON'S GRAVE:
LESSONS IN FAITH & FORGIVENESS

Jeremy Scott

Jeremy Scott serves as Pastor of North Street Community Church of the Nazarene in Hingham, MA.

They called it the "Dragons' Grave."

It seemed somewhat childish at first, even to a young 14-year-old. Even I knew that dragons were not real and dinosaurs were. If this excavation site was to have any kind of respectable validity, giving the exhumed ones the moniker of "dragon" seemed rather silly. However, after spending over a week at a dinosaur excavation site that was owned, overseen, and operated by 7-day creationists, my mind was as malleable as untouched Play-Doh.

Dragons?

You betcha. Even the fire-breathing ones.

I was a believer.

My memories of that week in the-middle-of-nowhere Wyoming are actually quite fond. Even when I think about the mind-bits that I swallowed, I have little but warm thoughts for the kind and gentle people I met from all over the United States and Canada. I don't remember the names of the individuals or organizations involved, but I do remember the loving fellowship we shared around early morning breakfasts (I made the omelets) before heading out for hours at a time to dig, poke, and brush for dinosaurs, or really, their remains. Even so, I think that some people were silently hoping for a real life 8,000 year-old one, which would once-and-for all settle the matter of the earth's age.

Each night after a hard day's work, I heard talks that informed me of the importance of literal creationism. This included ideas such as the coexistence of humanity and dinosaurs (they had a fossil of a human footprint in a dinosaur footprint from Texas to prove it!); a theory about the half-life of the magnetic field surrounding the earth, proving that it could not be anymore than 10,000 years old; and of course, fire-breathing "dragons" (after all, if we have beetles that blow up and bugs that light up, why can't we have dinosaurs that fire up? The fairy tales are true!). So while I may have unlearned much of the information garnered that week, I haven't forgotten it.

These things might seem silly now, but they seemed rather plausible then. I've since learned and am still learning that faith is hardly about a search for plausibility. Certainty might inform faith, but they cannot encompass one another. Otherwise, faith has lost its definition. Reasonable experience has its place (and an important one), but it cannot be my only foundation for faith. It is not God. It has failed me before, like that summer when I was 14 and came home sure that the world was some 10,000 years old because of the reasonable (to me) experience I had in Wyoming.

Like a computer, reason tends to lend itself to boiling down things into one of two options: Yes or no. Either/or. Zero or one. But other areas of my experience have led me to struggle with these black & white dichotomies. Even singularly-lined spectrums can fall far short of truly painting a decent picture of a given situation. Riding a swinging pendulum only tends to take one from one extreme to another.

So for instance, definitively saying, "Genesis has nothing to do with science" is as difficult as saying, "The earth was created in seven 24-hour days." Living in this either-or tension will only take us so far in life together until we determine that we must part ways because one end cannot jive with the other. Yet compromise so often only ends up weakening the strengths of the extremes. Maybe there's another way?

Perhaps we can look for our overlaps. The origin of the universe as we know it (created or not) predates science. And if science is the organization of observable data, then Genesis 1-2 might even speak to the idea of science without offering facts, figures, and timetables.

I believe that it was my father who first specifically pointed out Genesis 2:19 to me. We were discussing notions of open theism at the time when he reminded me of this passage:

> *"Now out of the ground the Lord God had formed every beast of the field and every bird of the heavens and brought them to the man **to see what he would call them**. And whatever the man called every living creature, that was its name." (Genesis 2:19 NRSV, added emphasis)*

The picture the writer(s) presents here is beautiful. As a father and co-creator myself, I like to think that I can understand how God felt in setting free this new creature:

"I wonder what she'll think about this one with the long trunk..."
"Hey watch what happens when I put this one with eight legs in front of him."
"Oooh...I forgot about these glow-in-the-dark ones...they're gonna love these."

In this narrative, we see a picture of humanity's classification of what is around them and the Divine's observation of the process. Genesis 2:19 is actually still in effect in that humanity continues to discover, classify, and name. I wonder what God's observation is like when watching the scientific process today?

While we might point to the multi-revolutions of the last several centuries as the birth of modern science, I propose that humans have been collecting, observing, and classifying data from the very beginning. And using our reasonable (to us) experience, we've made conclusions all along. Of course, the conclusions of our ancestors a few thousand years ago seem quite unscientific by modern standards, but I believe we can reject the notion that if one fact from a given source is incorrect, then the source itself is incorrect. We have indeed learned a lot as humans. However, what we haven't seemed to learn is to temper our desire to be eternally certain of our conclusions at the expense of relationship with others.

When I came home from Wyoming at age 14 with certainty sealed, I excitedly informed my parents of all that I had learned, happy to make them proud of my emboldened Christian faith. I came home with new books, a piece of a fossilized dinosaur bone, and a certainty sure to convict any who met me. But I didn't get very far before I saw that my convictions were not foolproof. The very first person I saw was less than receptive. The manner in which my mother spoke these words has never left me. She said cautiously, graciously, and without dismissal, "Jeremy, not all Christians believe those things."

In that moment, I think that I ran to my room to pray for her salvation, but as almost always with my parents, the passing of time revealed the sageness of her gentle warning.

And so my limited experience in discussions of science and theology has caused me to learn more about the things of grace and forgiveness than anything else. My mother wasn't the only one to receive the brutality of my certainty.

My freshman year of high school began the very day after I got home to New Hampshire from Wyoming, and with it came Mrs. Sawburn's honors biology class. That poor lady mostly smiled patiently through all of my dogmatic "proving" and "pointing out" to her all year long. She even accepted my offer of reading a couple of the books I came back with. But the only convincing I did of her mind was that there actually were people like me out there.

When I returned to my high school five years later to apologize, convicted that my treatment of her reflected poorly on my Lord, she smiled awkwardly and yet accepted my apology.

If we could all be so patiently gracious as my mother and as forgiving as Mrs. Sawburn, maybe we could get back to what science and theology are meant to do in their different and yet not unrelated functions.

53

MY EVOLUTIONARY WAR

Wilson Deaton

Wilson Deaton is Pastor at Kenosha Family Church--A Church of the Nazarene in Kenosha, WI.

As I write this I am anticipating Independence Day celebrations just a few days away. They're part of an annual ritual Americans observe to celebrate the freedoms won by the Revolutionary War. I find it very convenient that *revolutionary* rhymes with *evolutionary*. Because I experienced a personal war over evolution and found a sense of freedom as a result, I find the aforementioned rhyme irresistible. Thus I invite you to consider this particular aspect of my Christian testimony which I have titled, "My Evolutionary War."

There are many strands of influence twisted into this particular thread that contributes to the tapestry which is my life, but I choose to begin this story with the memory of going with my dad to a neighboring town to visit a Christian bookstore. Though a boy only recently arrived at a double-digit age, I was enthralled by a store that was devoted to products that were explicitly Christian--things like a ruler with the books of the Bible printed on the back. How cool is that? I also noticed a display rack of "evangelistic" tracts. I was especially drawn to one with a sketch of an ape's head next to the title, "Big Daddy?" (I'm not asking a question; the question mark was part of the title!)

I was only in fifth grade, but my science classes were beginning to part ways with my Sunday School classes. "Big Daddy?" was just what I needed (I thought). It was the story of a college student who stood up to his professor on the subject of evolution. The professor berated him, but he held his ground and methodically destroyed the professor's arrogant position. I had a new hero! I wanted to be just like that college student– a smart, bold, militant, defender of the Biblical faith. My *evolutionary war* had begun. I proudly argued with my fifth grade science teacher using the "facts" I had learned from the tract. Admittedly, the battle didn't go as well for me as it had for my hero, but I was neither humiliated nor discouraged. On the contrary, I was proud of myself for taking a stand.

However, something happened. Over the next few years I discovered I had been misled by that little evangelistic tract. I was slowly learning that evolutionary science was not a collapsing house of cards as the tract portrayed. The proud-of-myself feeling soon dissipated. In its place was a very uncomfortable tension. I was still fighting an *Evolutionary War*, but I was no longer fighting my science teachers. The war was now internal. On the one hand, I absolutely and wholeheartedly believed that the Bible was the Word of God and that it was true. On the other hand, I was observing the evidence and concluding that evolution was true. I found myself wanting to accept what I thought to be mutually exclusive positions. I wanted to believe that we humans were God's creation AND that we were the result of a long evolutionary process.

My faith demanded the former; my mind was campaigning for the latter. Having a strong faith foundation and a strong Christian support system, I responded by repressing what my mind was saying. I lived with the kind of faith described by Mark Twain as, "…believing what you know ain't so."

It was an uncomfortable and distressing way to live. I was supposed to love the Lord my God with all my heart and with all my soul and with all my strength and with all my mind. Couldn't I leave my mind out of it? Wouldn't three out of four be OK? If I tried hard enough couldn't I make myself believe that which, at some level, I knew I didn't believe? How long could I live with this distressing tension? Who will deliver me from this evolutionary war? Thanks be to God, the cavalry was on its way. It came in the form of more education.

I learned something at a Nazarene college that I had not learned at Sunday School. (Perhaps it had been taught, but I definitely had not learned it!) I learned that believing the Bible is God's Word didn't mean the Bible had to be interpreted literally. In fact, I learned that interpreting the entire Bible literally was to do a disservice to the Bible and ignore its purpose. That lesson was very recently expounded and restated in "The Report of the Scripture Study Committee to the 28th General Assembly of the Church of the Nazarene." Consider this key excerpt from that report:

> "... Article IV [of the Church of the Nazarene's Articles of Faith] makes clear the purpose of Holy Scripture: that it reveals the will of God '...in all things necessary to our salvation...' John Wesley was very clear that the purpose of being a person 'of one book' was to find 'the way to heaven.' The Bible is not to be treated as ... a text book of history or science. Its truth is expressed in the thought forms of the ancient world, in their culture, context, geography, cosmology, and language."

That means Genesis 1 and 2 weren't written the same way my science text book was written. That means Genesis 1 and 2 shouldn't be read the same way my science text book is read.

My own *Evolutionary War* was over. I had the freedom to love the Lord my God even with my mind--even with my mind fully engaged. I could now comfortably adhere to what I had earlier thought was mutually exclusive ideas--evolution AND God as Creator.

I remain concerned for others who may be fighting, or someday may fight, their own internal *Evolutionary War*. Might a perceived incompatibility between evolution and creation by God cause some to try to live with the distressing and uncomfortable tension of trying to believe "what they know ain't so"? Might it contribute to some deciding to walk away from the Christian Faith? Might it contribute to some failing to ever embrace the Christian Faith in the first place?

Fortunately, I think there is a straightforward solution: Let's stop perpetuating an environment in which it might be assumed that being a Bible-believing Christian is incompatible with accepting science.

54

MENDING WALL:

GOOD FENCES MAKE GOOD CHURCHES

Jeremy Hugus

Jeremy Hugus is a civil and criminal litigation attorney in Casper, WY with the law firm Murane & Bostwick and an adjunct professor of bioethics and health policy at Regis University in Denver, Colorado.

WHO AM I?

A lawyer, a Nazarene pastor and an evolutionary scientist walk into a bar, and the bartender says, "What is this, a joke?" The scenario sounds like a joke, but for me it is far more reality than joke. I am an attorney who married a Nazarene pastor (I am even a church pianist like a good Nazarene pastor's spouse should be). And although on paper my wife Libby and I may seem better suited for a "…walk into a bar" joke than an actual couple, day-to-day life in partnership with her is as real and as life-giving as anything I have ever known. But I am not a Nazarene simply because I married one. I myself went to a Nazarene church as a preschooler, I attended a Nazarene church camp every summer, I dated Nazarene girls in my teen years, I Bible quizzed my way through junior high and high school graduation as a Nazarene, I graduated from a Nazarene university, I have lived and served abroad with the Nazarene church, and I am a worship leader and a board member at a Nazarene church. The Nazarene church helped raise me, educated me, gave me the tools to engage the weighty conversations of our time critically and meaningfully, and has largely informed my thinking on evolution, especially as it unfolds within a broader Wesleyan theological context.

As a Nazarene high schooler I went to my advanced biology class with the perpetual quest to prove to my teacher that speciation was nonsense and evolution an evil, godless lie (never mind that I implicitly and unwittingly had affirmed a view of speciation that apparently transpired in a staggeringly short 6,000-year period). I ardently approached evolution and God's creative activity in the natural world as mutually exclusive. This belief persisted well into my college days at NNU as a biology chemistry major. As I encountered evolutionary theory in my science classes there, I slowly began to question and reexamine why I believed as I did and whether this view was scientifically and logically coherent. I eventually concluded that it was not. As you might expect, the evolution in my own thinking as a result of this informational variation did not occur immediately; rather, these permutations took place gradually over the course of many classes, conversations with students and professors, and much prayerful discernment. And, although my science classes initially prompted me to reexamine my position, it was ultimately my subsequent experiences in theology classes where I was given opportunity to engage conversations about a Wesleyan conception of divine love—especially as it relates to creaturely freedom, God's power, and *creatio ex nihilo* (creation out of nothing)—that convinced me there was a better way to understand the natural (and spiritual) world.

Specifically, what led me to affirm theistic evolution was a profound new realization that God's nature—the very essence of God—is love and that an indispensable element of that love-nature, especially in a Wesleyan context, is that God necessarily grants creaturely freedom. In other words, it is the very love-nature of God that precludes God from ever acting unilaterally or coercively as the sole actor. This "limitation" on how God can act in the world is not to reconceptualize God as diminutive or impotent anymore than saying God is weak because God is unable to hate people. Rather, it is simply a recognition that God cannot act in ways that are contrary to God's nature anymore than we can act contrary to our nature, and insofar as God's nature is love, God must necessarily always love, even if God has a degree of freedom in how God chooses to love. As this relates to creation theories, if God's love-nature requires that God cannot act unilaterally, then it makes no sense to speak of God as creating coercively or out of nothing because that type of power is inconsistent with the God who is love we read about all throughout Scripture. Instead Scripture tells of a God who in light of that God's love-nature necessarily grants creaturely freedom by co-creating with and out of that which already exists. Even the Genesis account supports this notion that God non-coercively creates out of something (Genesis 1:2).

This understanding, then, was a crucial turning point for me and was enough to convince me of what I was already learning in my science classes: the lion's share of serious science supports evolution. The scientific and theological disciplines clearly still had distinct spheres of expertise—I did not turn to the scripture to teach me about the role of mitochondrial DNA and I did not study molecular chirality with hopes that it would reveal to me the intricacies of divine love—but even in their separateness these two spheres were intimately connected and together worked to reveal to me a more complete picture of God's creative and redemptive love as it permeates every facet of life.

WHY DO I CARE?

I began by sharing how I am a Nazarene in my own right and not just by my wife's proxy. But, in truth, none of those reasons or experiences make me a Nazarene today either. I am still a part of the Nazarene church today because I choose to be, because I believe in her Wesleyan message of God's love that has the power to radically transform life, both physically and spiritually. The church plays an integral role in mediating that redemptive love to the world.

The narrator in Robert Frost's time-honored poem "Mending Wall" shares of his experience with a neighbor with whom he annually repairs a fence between their respective land. They carry on this ritual, despite the narrator's doubting questions of its necessity and recognition that the practice is outdated and irrational. Despite his probes, though, the neighbor maintains, "Good fences make good neighbors."

As this poem relates to our conversation here, I wonder if the opposite can be said of the church. I wonder if bad fences make bad churches. Even though I still actively choose to be a Nazarene today, I also doubt and have misgivings about the Nazarene church. There are days (and even months) when I do not want to be a Nazarene, and there are moments when I question whether I am Nazarene enough. I have these moments of doubt because I have seen the Nazarene church erect fences of exclusion that undermine her Wesleyan character by pitting spiritual integrity against intellectual and social integrity. To some extent our figurative fences can be beneficial insofar as they help demarcate what we believe and, more importantly, the kind of people we intend to be; they can help us to celebrate the unity of belief and practice within our community. Too often, though, we have erected non-Nazarene fundamentalist fences, all the while labeling them Wesleyan or Nazarene, and then used them not to celebrate who we are in Christ but as a means to exclude and ostracize others, often those who are no less Nazarene than we are. It is not altogether difficult to understand how this happens. If I say you must believe in all the livestock in fences A, B, and C to be a good Nazarene Christian and you think you only need to believe in the livestock in fences A and B, then by my very definition of a good Nazarene Christian, you are excluded because you do not believe in all the right livestock. Under this fundamentalist paradigm, I cannot simply agree to disagree with you (which you might be more than willing to do) because it is my very definition of a good Nazarene Christian that precludes your definition from being acceptable. Here, I will always be more threatened by the more liberal position because it has let escape that which I believe must necessarily be fenced in.

Increasingly, then, the effect of this "bad fence building" has been to push out of our Nazarene pastures, some of the most brilliant, capable, engaged, and passionate lovers of Christ and servants of the church. This is especially curious (and troubling) regarding the evolution conversation given the church's substantially blemished historical record when it comes to science. And, unfortunately, this brand of fence-building and the church's blemished historical record is not limited to issues of evolution or science; we have invented fences around a host of other sacred cows—social fences, political fences, economic fences, and even new theological fences. With this realization, we can hardly blame these "dissenters" for wishing to pasture outside of the artificial Nazarene fences we have fabricated, for it is outside of these fences that those leaving the Nazarene church are discovering new freedom in Christ to pursue full-orbed holiness—to doubt and question safely, think critically, live simply and peaceably, steward responsibly, advocate socially, love more generously, and co-create with God to establish the kingdom of God on earth more fully. All of these pursuits are hardly the deviation from our Wesleyan holiness roots these ever-tightening fences might suggest. In fact, they sound hauntingly like the Jesus we read about in the gospels.

This self-inflicted "Nazarene apostasy" concerns me, but I am also hopeful of a better way forward. I join the neighbor in Frost's poem, declaring that good fences make good churches. I believe there is space within our denominational fences to live peaceably with those who think differently than us without resorting to thoroughgoing relativism or completely abandoning what it means to be a Nazarene (after all, we recognize a variety of options when it comes to healthy food but can still distinguish food from poison). I believe that robust faith and intellectual integrity must walk hand in hand, that it is possible for and even incumbent on Christian men and women to love God with their hearts *and* their minds. Paul admonishes us to do as much when he says, "lead a life worthy of the calling to which you have been called, with all humility and gentleness, with patience, bearing with one another in love, making every effort to maintain the unity of the Spirit in the bond of peace. There is one body and one Spirit, just as you were called to the one hope of your calling, one Lord, one faith, one baptism, one God and Father of all, who is above all and through all and in all" (Ephesians 4:1-6 NRSV).

My hope is that the Nazarenes Exploring Evolution project becomes the catalyst for a revived loving posture toward Nazarene fence-building that extends far beyond science and theology. Perhaps, just as our denomination was known for its embrace of fundamentalist Wesleyans in the 1920s (which we were not at the time), we can join together to deconstruct and reconstruct good fences that help us to celebrate our unity in love of God and others, and in that same spirit of inclusivity, reclaim our Wesleyan heritage of charity towards those who contribute new, different, and even controversial ideas about the many other pertinent scientific, social, political, and theological issues of our time. And, if we are able to do that, perhaps someday attorneys, Nazarene pastors, democrats, stem-cell researchers, homosexuals and, yes, even evolution-ary scientists will all walk into a bar and sit down for a cold drink together and still be the (Nazarene) church God would have her be. And that is no joke—it is my earnest prayer.

Thanks be to God!

SUGGESTED READING

Floyd Cunningham, ed. *Our Watchword and Song* (Kansas City: Beacon Hill Press, 2009).

Rachel Held Evans, "Why Millennials are Leaving the Church." Web. 27 July 2013.

Thomas Jay Oord, *The Nature of Love: A Theology* (St. Louis: Chalice Press, 2010).

Al Truesdale, ed. *Square Peg: Why Wesleyans Aren't Fundamentalists* (Kansas City: Beacon Hill Press, 2012).

Kevin M. Ulmet, "I am a Concerned Nazarene" *Holiness Today* (March/April 2012).

55

EVOLUTION AND CREATION

Mike Schutz

Mike Schutz serves as Senior Pastor of the Avon Grove Church of the Nazarene in southeastern Pennsylvania.

I am not sure.

I am not sure if the Genesis account of creation should be taken literally. I am not sure how it was understood by those who first received it. I am not sure if they asked the same questions I ask today. I am not sure if they cared about the same issues as those who sit in my congregation every Sunday morning, or those who sit in our Sunday school classes and Bible studies. Were they asking, "How did God do this?" or were they asking, "Why did God do this?" Which question is the story of creation answering?

I am not sure.

I am not sure about evolution. I rely on scientists to understand and interpret vast amounts of data and develop a coherent explanation. In some ways, this is a fiducial relationship – I have to trust that they are honestly handling all the information available to them and not simply cherry-picking data to confirm their own biases. And I know enough about human nature to know this is a tall order. To be honest, it seems scientists change their mind every few weeks about what is [

eat or how to prevent disease. If they can't get on top of thos

can I be sure they know about something that happened th[

millions – of years ago? When I visit Ken Ham's Creation Museum, I realize that the arguments presented there sound persuasive. On the other hand, I read articles by my good friend Karl Giberson, refuting Ham, and I am attracted to those. I can see both sides. And I know that I am not smart enough to decide for myself. I need help dealing with these dueling experts (or at least self-proclaimed experts).

I am not sure.

My lack of certainty about the whole evolution/creation question might not be a very big deal – after all it doesn't seem to influence the way I live my everyday life. Except it does. I'm a pastor, and one of my roles is to help folks live their Christian lives in the real world. Thinking about the teens in my church, sitting in high school classrooms and preparing for college, I am aware that this is a big deal. When I think about the new person, who just moved to our community to attend grad school, I am aware that how we deal with this issue matters. And as I think of that member of my church board who has been inviting his neighbor to worship – and his neighbor happens to be a scientist – I know this question matters.

Perhaps we should consider the problem of the "litmus tests" created by the church.

Over the years, everyone from pastors to Sunday school teachers to camp speakers to youth leaders have offered our young people, and our not-so-young people, quick and easy answers as to how we know whether someone is one of "us" or one of "them." All you need do is ask for their opinion on one or two issues, and you would know. Sure, they might say they are a Christian, they follow Jesus, and they might even go to church. But we cannot be sure of their loyalties unless they pass our test. Abortion? End Times? Politics? Alcohol? Creation?

Really?

As a Wesleyan, I've always been comfortable with a bit of mystery. We don't claim to know all the answers to every question. We don't demand adherence to one stance on every controversy that comes down the theological pike. There's room for diversity about many issues that other groups argue over, even split over. We talk about unity on essentials and freedom on non-essentials. While we might even disagree a bit about what constitutes an essential, we've done a pretty good job of keeping the list short. Yet, when we use a non-essential issue as a test, in order to figure out someone else's spiritual state – well, the litmus test goes both ways. What happens when a young person who was told that every good Christian always votes with the _____ party finds out differently in the real world? And what happens when that student meets a professor – at a Christian college – who does not match up to the litmus test? And what happens when our young person's own views no longer match with the "correct" answers? Do we really want them to believe that to disagree with our opinion on a non-essential means they are no longer one of us – and that opinion separates them from the church and from Christ?

You see, as a pastor in the Wesleyan tradition, I've tried to preach and teach that we look to the Bible to answer the most important questions of our lives:

"What must I do to be saved?"

"What constitutes a meaningful life, and how can I live it?"

"How am I to treat others, myself, and creation?"

This is different from going to the Bible to answer *every* question of life. Scripture does not answer every question, nor is it the source of truth for every issue. When I misuse Scripture by expecting it to answer every question, including questions it was not designed to answer, I not only disrespect Scripture, but I find myself drawing strange lines that separate people in places where a separation is just not necessary.

And for me, this issue is not just a philosophical question or some abstract problem.

It has a face, several in fact.

It is Carrie, the young lady in my church who will be attending a major, prestigious university next year – and majoring in science.

It is David, the young, intelligent husband and father who has been coming to my church for awhile, and wants to know if his head, as well as his heart, is welcome in our church.

And it is Luke, my own son, who wants to know if there is room in the church for people like him, who are not satisfied with simple answers to complex questions.

I am not sure.

56

GROWING PAINS
AND BRAVE HUMILITY:
LEARNING TO LEARN

Seth Waltemyer

Seth Waltemyer is currently finishing his Master of Divinity degree at Boston University School of Theology.

"A man's pride will bring him low, but the humble in spirit will retain honor." Proverbs 29:23

As a kid I hated growing pains. I don't mean the TV show - that was a fundamental part of my youth. I'm talking about when you can feel your bones growing, when your tendons stretch as taught as guitar strings, and it feels like your whole body expands in unpleasant ways.

Ok, growth doesn't happen that dramatically. I don't even know if "growing pain" is a real thing or if my mom just told me that so I'd stop complaining about the bodily pain I endured from rough-housing with my brothers. However, this idea of growing pain has a strong spiritual counterpart. At one point or another we all go through a spiritual process of growing pains. There are many names for such experiences. "The desert" is a rich example of the type of difficulty and struggle that accompanies spiritual maturity. Indeed, spiritual growing pains happen in many different ways depending on one's circumstances.

Every year our colleges and universities receive a new batch of freshman, the majority of whom go through their own brand of growing pain. In classes like New Testament Introduction or the study of Church

History, students learn that what Christians believe today is not always what the church has proclaimed. The faith of the Early Church went through tumultuous revision(s) as Christians labored to express their understanding of Christ. Studying those theological debates and trying to still ground oneself in faith can be one of the most difficult processes a student will experience. Being confronted with bombshell after bomb-shell is a difficult process to say the least. For some students this "existential crisis" threatens their entire worldview because the way they thought about the world as a child ends up being drastically different than the way the world actually is. Such is the existential crisis, or, the growing pain.

But just as our bodies must first breakdown muscle in order to build up strength, it is our most trying experiences that offer us the greatest opportunity for maturity. Take an example from nature: the butterfly. As it sheds the pupal skin and begins working its way out of the cocoon, anecdotal accounts suggest that butterflies need the difficulty of emerging from their cocoons in order to become strong enough to survive. Therefore, if you came upon a caterpillar's cocoon and saw that a butterfly was almost ready to emerge, you would actually do it a disservice by trying to help it along. The butterfly needs to struggle in order to grow. The same is true of most students of theology; though the struggle may seem at times excruciating, we are inevitably the better for it.

The church as a whole has also experienced its share of growing pains. Throughout the entire life of the church, Christians along with the rest of the world have had to come to terms with many changes in worldview, often the result of various scientific revolutions. Just look at the Copernican Revolution. Shortly before his death in 1543, the Polish astronomer and devout Catholic Nicolaus Copernicus published his work, *On the Revolutions of the Heavenly Bodies*, which outlined a heliocentric (Sun-centered) view of the universe. Though he was not the first scientist to describe such a view, his influence upon the scientific revolution is unmistakable. 81 years after Copernicus died, Galileo Galilei wrote *A Dialogue on the Two Chief World Systems* in which he defended the Copernican system. Both Copernicus and Galileo were initially derided by the church for promoting a vision of the cosmos that contradicted traditionally-ensconced interpretations of Scripture. In the end it would take more than two-hundred years for the church to lift the ban on heliocentric scientific works, and it wasn't until 1993 that the Catholic Church officially acquitted Galileo of his heretical views.

It took a great deal of time and patience for the Copernican system to catch hold of popular imagination and even longer for the church to recognize that an accurate view of the world informed by science may indeed require a different understanding of the meaning of Scripture. Certainly this type of change and growth is quite painful, for it is no easy thing to admit one may be wrong, or that one's predecessors and tradition were hindered from seeing clearly. Today we are witnessing another type of revolution. One of the most pressing growing pains for the contemporary church concerns the debate over the validity of evolutionary theory for the Christian worldview.

But in order to have constructive dialogue and a true exchange of ideas, supporters and detractors of the theory of evolution must take the first step to intentionally prepare their hearts and minds for the journey ahead. Prepare to be taught, to learn something new. Prepare to recognize that no one has all the right answers, though some answers are more helpful than others. And we must all prepare our hearts to recognize the limits of our understanding - concerning both evolutionary science and holy Scripture. What I am trying to illustrate is an idea that I like to think of as "brave humility." Before we can truly learn from a spirited conversation about evolution, we must address the ways of thinking - which we have all built up - that determine how readily we are willing to entertain new ideas, to allow our worldview to change. But this process is not an easy one, and therefore requires great courage. Are we prepared (and if so, how?) to handle new information in situations such as the study of biblical literature or the study of biological evolution? The truth contained in Scripture may be timeless, but our knowledge and understanding of that truth will always be dimly lit.

My point is this: if and when we approach the subject of evolution, or Genesis and biblical studies, we must not mistake pain and difficulty with error. For fear of change, or because of the difficulty (and pain) of the endeavor, I am afraid that far too few evangelicals are giving evolution a chance. There are innumerable reasons why a person may seem closed off to the possibility of recognizing evolution as a valid way of understanding our physical universe. But for me it all comes down to fear. What will happen to my faith if...? If evolution is true? If acceptance of evolution disrupts my worldview? What does evolutionary theory mean for my understanding of God and creation? These and many other questions may come to those who venture down this path, but we should not shy away from them simply because they are difficult.

I make this plea because my heart grows heavy when I consider the church in the world today. My heart is heavy because I believe the posture the church takes right now concerning evolution will be a strong indicator of the church's growth, health, and social influence in the decades to come. And isn't it amazing? Right now we stand at the cusp of a new epoch in human understanding and knowledge about God's creation. It is beautiful and amazing that our technology and science in the twenty-first century can allow leading scientists to study the available evidence and find that evolutionary theory seems to offer the best explanation (so far) for connecting all the dots.

But to ignore the evidence, or to misconstrue the evidence in unscientific ways, or to cast evolution aside because it doesn't meet our preconceived ideas or traditionally-held beliefs is to retard the church's maturity. To approach evolution with assumptions and battle plans instead of with brave humility is to neglect the opportunity for maturity and growth.

In the end, all that I want to do is encourage my fellow Christians to recognize that our own growing pains *will* come, and in their coming, to employ brave humility. Do not run at the first sign of difficulty in favor of familiar surroundings. If the butterfly stopped trying because it found escaping from its cocoon too difficult it would surely die never knowing the fullness of flight. Similarly if the church remains in stiff ways of thinking instead of humbly asking what we can learn from the scientific study of the world, the church will be doomed, at most, to die, and at least to never fully live.

57

EXPLORING EVOLUTION:
DOES IT MATTER TO THE CHURCH?

Trent Friberg

Trent Friberg is Pastor of Family Life at Centralia Church of the Nazarene in Centralia, Washington.

On the western side of the state of Pennsylvania, nearly equidistant from the northern and southern borders, there is a sleepy little town of less than ten thousand people. There, once a year, people celebrate something that they say matters. A small rodent emerges from its burrow and supposedly is able to predict the weather patterns across the nation. It makes no sense because it does not matter. It is a nice tradition. It might be a fun story to talk about, but there is no real significance.

As a pastor of a congregation, I'm compelled to ask whether the question of evolution really matters to the church. Is evolution like Punxsutawney Phil, a question that pokes its head out once in a while to see what might happen when it does but matters very little? After all, even if evolution is true, the process is so slow, practically indiscernible, and people are going to look very similar to me for a very long time.

I certainly am not a scientist. I have neither the right nor the knowledge to persuade people through discussions about the validity of archaeological evidence or carbon dating. I am far from the wisest or most well-read theologian. I can say with certainty that I am not the one you should come to in order garner a reputable defense for any position in the creation/evolution discussion, but I do know the church. I have studied this bride of Christ, served her, nurtured her, prodded her, wept for her, worked for her, been challenged and humbled by her, supported her, exhorted her. She is the context wherein I find the fulfillment of my call. And as I consider this matter of exploring evolution and whether or not it matters to her, the answer is a clarion, "YES!"

To be fair, I am not claiming that evolution has happened or ever will. I have seen evidence that species and creation as a whole tend to change and improve over time. It seems plausible that stronger and more advanced mutated specimens might have the opportunity to live longer, reproduce more often and perhaps pass along genetic or physical anomalies that would give them an edge in survival. I am also not purporting that God created, at the whim of verbal instruction, the world, universe, cosmos and creatures during six twenty-four hour periods of time as literally recorded in either Genesis 1 or 2. I do not believe that I am qualified to argue either of these two theories.

However, this question is still relevant to the church, and as such, the church must engage in the exploration of evolution.

The process that has too often been left to the academy to delineate, discuss and debate must begin to filter down into and throughout our churches. The church does not need to worry about definitively solving the question. Rather, the church must worry about creating a culture in which our people feel safe to lean heavily into conversation with one another about topics that have deep significance.

The role of the pastor is changing. While we must always retain the edge of the prophet and boldly speak God's message to the people, we must also tend to the environment of our churches by creating space for discussion and dialogue. The church needs the literal fundamentalist who believes that the earth is young and that creation happened in a time span of 144 hours. The church equally needs the scientist who is compelled by the evidence available to believe that creation is millions of years old and has been guided by a loving Creator to this moment. While it is possible that people who hold these differing opinions may never be able to reconcile their beliefs about creation and evolution, certainly they can worship together and journey with one another in caring, loving and mutual respect.

The church cannot afford to sidestep these discussions any longer. We need not fear them or run from them. I argue that the church must embrace these discussions, particularly in order to hold and retain our generation of young adults who are largely unimpressed by pat-answers and one-sided opinions. They are a Google search away from hundreds of thousands of bits of information designed to inform them and sway them. This evolution/creation discussion is one of many topics about which the church must be able to have meaningful and significant conversation.

The question about whether or not God created through evolution pales in importance to a deeper, more fundamental question about the church: Can we endure differences of opinion about portions of our faith that we hold passionately and still be the unified body of Christ? If so, what will it take to establish this kind of interaction and engagement within the church? And, like a mentor of mine has often encouraged me to consider, do our people truly believe that it is more important to be "rightly related" than it is to win the argument? The churches that choose to cultivate environments receptive of these conversations will thrive because of them.

58

PUTTING CHILDISH WAYS BEHIND US

Joe Foltz

Joe Foltz is Senior Pastor at Drexel Church of the Nazarene in Missouri.

Mrs. Andrews was my fourth-grade teacher. I don't remember much about fourth grade. I read C.S. Lewis' *The Chronicles of Narnia* for the first time. My twin sister had an in-school suspension for bringing a steak knife to school. (She brought it to share the 7 oz. Hershey's Kiss she had received for a special occasion with some of her friends, since the "sporks" we had in the cafeteria were not strong enough to cut through the solid piece of hard chocolate.) I had a short-lived relationship with a girl named April, who also had short-lived relationships with two other boys who would become my best friends as we moved into middle school and high school. I also learned about evolution for the very first time. I remember sitting in class thinking how this might be what they taught in schools, but I knew the truth! God created, and Charles Darwin and evolution was a bunch of hooey.

Mrs. Andrews wasn't just my fourth-grade teacher. She was also a pastor's wife. Her husband was a United Methodist minister, who wrote a little devotional thought in the small-town weekly newspaper. I knew Mrs. Andrews was a fellow Christian and a pastor's wife, and I recall that I asked her what we did with this whole evolution business as Christians. Sadly, for the life of me I cannot remember what she said, but I do remember how sweet and wise she was.

It's a complicated issue, isn't it? Before this project, the last grand discussion on evolution in the Church of the Nazarene was at the 2009 General Assembly in Orlando, Florida. Prior to this General Assembly, *Manual* paragraph 903.8 read:

> *"The Church of the Nazarene believes in the biblical account of creation ("In the beginning God created the heavens and the earth..."—Genesis 1:1). We oppose any godless interpretation of the origin of the universe and of humankind. However, the church accepts as valid all scientifically verifiable discoveries in geology and other natural phenomena, for we firmly believe that God is the Creator. (Articles I.1, V.5.1, VII)"*

At the 2009 Assembly, there was a resolution to move the parenthetical reference to Genesis 1:1 and to delete the final sentence of the paragraph and add the following new text:

> *"The biblical account states that God created the heavens and the earth. ("In the beginning God created the havens and the earth..."—Genesis 1:1). Also, the biblical account explains: 'For in six days the Lord made the heavens and the earth, the sea, and all that is in them, but he rested on the seventh day' (Exodus 20:11a). And, Jesus taught: '...at the beginning of creation, God made them male and female' (Mark 10:6). The church affirms that the truth of God's Word and the truth of all valid scientific evidences are the same truth."*

This was just one of many resolutions that asked an underlying question: Is the Church of the Nazarene a fundamentalist church or not? This particular resolution was the only one dealing with fundamentalism that gained much traction. It seems that the delegates were in agreement that they did not want a fundamentalist view of the Bible, just its first book. Even so, this resolution was heavily debated and was amended by both the legislative committee that dealt with it and the General Assembly. The statement finally adopted now reads, as paragraph 903.9 in the current *Manual*,

"The Church of the Nazarene believes in the biblical account of creation ('In the beginning God created the heavens and the earth...'—Genesis 1:1). We oppose any godless interpretation of the origin of the universe and of humankind (Hebrews 11:3). (1, 5.1, 7)"

As I sat in the visitor's section, I became sad as the resolution was adopted. In 4th grade, I had allowed the Scopes trial to play out in my mind as I listened to Mrs. Andrews teach about Charles Darwin and his *On the Origin of Species*. In 2009, entering my final year of seminary, I was saddened by the fact that the church I so dearly love was choosing to ignore 150 years of scientific research. As I reflect back on it now, 1 Corinthians 13:11 comes to mind- "When I was a child, I spoke like a child, I thought like a child, I reasoned like a child; when I became an adult, I put an end to childish ways" (New Revised Standard Version). What might it look like for the Church of the Nazarene to put an end to childish ways in regards to evolution?

We must embrace who we are. As Nazarenes, we are a holiness people called to love both God and neighbor. 1 John 4:18 says that perfect love casts out fear. Yet, the sense I gain from my Nazarene brothers and sisters who are very worried that other Nazarenes might embrace evolution is that they are operating from a posture of fear. Often, this is expressed through a slippery slope argument: "If we start to believe that Genesis 1 isn't an historical account, than it's only a matter of time until we won't believe the resurrection didn't happen." Friends, slippery slope arguments are an informal fallacy, meaning that the premises don't support the proposed conclusion. To continue with our example, there is no way to prove that believing that Genesis 1 is not an exact, historical account would cause a person to also believe that the resurrection is not an exact, historical account. When we embrace such arguments, we do so out of a needless sense of fear.

We must embrace what we believe. Part of the brilliance of the Church of the Nazarene is that it has always been a "big tent" movement. As Phineas Bresee brought together holiness groups from all across the United States that often had very different points of view on particular issues of theology and polity, he became known for a saying, even though it wasn't original to him: "In essentials, unity. In nonessentials, liberty. In all things, charity." The spirit in which Bresee used that saying led to our Agreed Statement of Belief, which is brilliant in that just about any orthodox Christian can agree to it. The Agreed Statement of Belief doesn't contain anything about the origins of the universe and humankind. It does say that we believe in the Triune God. I believe we can trust the God that created enough to not get too hung up on how He did it.

These days, most church practitioners are very concerned about whether or not my generation, the Millennial generation, is going to embrace the church. Right now, the odds seem against us. If you do an online search for why Millennials are leaving the church, you'll get over 200,000 results and probably thousands of different reasons why. I once read an article on such things that said Millennials are leaving the church because they consider the church opposed to science. The Church of the Nazarene has been blessed to have great institutions of higher education and to have gifted scholars in the fields of Bible, theology, and science. We must make room for all fields of inquiry and love one another even when we disagree on nonessential matters. That's part of what I love about the Church of the Nazarene being a big tent movement. We'll let you be a Nazarene if you're a young earth creationist, an old earth creationist, a gap creationist, or a theistic evolutionist. We'll let you be a Nazarene if you agree with Bishop Ussher that creation began the nightfall before October 23, 4004 BC. Once we have all those different kinds of people in the Church of the Nazarene, we'll let everybody argue for their position till either we all die or Christ returns.

We can have that debate until we're all blue in the face. What we can't do is move from debating a nonessential issue to calling one another heretics or doubting one another's salvation. That'd be embracing childish ways like I did sitting in Mrs. Andrews' 4th grade class at New Manchester Elementary School. Don't you think it's time to put childish ways behind us?

59

SETTING GOD FREE

Ryan Scott

Ryan Scott is the Pastor of a non-traditional missional engagement in Middletown, Delaware.

I grew up in a very conservative environment; a nice, comfortable box. Whether or not it was explicitly taught, I was well aware that no one could be Catholic or a Democrat and also be Christian. I remember reading picture books with Adam and Eve riding dinosaurs. I have no recollection of my parents teaching me any of these things, but these ideas were certainly rampant in the religious culture of my childhood.

I've always been a bit of a contrarian, even as a child. I took advantage of "the letter of the law" when it was convenient and I always asked 'why' – I still do. At a young age, I remember asking my Dad why God couldn't have used evolution to create the world. To his credit, without hesitation, he said it was entirely possible – nothing in the Bible said it didn't happen that way.

His answer was like gold to me. My religious box began expanding rapidly. Now the walls weren't defined by what the Bible said, (at the time I had no idea there could be multiple interpretations of what the Bible said) they included just about anything, so long as the Bible didn't specifically prohibit it. I was quite satisfied.

A few years later, I heard a preacher, whom my dad trusted and respected, spend an inordinate amount of time explaining, from Scripture, or at least using Scripture, why he thought the world was very, very old. Now it wasn't just ok to believe in a week's worth of evolution, but millions of years of it. I could tell people evolution was perfectly fine, so long as God created evolution.

It became less of a shock when I got to college and had Christian professors explain the same thing from the perspective of science. The boundaries of my box continued expanding when I arrived in seminary and discovered what the Bible says is more complex than simply what it means to me.

To say my religious box was whittled away sounds like a negative. But I've never seen it as a destruction of faith or the abandonment of orthodoxy. It is immensely freeing. The idea of a Spirit moving, breathing, and acting in the world like a mighty rushing wind just doesn't seem plausible inside a buttoned-down, well-defined, limited box. Without the box, I could experience all of God, the majesty and the immensity, and not be limited by what was "safe."

As C.S. Lewis famously wrote of Aslan, the Christ figure in his Narnia series, "Safe?... he isn't safe. But he's good."[1]

Freed of those constraints, I came to realize just how much the scientific explanation of creation echoed the spiritual explanations of life, faith, and salvation I'd been taught in the Church of the Nazarene. Everything about holiness is growth, development, and continually moving toward Christ-likeness. There are even crisis moments – the missing links of holiness theology – seemingly miraculous changes marking our movement from one phase to another.

It all began with the discovery that The Fall is not a story of failure, but of grace. God says Adam and Eve will die if they eat the forbidden fruit – it's not a statement of long term consequences, it's akin to your mother saying, "If I ever catch you smoking again, I'll kill you." You may understand your mom is not entirely serious, but God certainly didn't have to be. It's an illustration, right away, that our inevitable human frailties do not keep us from God's love.

The second step was dealing with the historic Christian conviction that Christ's incarnation was not a reaction to sin, but a pre-planned event. If we hold that God did not change the plan because of human sin, there must have been a purpose to the incarnation all along.

Both of these added up to the very real notion that perhaps God created human beings with an insatiable desire for selfishness, with a created drive to self-fulfillment. It sounds a bit like blasphemy, but it makes sense in light of scriptural, biological, experiential, and relational evidence.

First of all: death. There had to have been death before sin. Death wouldn't have been a deterrent without a working knowledge. Children have to learn about death through experiencing death around them – a relative or a pet. It's not an inborn concept. Perhaps Adam and Eve took death for granted because it had been happening for millions of years?

It doesn't negate the possibility of some sort of eternal destruction for the finally impenitent at the end of time. If you believe in resurrection, the death we face here and now is simply a bump in the road. Couldn't it just be another part of God's continued nurturing of life, like birth or adolescence? If we affirm the resurrection, death is not a punishment for anything, just a consequence of life.

Of course that still leaves us with a less than perfect world. Why would God create a world incapable of functioning as God designed? We have to ask what perfect means and also whether our conception of God's design is in line with what we know and claim of God. When God calls creation good, the implication is that it's fit for the purpose to which God created it. Things are as God intended them. There's no indication that nothing will go wrong; that's a faulty inference on our part.

Additionally, it doesn't make much sense to assume God wanted creation to function exactly the same way for all eternity. We affirm a God who is constantly at work, continually pulling us and challenging us to grow in grace and Christ-likeness. It's tough to imagine that this core element of God's action was unintended, a plan B.

There is an old philosophical trope – that we only appreciate joy because of sorrow and love because of loss. What if that were true? What if we posited that failure and pain have always been part of God's plan for the world? Not because failure and pain (or even death) are good things, but because forgiveness, redemption (and resurrection) are. It's not difficult to imagine a world without pain and death being less beautiful, less loving, than a world without forgiveness and redemption.

If we claim that God is loving and that God is relational (which seem to be the ultimate ends of the doctrine of the Trinity), wouldn't it make sense for God's creation to have inborn need for both? If our natural inclination is towards self-fulfillment and our only means of self-fulfillment is forsaking ourselves and loving others, then realizing our creative purpose requires an intervention. We're never going to figure that out on our own – and if we did, we could never hope to actually accomplish it within our own power.

This world is constantly moving towards something, a purpose. It is becoming more fit, more appropriate, more in line with God's design. The narrative of history is not God calling back a wayward people, but God fostering the growth and development of a good creation into something even more beautiful.

I've come to see the evolutionary model as the framing narrative of Christian life. God has a plan, an end-game. We try so hard to figure out the specifics, we fight holy wars over the interpretation of Revelation, but in the end we all agree: God wins, the dead are raised, God and creation once again dwell together. This requires movement, development, growth– evolution.

Evolution does create some difficulties as we move beyond the human realm. When we think about the vast majority of creation without self-determination or at least without any choices in self-determination, things get a bit tricky. One of the downsides to freeing God from the theological and interpretive boxes we build is that our neat, clean, self-contained, well-understood narratives have to go as well.

Here, I think the unique nature, purpose, and calling of humanity comes into play. We've often claimed that God created the world for us and have used this claim to our own, and creation's detriment. Genesis 2 seems pretty clear that God created humanity for creation, not the other way around. God seems to have made this wild, rugged world that, left to its own devices, would literally devour itself. God created human beings to tend and care for creation, to help keep it in line with God's purposes.

From a perspective of pure results, there's really no better means of creating a universe than survival of the fittest. It's a great descriptor of functional, efficient biological development. But it seems kind of mean. Those creatures born on the losing end of genetic odds are cast aside quite cruelly. One of the real detractors from Christian acceptance of evolution is simply how unlike God the process seems.

Here, I think, is the most profound, beautiful aspect of incorporating evolutionary ideas into our understanding of theology. God is always at work subverting our expectations. Value is no different. Whether we like it or not, we tend to value things for the benefit they bring. The rich, the wise, the strong, the resilient – we elevate them. We recognize the error in this perspective because of the revelation of God. All are loved, all are accepted, all are valuable, because all are beloved creations of God.

Left unchecked, evolution does produce error – creatures ill-suited for survival and less valuable to the system as a whole, creatures doomed to die. But evolution was never meant to be left unchecked. Part of human purpose is to keep creation in line, prevent it from growing out of control. Humanity is the image of God, meant as a constant presence in the midst of the world to represent, through being and action, the very character of God.

A child with Down's Syndrome is an evolutionary error. Someone born with a genetic predisposition to addiction is an evolutionary error. Neither one is actually an error. Because we carry the image of God within us, we do not allow "natural" processes to take their toll. We love and support all people as the beautiful creations of God they are.

Why? Because ultimately we recognize that none of us is equipped to live life the way God created it to be lived. We need each other and we need God – those traits are just as inborn in us as any evolutionary genetic result.

Too often we define heaven as a place where everyone is the fittest, rather than a place where everyone fits. Survival of the fittest only works when paired with God's selfless love and grace. Evolution needs purpose and that's exactly what the Christian narrative provides. We're not living for a faultless Kingdom, but a Kingdom that overcomes our faults.

If we were perfect, we wouldn't need God. This is exactly the point.

Admittedly, this is all a bit confusing. I suspect seeing the world from this perspective raises more questions than it answers. There are certainly no boundaries, no box remaining from the structured faith of my childhood. Yet, I'm supremely confident that all facets of Wesley's Quadrilateral – Scripture, tradition, reason, and experience – push us in this direction.

I believe God created a world bent to its own self-interest, yet at the same time, God created a world perfectly fit to achieve all of God's aims. Evolution is one force, countered by the force of God's love. Both are infused within creation in powerful, often overwhelming ways that will ultimately achieve everything God has planned for this crazy world of ours. We, who are created to cultivate and nurture this world, must set aside our own interests, our own selfishness, and embrace God's call, follow God's example, to selflessly love the world.

That is way outside the box, but it sounds like gospel to me.

ENDNOTES AND SUGGESTED READING

1. C.S. Lewis, *The Lion, The Witch and the Wardrobe* (New York: HarperCollins, 1950) 75.

60

MY VIEW FROM THE WINDOW

Eric Frey

Eric Frey is currently pursuing a DMin in Liturgical Studies at Trinity School for Ministry and serves the Church of the Nazarene in Toronto, Ohio.

The landscape was a vivid swirl of bright colors as I was perched in the windowsill of a hospital room. It was graduation day at Case Western Reserve University, and I was sitting with my four-year-old little boy who was slated for surgery in the coming week. With him sleeping, and with the regalia-clad crowd swirling below me, I sat there questioning my decision to write this essay. *What do I have to contribute?* I asked myself over and over again. Truth be told, I haven't really ever given the issue much thought. It just isn't important to me. Affirming God as Creator is sufficient for the composers of the early creeds, and it has always been sufficient for me. Why worry myself with more than that? Why let myself get drawn into the fray?

As I sat there questioning my involvement in this project and wondering what value I have to add to this conversation, it occurred to me that while the question may not be very important to me, it very well may be important to them. "Them" in this case is the myriad of academics colorfully milling about outside my window. CWRU is well known for its programs in the sciences, and it was highly likely that many of the graduates and faculty alike were scientists of some sort. I began wondering how many of those scientists, at various stages in their career, think about the origins of the universe. I wonder how important this question is to them.

Time has passed since graduation day, and I have begun to see this issue quite differently. It is no longer a question that does not matter to me. If it is a question that matters to "them," it has to be a question that matters to me. No longer is it a question of science. No longer is it even a question of Bible. Now, for me, it is a question of mission. If I am going to be the means of grace to them that faith requires, I have to be open to delving into the origins of the universe with them. I have to be open to exploring evolution with them. The mission demands it. If I want them to value me -- my work, my ideas, and what I have to share with them -- then I have to value them in those same ways. This is where the issue seems to unfold for me from the single question of evolution to the often terse relationship of faith and science. It is a relationship that has been strained at least since Copernicus was condemned a heretic for having the audacity to say that the earth revolves around the sun.

Sometimes science is loved and embraced. My son, for instance, was hospitalized because he has a rare genetic disorder. As recently as the 1980's it would have been a life threatening condition. The HIV/AIDS epidemic nearly wiped out an entire generation of those affected by his condition. Now, thanks to science, there are safe treatments, and it is highly likely that my son will have no more than mild arthritic symptoms. The future is even brighter. Advances in genetic therapy are giving signs of even greater hope of bigger steps in treatment.

We love science when it improves our lives, but we are quick to write it off when it confronts our worldview and all our preconceived notions of reality. Evolution continues to be dismissed by vast segments of Christianity. Not because of bad science (though the science is certainly debated, even amongst scientists), but often because it would mean we have to re-evaluate the way we think about Scripture. We reject the science because it would cost us too much. Beyond the issue of evolution, consider the ongoing debates about global warming between "liberal progressives" and "conservative Christians." Is the science that leads to theories of global warming rejected on scientific grounds or because acknowledging the science would be too costly? To accept some culpability in a climate-change crisis would require life-style changes on a grand scale that many are not willing to accept. Such examples show clearly that in large portions of the Church, science continues to be seen through the lens of skepticism, resulting in a dynamic where faith and science are seen in opposition.

Perhaps many in the scientific community view faith and science the same way. If this is the case, then being a means of grace to the scientific community begins with rethinking the relationship between faith and science. Fortunately, our *Manual* provides us help in this task. In addressing creation, the *Manual* opposes only "any godless interpretation of the origin of the universe" (903.9), leaving the question of creation open to science. In every other instance to which science is appealed, its goodness is affirmed within an orthodox theological framework (cf. 18, 36, 903.1). As it turns out, the two are not opposed at all, but rather "the humble and persevering investigator of the secrets of nature is being led, as it were, by the hand of God in spite of himself, for it is God, the conserver of all things, who made them what they are."[1]

This finally brings us back to the question of mission. How do we cease being opponents and realize we are teammates? When two communities see each other as opposed to one another, discussion is impossible. When two communities see each other as working against each other, conversation is impossible. No one gets heard when both communities are shouting each other down. Perhaps in order to be heard, we might first have to listen. Perhaps in order to be respected, we might first have to respect. Perhaps in order to be trusted, we might first have to trust. Could it be that their willingness to explore faith might require us to first explore evolution?

ENDNOTES

1 *Catechism of the Catholic Church*, 2nd Ed. (Washington, DC: United States Catholic Conference, 2000) 43.

61

EVOLUTION AND ORTHODOXY

Steve Estep

Steve Estep is Pastor at Grace Church of the Nazarene in Clarksville, Tennessee.

In chemistry, litmus tests are used to determine pH, the level of acidity in different substances. Around 1300 A.D., Spanish alchemist Arnaldus de Villa Nova was credited with developing these strips of paper that quickly reveal levels of acidity so chemists know what kind of material with which they are working. The term "litmus test" has become an apt metaphor in politics and theology. Potential Supreme Court justices are grilled with questions before Congress and have to contend with dozens of differing ideas about what one issue–what "litmus test" question–might disqualify them for service. What may be "THE" issue for one politician will likely be different from "THE" issue in the mind of a colleague across the aisle. They have determined their own litmus tests.

The same can be said of theological and sometimes not-so-theological issues throughout the history of Christianity. Theologians and pastors (which is the perspective from which I write) have had to address a variety of doctrinal statements, practices, and deeply held convictions that followers of Christ have determined are their "litmus test" issues. King James only, women in ministry, infant baptism, frequency of communion, Sunday night services, and styles of music have all been "litmus tests" I've run into as a pastor. God-loving people have found these issues to be so significant that they become the lens through which everything else is viewed - or skewed. I'm sure in the next 20 years of ministry there will be new twists and new tests that emerge in these conversations among Christians.

In recent years, the question of how Genesis 1-2 is to be interpreted has been added to the list of litmus tests. I've been given "scholarly" papers, videos, and links to websites by well-meaning people who have deep convictions about the importance of promoting an orthodox view of creation–which they understand is a literal, six day, twenty-four hour period of God's creative work. Any other options have been deemed heretical and a threat to the foundation of the faith. As a pastor, I have read (some) of the papers, watched (some) of the videos, and believe it is part of our pastoral responsibility to engage the issues, and the people who bring them, with a commitment to patiently speak the truth in love. Part of our responsibility is to help God's people navigate the depths of their convictions, which are often based more on emotion, or "what I've always been taught," than on sound theology or good science.

One approach that I have taken is to frame the conversation in terms of the "litmus test." The Apostle's Creed was by and large an answer to legitimate "litmus test" questions about the nature of God. Since the fourth century, it has been held as a standard for orthodox Christianity and has been an effective way to distinguish right-thinking Christians from unorthodox cults. Christians around the world can and do have beliefs that differ greatly, yet are still on the same page with the essentials of the faith in affirming the Creed.

While the creation/evolution debate was nowhere near the horizon when the Apostle's Creed was forged (or when Genesis 1 was written for that matter), there is a simple yet profound statement that comprises the first stanza of the Creed that can speak directly to the issue. "I believe in God the Father Almighty, Maker of heaven and earth." The Creed affirms God as the Maker of heaven and earth even more succinctly than our statement on Creation in the *Manual of the Church of the Nazarene*. The Creed, just like Genesis 1-2, is concerned with the question of the "Who" more than the "how" of creation. When in worship we sing or speak the words of the Creed, "I believe in God the Father Almighty, Maker of heaven and earth," we are joining with the voices of Christians past and present in making one of the boldest statements of faith we can make. God is the Source of our existence. God is the Creator. God is the Maker.

If we consider the issue of origin a part of the litmus test of orthodox Christianity and feel the need to come up with something that will protect truth and guard against heresy, that has already been done. *I believe in God the Father Almighty, Maker of heaven and earth.* A literalist can affirm the Creed. A theistic evolutionist can affirm the Creed. An evolutionist who does not deny the hand of God at work in the process can affirm the Creed. To move beyond the who to the how is a worthy intellectual pursuit, but simply does not carry the freight required to determine orthodoxy. Theologically and pastorally, the Creed offers us a good litmus test for any view of creation: *I believe in God the Father Almighty, Maker of Heaven and earth.*

62

BREAD, CUP, AND A BARREL OF
MONKEYS, WOLVES, AND LAMBS

Jon Middendorf

Jon Middendorf is Pastor Oklahoma City First Church of the Nazarene.

I have the great honor of pastoring in a college town. With dozens of colleges, business schools, universities and technical schools around, there is no shortage of teachers and learners to season every conversation and challenge every assumption. Every week our pews are filled with chemists, physicists, biologists, social scientists and doctors of all kinds. Throw a hymnal around in our sanctuary and you'll probably hit a scientist or two.

I love it. There's something so.....Wesleyan about it, especially when that spirit of learning and growing reaches into our churches. It doesn't always happen, but when it does, there's something beautiful, powerful and God-glorifying about it.

At OKC First Church of the Nazarene, we embrace science. In keeping with our Wesleyan tradition, we are people who do not view science as a threat to religion. We don't worry that science will contradict God; we believe science will continue to reveal God. Eyes-wide-open study is encouraged, and scientific discovery is celebrated, all with the full and complete blessing of our tradition and church.

The scientists in our fellowship hold to a theistic concept of evolution; they are convinced by the research that indicates the cosmos to be in a constant state of growth and development. Finding evidence in the movement of the stars and the slow, incremental changes seen throughout the variety of species, our parishioners use words and phrases like "adaption" and "natural selection"- all to the glory of God. There isn't the slightest hint of sacrilege in their voices. To the contrary, they celebrate the genius and the creativity of the Creator God as they teach the movement of creation.

These scholars are knowledgeable and respectful where Scripture is concerned. They don't proof-text the Bible to support their beliefs; they understand the grand narrative. More importantly, they know the character and nature of the Creator. These scientific findings don't compromise their beliefs; they are, to a person, very comfortable with this understanding of God, creation and evolution.

And I'm very comfortable with the concept of theistic evolution as well. I'm deeply convinced of God's authorship, and, like my fellow parishioners, I've never expected Scripture to give me a scientific explanation of the entire process of creation. I expect science to do that. Scripture, in every form and genre, testifies to the nature and character of God and to the dream of God; science describes how the dream of God moves and breathes and coheres.

Creation is the dynamic creation of a dynamic God; I assume things are always moving, changing, maturing, growing- even our fruits and vegetables! Given that creation is dynamic and all the targets move, our teaching and learning must also be dynamic in nature. The best learners are always on the move; they know the best education happens because of the dynamic journey and not the static destination. Again, this sounds like home, if you consider the Wesleyan tradition to be your home.

But there's more to say.

This is another of those debates that seems to be polarizing our Church. You've heard me access our tradition to voice my opinion where the content of the debate is concerned; now hear me access it again to voice my concern over the tone of the debate.

The hope of this debate is not some mythical middle ground. These two camps and mindsets are firmly entrenched, and a compromised, negotiated via media seems contrived at best and disingenuous at worst. Our best hope, where this and other similarly contentious debates are concerned, is not the middle ground but holy ground, on which the people of God stand together while in the midst of serious (and perhaps permanent) disagreement.

"Love your enemies." (Matthew 5)[1]

"If your enemies are hungry, feed them; if they are thirsty, give them something to drink; for by doing this you will heap burning coals on their heads." Do not be overcome by evil, but overcome evil with good. (Romans 12)

The evils are named hatred, discord, strife, slander, etc. We will overcome these evils, not by a false sense of compromise but by the regular and consistent practice of the Open Table.

What? What do the Cup and the Bread have to do with it?

Recently, I discussed our theology of the Open Table with a dear friend and fellow parishioner. I described our liturgy as a rehearsal, a practice. My friend responded with a quick and pointed question, "What are we practicing for?"

I was jolted. He made a brilliant point, one that we should make over and over, perhaps every time we celebrate, observe and practice our understanding of the Eucharist. Surely, as we practice an Open Table, we are practicing for something beyond the Table itself, right?

If yes, then what are we rehearsing? And for what do we practice? I very much enjoyed Dr. Staples' contribution to this discussion. In his book, *Outward Sign and Inward Grace: The Place of Sacraments in Wesleyan Spirituality*, Dr. Staples artfully and beautifully explains our Eucharistic posture, distinguishing between our tradition and all traditions that bar outsiders from participation. In that sense, we are an Open Table tradition; we welcome Christian believers of various stripes to participate side by side with us.

But we are an Open Table in another sense as well. Quoting Scripture and some of our most treasured Wesley hymns, Dr. Staples reminds us of the Eucharist's salvific potential. Though we don't say it often enough, all who are aware of their need of Christ are welcome at the Table. You don't have to be healthy or right or finished or onboard or in line or in agreement to eat and drink with us. We understand the Table to be a great equalizer, a unifying influence capable of taking many and making one Body, and we know that the one Body eats together as a present manifestation of the Dream already won but not yet fully established.

God's call to salvation is universal. He has invited everyone to feast with Him in His final Kingdom. And the invitation to the sacrament Supper, which is the foretaste of that final feast, must therefore, likewise, be universal.[2]

The Kingdom, launched at the Resurrection, amplified by the Spirit and *practiced and rehearsed at the Open Table*, is present now, and we should start behaving as such.

In the Kingdom, as you know, wolves and lambs get quite close. It's not that they are somehow melted and blended into something in the middle (a wamb?), but the lamb and the wolf, the predator and the prey, are knit together by something larger and more powerful than that which would otherwise keep them apart.

Andrew Dragos, writing for the Seedbed blog, reports Wesley scholar and author Ken Collins saying it like this: "Phariseeism is delighting in the difference brought about by holiness. Communion thus operates as a counter movement to separatism and phariseeism."[3]

The Kingdom does not advance when we insist on a contrived and "compromised" middle ground between the creationists and the evolutionists; the Kingdom advances when each side recognizes the power and possibility of Kingdom Hospitality and the spaces we make for one another.

Unity, but not uniformity. One, but not the same.

In saying this, I don't mean to minimize the theological ramifications of these positions. Regarding the life of faith, the work of the Church and the view and use of Scripture, the creationists will tend to see things one way and the evolutionists the other way. As you know, I've made my choice; the evidence seems clear. But there are others in my fellowship with differing opinions, and they are just as convinced in the other direction. The result is a church with muddy, complicated, delicate issues--issues that, in any other context, would keep wolves and lambs far apart.

But, in our tradition, with the Cup and the Bread in hand, we now see why we practice.

With all due respect, I submit that we have other, bigger debates on the horizon. And like this one, I suspect these other discussions will again pit parents against their children, brother against brother, insiders against outsiders, and there will be no middle road in sight.

Perhaps by then we will better understand how to fight, how to eat, how to drink, how to be the Kingdom- on earth as it is in Heaven.

A final warning from Scripture, from the opposite end of the Biblical spectrum. Hear the voice of Christ as reported by John in Revelation 2:

> To the angel of the church in Ephesus write: These are the words of him who holds the seven stars in his right hand, who walks among the seven golden lampstands: "I know your works, your toil and your patient endurance. I know that you cannot tolerate evildoers; you have tested those who claim to be apostles but are not, and have found them to be false. I also know that you are enduring patiently and bearing up for the sake of my name, and that you have not grown weary. But I have this

against you, that you have abandoned the love you had at first. Remember then from what you have fallen; repent, and do the works you did at first. If not, I will come to you and remove your lampstand from its place, unless you repent."

We're told at the end of chapter one that the lampstand represents a church. Here in the fifth verse of the very next chapter, Jesus issues a not-so-subtle threat: if you do not repent and return to the love you had at first, you will lose your permission to call yourself a church of Jesus Christ.

Planting a church in Ephesus was no small feat. Ephesus, a large and bustling city of 250,000 or more, had more than its share of competing ideologies and theologies. According to the 19th chapter of Acts, when the Kingdom of Christ showed up in the form of the Apostle Paul, "no little disturbance" was the immediate result.

Christianity was now part of the conversation, and every other competing interest had to account for it. Paul left Timothy to shepherd the small and vulnerable congregation, and under his leadership the church developed the filters necessary to sniff out false prophets and bad theology.

At the time of this warning to the church in Ephesus, they were commended for their precision and their passion for the right answers, and at the very same time warned that the pursuit of the right answer can come at an enormous cost- the love that is the hallmark of the Christian faith and the Church. When that love is lost, our identity as the people of God is soon to follow.

This conversation is an important one, and we should have it. We should explore the ramifications of creationism vs. evolutionism, working it out to the last detail. We should point out the faulty reasoning and questionable thinking in the other side and work toward better answers and questions. We should encourage dialogue while not being afraid of debate. We should debate and even argue our points with great passion and conviction. You've heard me say it earlier- I lean heavily toward one side of this debate, and I believe the ramifications to be significant.

But we can't give away our birthright in the process. We are the Body, the Church, historically extending and culturally embodying the very person and passion of Christ. We must be these same people in the midst of painful argument and debate, even if the "right answer" or the "winning" answer is within our reach. The right answer, when it comes at the cost of love, is too costly.

For us, some things are more important than the right answers. We remember, rehearse and celebrate those things at the Table.

Eat, drink and be loving, always and every time.

ENDNOTES AND SUGGESTED READING

1 All Scriptures taken from the New Revised Standard Version (1989).

2 Rob L. Staples, *Outward Sign and Inward Grace: The Place of Sacraments in Wesleyan Spirituality* (Kansas City: Beacon Hill Press, 1991) 261.

3 Andrew Dragos, Seedbed- "John Wesley's Open Table Communion: Counteracting Pharisaism", http://seedbed.com/feed/john-wesleys-open-table-communion-counteracting-pharisaism/, June 26, 2012

Made in the USA
San Bernardino, CA
24 December 2013